Promoting Maternal Mental Health During Pregnancy

Theory, Practice & Intervention

JoAnne E. Solchany, PhD, RN, CS

ncast
programs

Promoting nurturing environments
for young children

NCAST Publications Seattle

NCAST Programs
University of Washington
Box 357920
Seattle, WA 98195-7920
206.543.8528
ncast@uw.edu

Library of Congress Control Number: 2001094123
Solchany, JoAnne

Promoting maternal mental health during pregnancy/JoAnne Solchany

p.   cm.

Includes bibliographical references and index

ISBN 1-930949-95-2

1. Pregnancy.   2. Mental health.   3. Prenatal psychology.
4. Interventions   5. Mother-child relationships

I. JoAnne Solchany   II. Title

First Paperback Edition

Printed in the United States of America

Design assistance Publications Services

Cover Illustration — *She Goes With Grace*
acrylic on canvas, 18 x 24 in.
© 1995 Mara Friedman

To inquire about original paintings, prints, and notecards , please contact Mara c/o:
New Moon Visions, PO Box 23, Lorane, Oregon 97451 • 541-92-9057
mara@newmoonvisions.com, www.newmoonvisions.com

Mara lives with her family in a gentle river valley in the Pacific Northwest. In her country studio, she creates images that both honor and express the spirit, grace and beautiful strength of the Feminine. Mara's work first blossomed in Hawaii, once home and always a source of inspiration when she returns to visit. Her paintings focus upon images of women, and can be described as richly colorful, deep and spiritual. In her work, Mara explores the healing qualities of color, of harmonious rhythms and of universal symbols and form. Inspiration comes in many ways ~ the beauty of nature, the art and teachings of native cultures around the world and from the great circle of women, past and present, that she is a part of.

Dedicated to

the generations of women in my family,

past, present, and future

My grandmother, Johanna

My nana, Anna

My mother, Swanhild

My aunts, Borgny, Audrey, Nora,

Betty Ann, Gabriella, and Val

My sisters, Sandy, Susan, and Diane

My daughter, Anna

FOREWORD

This book is the result of my vision for addressing the mental health issues in pregnancy and the child's first year. The collective writings of nurse colleagues such as Reva Rubin and Ramona Mercer have documented the psychological work necessary to take on the mothering role. While we knew about these mental processes in the early 90's, there was limited application of their theoretical assertions by nurses, physicians, midwives social workers, or psychologists. I pledged to myself to take Rubin's and Mercer's ideas to the front line of practice. The opportunity to do this came in the mid 90's when several colleagues and I primarily Drs. Susan Spieker and Colleen Huebner at the University of Washington, began working within a research partnership with the Children's Home Society Early Head Start Program, which at the time was directed by Peg Mazen.

With this opportunity to develop a pregnancy related intervention for poverty mothers enrolled in the Early Head Start program, I began first involving students in my Infancy course. We developed the basic ideas for the resulting intervention program beginning in pregnancy and continuing through the child's second year. The pregnancy components dealt with helping the mother identify or develop her support system and establishing a niche for the expected child, reviewing and rehearsing the mothering role, and exploring attachment issues. We further developed our ideas with the home visiting staff associated with the Children's Home Society Early Head Start program. They were the first to implement the pregnancy protocols. We found that interventions could be used and that women were eager to think more about their unborn child and mothering.

This book contains the revision of our thinking about mental health issues and ways to assess and provide directed support for maternal role attainment during the pregnancy. The book will be a classic in the field. It provides a synthesis of the theoretical assumptions of mental health with the practical application of assessing the women's mental health and provides a number of activities to help guide the mother through the psychological work necessary to become a mother. While many mothers do this work on their own, a sizeable number do not. Doing this preparation for mothering is one of the best preventive interventions for promoting both maternal and child health.

We are rapidly beginning to understand the role emotions have in health and in particular the role they have in promoting the intrauterine conditions for brain development. Prenatal stress that is high and continuous is proving detrimental to fetal and later infant brain development.

It is my hope that professionals in the field of maternal-child health will use this information for evolving a new emphasis in primary health care and in prenatal education to assist mothers in preparation for mothering. Some will ask what about including the partner? This book sought to specifically address the woman's work during pregnancy, some of which involves her partner. It is my hope some of you will apply these concepts with the couple; that will be exciting to see the dyadic emphasis on parenting preparation evolve from the background where it is today in 2001 to one of the major aspects of prenatal care by 2010.

There were individuals whose support of this work is important to recognize. Dr. JoAnne Solchany, the author, did a masterful job of blending the worlds of theory and science of maternal and child health and psychiatry to the platform of primary care and the reality of daily practice. Anita Spietz, Associate Director of NCAST (Nursing Child Assessment Satellite Training Program, University of Washington, School of Nursing), an expert at clarifying and disseminating knowledge, served as editor and producer of this volume. Georgina Sumner, Director Emeritus of NCAST, supported this publication as one of her last accomplishments before retiring in May 2001 after a quarter of a century of commitment. NCAST as an organization has been devoted to the mission of bringing new knowledge to the practice community. This is another concrete example of NCAST's promotion of knowledge for practice.

It is my personal goal to speed this work to the front line of practice. By 2010, my hope is that this knowledge is incorporated into the practice of all prenatal clinicians striving to make a difference in the lives of women and children. If we can accomplish the work described in the pages of Promoting Maternal Mental Health During Pregnancy, we will reduce the rates of preterm birth, child abuse and neglect, postpartum depression, subsequent unwanted pregnancies. Even more importantly, we will increase the quality of life for families and children and eventually the total society. Caring for caregivers of children is the best way to bring about both health and peace.

Kathryn E. Barnard
Professor of Nursing
Scientific Consultant to
NCAST - University of Washington
Seattle, Washington
Summer, 2001

INTRODUCTION

In 1995, I became involved with a research project designed to look at the impact of specifically designed interventions on the developing parent-child relationship. This was an Early Head Start program working with women from the beginning of pregnancy through the child's third birthday. Delivering the services were a group of "home visitors" whose background and training was mainly focused in child-parent interaction and child development.

Home visitors, in general, had not received training about pregnancy or about providing relationship-based interventions to pregnant women. This challenged them to develop new ways of interacting with these women and to develop content appropriate for their visits. Within the research we were doing, home visitors had helped to develop a small group of interventions to use in pregnancy. Home visitors reported these as successful, as well as helpful and interesting to the women in the program. Program women reported liking visits while pregnant. Despite these positive experiences, it was not uncommon to hear home visitor concerns over their interventions being inadequate.

In response to these concerns we made an exhaustive search of the literature. It revealed little written on relationship-based interventions during pregnancy. Neither was there much on the "other side" of pregnancy—the psychological and emotional components. The literature was abundant with the physical issues of pregnancy; for instance, nutrition, weight gain, expected body changes, and so on. While this was valuable information, there were few connections between the "physical" information and the "emotional and psychological" needs of pregnant women. Based on clinical experiences and what was written about pregnancy, it was not difficult to see the holistic connection between the two sides.

Working within the context of parent-child interactions for many years has made me a firm believer in the idea that how parents think and behave during pregnancy and in the early years of their child's life greatly contributes to each child's future. The minds of parents are powerful forces. What we think of our children and the manner in which we think about them contributes heavily to who our children are to become. The scientific community generates more and more support each day for the concepts that the parent-child relationship begins in pregnancy and it influences the child throughout life. This relationship is not merely a caregiving relationship, but one that helps to construct the psychological make-up of the child, as well as helping to shape that child's emotional literacy. This, in turn, feeds social interactions and social success.

With all of this in mind, the reason for writing this book came down to three main reasons:

1) to educate people working with pregnant women on the emotional and psychological needs and changes during pregnancy.

2) to provide clinicians and home visitors with a series of interventions that support the emotional and psychological course of pregnancy.

3) to support the budding mother-child relationship through proactive interventions preparing for baby, preparing to mother, developing a nurturing mother-child relationship, and healing past maternal trauma and losses.

A mother and child who, from the very beginning, are healthy on all levels-physical, relational, psychological, emotional—become the best predictor for a positive life trajectory for any child and a satisfying mothering experience for any woman.

JoAnne E. Solchany, PhD, RN, CS
Assistant Professor
Family and Child Nursing
School of Nursing
University of Washington
Seattle, WA

ACKNOWLEDGMENTS

Giving birth to this project could never have been accomplished without several very key people.

ANITA SPIETZ

Anita was the chief midwife for this project. It was her compassion, diplomacy, eye for detail, and naturally loving way of being with others that truly brought this project through the literary birth canal and into waiting arms. Thank you for who you are and everything you have done.

GEORGINA SUMNER

Georgina's boundless energy and enthusiasm kept us all focused on the goal of completion, as well as grounded in what people needed to do the best work possible. Thank you for this. As this project comes to completion, Georgina moves forward to retirement. Her legacy with NCAST is great. There are more babies throughout the world who have experienced better relationships with their mothers and fathers due to Georgina's commitment to them than there are stars in the nighttime sky.

KATHRYN BARNARD

It was Kathy's ideas and thinking that led to the conception of this project. Thank you for the chance to make it happen. I am forever grateful for the mentorship, friendship, support, and confidence you have offered me.

VICKI LONG

Thank you for your continuous support for the production of this project.

DENISE FINDLAY

Thank you for field-testing this project, for your insight from an interventionist's point of view, and for your excitement.

MOLLY GERHARD

Thank you for your editing of the manuscript for this project.

MARY ANN BEST

Thank you for your thoughtful examination of content and your insightful feedback and direction.

GREG OWEN

Thank you for your patience and for your artistic assistance.

MARA FRIEDMAN

Thank you for allowing us to use your moving artwork that represents women so beautifully.

CAROL CLARK-LINSE

Thank you for your creative illustrations.

Finally, thank you to all the mothers and babies who told us their stories and shared their lives with us.

TABLE OF CONTENTS

Our Mighty Mothers, here we honor:

Earth, release the blessed spirits, brown and black and pale

and golden, whose bodies birthed and souls inspired us from

womb to womb, since the world's beginning.

A Ritual for Mothers, Diana Paxson

Section I

Theory: Understanding the Mental Health of Pregnancy

The focus of this section is on the emotional and psychological experiences of the pregnant woman and how these impact not only the course and eventual outcomes of her pregnancy but also her developing relationship with her child. Five chapters summarize these mental health issues. Chapter 1 provides an overview and answers the questions: "Why is the emotional and psychological work of women in pregnancy so important?" and "How does the woman's experience impact her ability to become a mother to the child she carries?" Chapter 2 explores the transition from pregnancy into motherhood. Chapter 3 looks at how the woman goes about accepting her identity as a mother. Chapter 4 addresses the establishment of the relationship between mother and child. Finally, Chapter 5 explores the current information on the influence of maternal factors, such as stress, on the course and outcomes of pregnancy.

Oh mirror in the sky

What is love?

What is child within my heart rise above?

Can I sail through the changing ocean tides?

Can I handle the seasons of my life?

Well, I've been afraid of changing,

'Cause I've built my life around you.

But time makes you get bolder,

Even children get older,

And I am getting older too.

Stevie Nicks (Fleetwood Mac), Landslide

1

The Other Side of Pregnancy

This chapter presents an overview of the current views of pregnancy, the psychological and emotional issues of pregnancy, the levels of psychological well-being and related issues during pregnancy, the issues pregnant women face, and the options for intervening within each level.

The Significance of the Psychological Work of the Mother

During the last several decades, great strides have been made in improving the outcomes for pregnant women and their babies. Much effort has gone into helping pregnant women take care of themselves during pregnancy, successfully navigate childbirth, and welcome healthy babies into the world. National goals were set to ensure that babies would not be born with low birth weights or birth defects. In addition, attempts were made so that these babies would not be born into families where they would be abused or neglected. Many intervention programs were designed and instituted to promote the best outcomes. These programs secured prenatal care for high risk women in pregnancy; provided prenatal labor and delivery courses; encouraged sound health practices such as stopping the use of cigarettes, drugs, and alcohol; recommended regular exercise programs, and healthy diets rich in certain nutrients; prepared mothers to breastfeed whenever possible; and educated women on family planning methods. In addition, programs were set up to improve the relationships between mothers and children and to improve the mothers' knowledge and skills to foster good cognitive, emotional, and developmental outcomes of their children.

There is no argument that many of these programs have been successful in meeting the goals they targeted. Infant mortality and morbidity rates have decreased throughout the last decade [1], as have teen pregnancy rates [2]. In fact, there have been drops in not only overall teen pregnancy rates (18% drop), but most specifically in the occurrence of a second pregnancy during the teen years (21% decrease). Although overall rates of teen pregnancy have decreased, the rates for Hispanic and African-American teens continue to be double those for non-Hispanic Whites. Racial differences persist within the death rates for infants as well, continuing to be higher for Blacks than Whites.

Many other pregnancy-related issues have also remained unchanged. In the number of neonatal deaths that occur, over one half can be attributed to congenital abnormalities, low birth weight, and the effects of maternal complications of pregnancy. These causes of death are often preventable with adequate prenatal care. The Center for Disease Control [3] reports that 2-3 women die each day from complications of pregnancy. Once again, many of those deaths are preventable with proper prenatal care; the percentage of preventable maternal deaths is estimated as high as 50%. Racial inequalities exist as well. When compared to Whites, Hispanic women are two times more likely to die during pregnancy and Blacks are four times as likely to die. Other gaps can be seen worldwide; in developing countries there are 480 maternal deaths per 100,000 women. This is 18 times higher than the number of maternal deaths in developed countries[4].

The number of cesarean deliveries continues to be high. The Center for Disease Control [5] report stated that, based on 1997 statistics, over 2000 of the reported 10,000 births per day, or one fifth, were surgical births. The same report found that violence during pregnancy ranged from between 4-8 %. They suggest that pregnant women may be at higher risk to experience violence than to experience pregnancy-related health problems.

Child maltreatment, a problem embedded within the parent-child relationship, remains especially high for children during the early years of life. In 1997, almost 3 million children were reported to child protective agencies for concerns of child maltreatment; about two thirds, or 2 million children, warranted further follow-up [6]. These figures are thought to be a gross underestimation of the true number of children being victimized. True figures have been suggested to be as high as 42 abuse victims per 1000 children versus reported statistics of 23.1 abuse victims per 1000 children [7,8]. Between 1986 and 1993, rates for physical abuse, sexual abuse, emotional abuse, and child neglect all doubled[9]. The highest number of victims fell into the 0-3 age group[10]. Of the reported child fatalities, 37.9% were under one year of age and 77.5% were under the age of five[11]. Maltreatment—physical abuse, sexual abuse, emotional abuse, and child neglect—of a child by a parent cannot be separated out of the context of the parent-child relationship. To effectively intervene, the focus needs to be within that same context. Recent research indicates intervention should begin in pregnancy where significant effects have been seen with the parent-child relationship[12].

The news often reports stories of mothers showing obvious signs that something has gone wrong in the mother-child relationship. We hear of mothers drowning their children and of newborn babies abandoned in gas station bathrooms or left in dumpsters. One mother left her 14-month-old son alone in an apartment, dropping by to leave him sandwiches every few days; she did this, she said, because she was afraid she would lose her boyfriend if he found out she had a young baby. Another mother abandoned her naked 9-month-old baby in her apartment when she was arrested for a separate incident. She did not feel it was important to let anyone know of this child.

What goes wrong in mother-child relationships where the mother neglects, abandons, abuses, or even kills her child? Did she feel like a mother? Was she bonded to her child? Did she feel any connection to her child? Was she overwhelmed by the new role she acquired when she gave birth and chose to parent her child? Did she have support? Had she wanted this baby? Had she wanted to be pregnant? Had she herself been neglected, abandoned, or abused as a child? What could have possibly gone so wrong that a mother would choose to treat her child in such an inhumane manner?

These kinds of situations and questions force us to take a second look at our beliefs about pregnancy and motherhood. We no longer believe a child is a blank slate at birth with no ability to feel or interact with the world. We no longer believe that children are so resilient that the effects of a traumatic experience simply fade away with their diapers and high chairs. And, we no longer believe that a pregnant woman just "births a baby." We now know that children are impacted by the relationships and environments that surround them, beginning at the point of conception. We know that babies may experience the generational effects of any trauma, addiction, attachment disturbance, or pattern of relationship dysfunction (see Chapter 5). We know that the period from pregnancy through age three is one of the most active and rapid periods of development. We know that the experiences parents had throughout their lives will impact how they care for and parent their baby[13].

Myths of pregnancy still exist, many strongly rooted in traditional medical practice, "old wives' tales," and family belief systems. Old, established beliefs are difficult to change, especially when people latch on to any example contrary to the new ideas being introduced. The scientific community has made major strides in establishing evidence dispelling many of the myths and traditional practices of pregnancy and motherhood. However, the acceptance of this information has not kept up with the discovery. For instance, it is common to hear mothers, as well as members of their families, denying the validity of information, discounting the impact the information might have on the child or the role and responsibility of the parent.

One of the most challenging myths of motherhood is the idea that responding to a baby's cries will spoil the baby; this myth is contrary to mountains of evidence that **responding quickly and consistently to** a baby's cry not only decreases crying, but supports the development of a secure, loving bond between mother and child.

In one of our research projects at the University of Washington, we examined the types of protective factors present in a low risk, well educated, and well-supported group of women. We wanted to find out what maternal factors served to protect the baby from maltreatment. One of our findings surprised us. We found several highly educated mothers disregarded evidence on the negative impact of marijuana on themselves or their babies during pregnancy. The mothers made active choices to continue using this drug on the basis that it was a "natural substance." The impacts of marijuana on the fetus have been found to include low birth weights, shorter gestational periods, and "colic-like" behaviors in some babies that make them difficult to settle[14].

In the medical world, the focus in pregnancy has traditionally been on the physical well-being of mother and fetus. This traditional model of medicine has only been partially successful in meeting the goals for pregnant women and their babies. This is even more apparent when other countries focusing on social as well as medical models of care have demonstrated greater success in reaching similar goals for pregnant women and babies.

We know that the delivery of social interventions, including psychological and emotional interventions, can have a dramatic impact on pregnant women, their babies, and their families[15]. We know that what happens during the prenatal period, infancy, and early childhood echoes forever in a child's life[16]. Furthermore, we know that these echoes can send a child down a life trajectory of resounding positive energy or one of chaos and instability. We have the resources to support both mothers and children during these periods. We have the ability to insure that the resounding echo children hear throughout their lives is supportive and conducive to a life filled with possibility and hope. Why then are the psychological, emotional, and social segments of pregnancy rarely the focus of, or included in, medical care, intervention programs, or treatment plans offered to women?

The focus of this book is to help develop an awareness of the psychological, emotional, and social work women do during pregnancy; to increase the understanding and significance of this work; and to develop an appreciation for the impact of this work on the baby both before and after birth. In order to meet these objectives, it is first necessary to explore why the pregnant period is the best period for intervention.

Why Begin in Pregnancy?

Pregnancy is often seen as an idyllic period when the mother-to-be waits patiently as she radiates a glow of love and eager anticipation. This, unfortunately, is rarely the case. In fact, it has been estimated that up to half of all pregnancies are unplanned, and these pregnancies in turn contribute to unexpected stress [17]. The Journal of the American Medical Association reported that, in 1994, 76% of unintended pregnancies occurred in women older than 20 years of age[18]. Even when pregnancies are desired and planned, the many changes that accompany a pregnancy create a host of new stressors on the mother-to-be. Pregnancy is a time of change for a woman: her body changes, her view of life changes, and her understanding of her relationships and her own life history change as well.

Transitioning from a woman without child to a woman with child requires a lifetime of changes and adjustments not only with the pregnancy and birth of the child, but each time the child reaches a new developmental stage. Having a child, whether through birth, adoption, marriage, or whatever circumstances, changes every molecule of a woman's being. Nothing is the same anymore; the woman shares her body, her time, her sleep, her health, her thoughts, her place in the world, her family, her friends, her roles in life…everything. Introducing a child into one's life means change, and change brings crises. However, the result of these changes and crises can be beneficial to both mother and child.

In the early 1960's, Grete Bibring and her colleagues[19] identified pregnancy as "a crisis that affects all expectant mothers, no matter what their state of psychic health". They defined *crisis* as "any turning point in a person's life, which leads to acute disequilibria, which with favorable conditions can lead to maturational steps toward new functions." Basically, this means that a crisis can be a positive event, allowing people to go through a period of chaos and confusion, eventually allowing them to move on to higher levels of understanding of themselves and greater behavioral maturation. Bibring's group also suggested that there are certain events throughout life that could be considered points of no return. The old ways of dealing with life were no longer relevant; the next phase of life demanded new approaches and tools to be successfully mastered [20]. They saw pregnancy as one of those "developmental phenomena," meaning that once a woman becomes pregnant, she can never go back to having never been pregnant and once a woman gives birth to a baby, she can never reverse the process. Conception and birth are two "points of no return" or passages from one phase of life to another. These passages impact a woman's life as no other experiences can. They cause her to rethink her approach to life and to re-evaluate the tools and skills she has and the manner in which she lives her life. A final addition to Bibring's beliefs was that these passages in life have a huge psychological impact on the pregnant woman and have far-reaching effects on the early mother-child relationship.

Another researcher from the late 1950's, Therese Benedek[21], described the transition during pregnancy into parenthood as a developmental phase. Through her work, she demonstrated how the periods of pregnancy and parenthood serve as opportunities for personality development as well as mental growth and development for the baby, the mother, and the father. She saw this as a time for the mother to work through some of her own past issues. Through her developing relationship with her infant, she was also provided the opportunity to organize and reorganize her ideas of mothering and her role as a mother.

In summary, normal, expected psychological work accompanies the woman's natural progression from pregnancy to birth. Some of this work includes re-thinking her childhood, how she was parented, and how she wants to parent her own child. She also begins to view the risks, benefits, and experiences in life as not only impacting herself, but also impacting her child and her relationship with that child; she begins to think about herself as not only a woman but as a mother, and she begins to transform the idea or image of her baby-to-be into her real child. Two central goals emerge as the most desirable end results of this very important work: (1) that the woman be successful at maternal role attainment— the acceptance and embodiment of the role of mother; and (2) that the woman develop an awareness of the fetus as her child and begin to form a bond with that child.

What Happens to Mothers Exposed to Multiple Risk Factors?

Pregnant women are often exposed to high risk situations, such as domestic violence, drug use (either by them or those around them), lack of support, homelessness, and multiple traumas. Histories of poor, dysfunctional family relationships leave them without any models by which to gauge their current circumstances. Even women in situations generally considered low risk are often challenged in pregnancy with regard to the isolation, changes in their body image, disruption of their career or life plans, and significant changes to their income and sometimes lifestyle, thereby creating an element of risk in their lives. There are also those women who consciously decide to expose themselves to certain risks in order to become mothers. These women often become pregnant despite immense odds and often endure continual risk not only to the life of their fetus, but to their own lives as well.

Through intervention programs as well as through high tech medical care, many of these risk factors are eliminated, lessened, or at least managed during pregnancy. How do women at risk deal with the situations affecting them? If they are investing most of their energy into eliminating or managing their risk factors, how are they able to do the necessary preparatory psychological and emotional work of pregnancy? Are there persons or programs available to help with this important work? If this work is not done in pregnancy, how does the mother's experience impact her development of the maternal role and her relationship with her child?

The answers to these questions depend on the many factors surrounding each woman's situation. Assessment of three areas can help to provide the needed information. These are areas of concern:

1) the risk factors involved

2) the woman's available support system

3) the circumstances behind the risk factors

First, what are the risk factors involved? The type and intensity of risk will have a great impact on not only the quality of the psychological and emotional work the mother does, but also on whether she does any of the work at all. For example, a woman who has a history of bulimia and subsequently develops a fear of the changes to her pregnant body, but has a wealth of support including her spouse, her parents, and a strong social network of friends, will most likely be able to do much of the psychological work necessary for a successful transition into motherhood. On the other hand, a woman who has a multi-generational family history of poverty, has a spouse working two jobs because she has had to quit hers when she developed medical complications with her pregnancy, and has no extended family or friends in the area, may have the ability to do the work necessary but may not have the support or opportunity.

Not only do the risk factors vary greatly between these two women, in terms of intensity, length of exposure to, and possible consequence of risk, they also vary greatly in terms of available support. Reva Rubin, a nurse researcher who studied pregnancy and developed a theory of the work of pregnancy, once stated "The absence of a female support system during pregnancy seems, in itself, a singular index of the high-risk pregnancy."[22] If you consider the added risk of a lack of support system on top of the other risk factors present, it becomes evident that the second area of concern should be "does the woman have an available support system in place?"

When evaluating the answer to this question, it is important to look first at the presence of support, generally found in relationships with the woman's spouse or partner, family members, friends, and acquaintances. Each of these potential support sources should then be evaluated as to the quality, type, and amount of support they could offer. A woman with a severely dysfunctional family may be surrounded by people who are not helpful or healthy. In some cases, while the family and friends of the pregnant woman believe they are being helpful and supportive, they may actually be draining on the psychological and emotional resources the mother-to-be may have.

The third area of concern to consider is "what are the circumstances behind the risk factors?" Many things come into play here. Does the woman have some control over the risk factors? Helplessness and/or hopelessness often compound the impact of a risk factor or stressor. Are these risk factors a part of the woman's pre-pregnant life? If so, the impact on the woman may be less than it would be for the intro-duction of a new risk factor, especially if she has not had any prepara-tion to deal with that particular issue. For example, is this a woman who has lived her whole life in poverty or is this a woman who has been forced to live in poverty due to her changing life circumstances resulting from her pregnancy. Another significant question to think about is whether this woman has the ability and/or the inclination to address the psychological work required of pregnancy. A woman with a painful relationship history of abuse and neglect has often developed a wealth of defenses to protect her from emotionally or psychologi-cally intense situations. For these women, thinking about what kind of mothering they had and what kind of mother they want to be might require them to consider abuse or neglect they experienced from their mothers. Often, women in this type of situation deny either the reality of their past, the impact of their experience on their present life, or both.

What About Those Women Unable to Do the Psychological Work Due to Mental Illness?

Another group of women to consider are those who are experiencing mental illnesses before or during their pregnancies. For many years, the medical community believed that pregnancy was one of the most stable times for women's mental health. Pregnancy was seen as a safe harbor from the development of mental illness, with the risk of mental illness falling in the postpartum period. Women having histories of mental illness often demonstrated fewer symptoms during pregnancy. These beliefs have been upheld by several research studies; however, other researchers have found these beliefs to be a little over simplified[23].

It is interesting to think about how these beliefs came about. During pregnancy, as women begin to do some of their psychological work, they tend to go "inside themselves." Most women grow quieter, think about things with a deeper awareness, think about the emotional content of their lives, and perhaps, even experience their life events in a different way. The birth of their child is often a long anticipated event; it becomes a goal to reach. As with any goal or anticipated event, the build-up and anticipation can be intense and sometimes stressful; however, it can also "hold" you together emotionally or psychically. Christmas is often a much-anticipated time for children. During the month of December, they are often on their best behavior, holding it all together. Once Christmas is within reach (usually the last day or two before), they frequently "fall apart" or act out. The stress of the wait and anticipation overwhelms them. Once the event actually arrives and then passes, the letdown can be enormous. The floodgates may open and all of those emotions come rushing out, often quickly followed by an emotional disappointment. This same pattern can often be seen with those persons affected by mental illness. When some goal or long anticipated event, especially a life-altering event, is in the future, the symptoms of their mental illness may fall to the background. This does not mean their mental illness has disappeared; it is merely not affecting them in the same manner. It is important to remember that mental illness is not a choice; a woman cannot simply turn it off or on depending on the current circumstances of her life, since many of these illnesses have their root in the biology of the body.

Many women do not experience a decrease in symptoms. A fear of harming their baby causes some to go off the medications that stabilize their symptoms. This can exacerbate their symptoms. The decision to continue using a particular medication or to stop its use is one that should be left to the woman and her prescribing health care provider. Furthermore, the changes in body chemistry and hormonal fluctuations during pregnancy can exacerbate symptoms or even facilitate the expression of symptoms not evident before pregnancy. Dealing with the issues related to mental illness requires a deeply significant level of intervention.

The Psychological Work of Pregnancy, Levels of Risk, and Focus of Intervention

It might be helpful to think about the levels of impact of psychological, as well as psychosocial, risk factors and issues during pregnancy. Level I would be the "normal" or "typical" psychological work every woman goes through as she transitions from woman without to woman with child. Pregnancy and the transition to motherhood are normal parts of maturation and development in the life course of women. Essentially the significance of risk at this level would be zero. Even if a woman chooses to be child-free, she has most often thought about what a child would mean to her, in her life, under what circumstances, and reevaluated her choices in life and her relationships with significant others. Some women may spend years doing this work, others only moments; it is an individual process. Some do this all at once, some intermittently, some smoothly and thoughtfully, yet others with resistance and dysfunctionally.

Level II would focus on those women who have only one stressor or risk factor present in their lives. For instance, unemployment, inadequate housing, or lack of support. Even with the presence of one risk factor or stressor, the impact on the woman, her developing pregnancy, and her transition into motherhood can be powerful. Intervention efforts would focus on supporting the woman in eliminating or modifying the specific factors involved.

Level III would include those factors that impact a woman and her child during pregnancy, such as the impact of abuse, stress, poverty, lack of support, a history of addiction, medical risk, the inability to cope with pregnancy-related changes, etc. All of these factors impact how a woman progresses through her pregnancy and the ultimate outcome status of her child. Women affected by these risk factors have not always been able to develop a good, working repertoire of coping skills and abilities to deal with additional stressors. Another crisis, such as pregnancy, further taxes their existing abilities, leaving them with little energy to deal with the multiple factors impacting their lives. Addiction may affect the decisions a woman makes around the use of substances during pregnancy; the attitude she has about the conception, the pregnancy, and the eventual birth of the child; and her ability to deal with stress and cope with the pregnancy physically and psychologically. Poverty generally limits choices; women are not able to choose the type of birth or afford the "baby things" needed for the child or appropriate maternity clothing—all of these filter into the woman's self esteem and affect her outlook, her ability to plan and prepare for this child, and her own sense of self as a woman and a mother.

Level IV would include those women who have experienced major loss and trauma in their lives and who remain emotionally unresolved with regard to those losses or traumas. It is not actually the fact they experienced a significant loss or that they were traumatized, it is rather the fact they have been unable to resolve the emotional issues around the loss or trauma. The losses most often include primary caregivers, special family members, or endeared friends. For some, it may not be the person they lost, instead it may be the nature of the loss or how the person died, or even the number of losses the woman might have experienced over a short period of time. Regardless of the nature of the loss issues, if the woman fails to heal her sense of loss, her relationships will be impacted. The impact of this lack of resolution may also reach beyond the existing relationships and extend into the developing relationship with the unborn child. Without intervention, this can spread to also infect the mother-child relationship following the birth of the baby.

The traumas generally include chronic relationship-related traumas such as sexual, physical, or emotional abuse or physical or psychological abandonment. It may be difficult to stop thinking of oneself as the traumatized child, especially if the relationships in which the trauma took place are still active and impacting the woman's life. The trauma becomes embedded in who the woman believes herself to be; it continues to permeate into her ability to form and nurture positive relationships. The traumatized woman may have generalized her experiences to many of her other relationships, making it difficult for her to trust anyone. Her ability to reciprocate any emotion within relationships may also be limited, which in turn also limits her ability to make and maintain supportive relationships even with professionals whom she may have initially sought out.

Even if the traumas and losses occurred when the woman herself was an infant or young child, the impact can be quite dramatic. This was noted many years ago in the classic report, "Ghosts in the Nursery," by Selma Fraiberg [24], who was able to locate remnants of women's experiences of being cared for during infancy and early childhood within the woman's caretaking relationship with her own infant. If the woman is unable to integrate her past traumas and/or losses into who she is or if she is unable to adequately heal emotionally, she will continue to be haunted by the past. When these issues have been embedded within a relationship context, this haunting will become evident with both the woman's present day relationships and her developing relationships. Essentially, the traumas and losses continue to be alive in their present lives.

Level V would include those women who have mild to severe psychological problems such as depression, anxiety disorders, or schizophrenia. Pregnancy can complicate these illnesses. Sometimes there can be an increase in already present anxieties, such as fear of death; new anxieties, such as losing sexual attractiveness in the eyes of their spouse or partner, can develop. Anxiety can be elevated to the level of preoccupation. This means the woman would focus on these issues and think about them almost all the time. High levels of anxiety in pregnancy have been associated with higher rates of postpartum depression.

Denial of pregnancy is another significant issue on this level. Without intervention, the woman often has difficulty developing a relationship with her fetus, and later with her child. With the proper support, women in this situation can come to terms with their pregnancy and decide whether they can parent a child or not. They should be supported with either decision; not all women want, nor are they able, to develop a relationship with the child they carry, and adoption should always be a supported alternative. Ambivalent mothers and those forced to parent unwanted babies have been shown to have the most dismal outcomes during their babies' infancies and throughout their subsequent childhoods[25].

It is important to think about the intervention needs for women at each of these levels. Within each level, there will be wide variations in impact, response, and need. Women falling into Level I will all have different capacities and abilities to go within themselves and re-evaluate the many significant components of their lives. Women falling into Levels II or III will experience these same variations in the ability to self-explore. They will also have variations in the number of risk factors, the quality of these factors, and the impact, response, and need evoked by the risk factor(s). The experiences of Level IV women may be further complicated by their lack of emotional resolution around loss or trauma issues. This lack of resolution often leaves them "tied up" emotionally and prevents them from being able to invest the needed emotional energy into the relationship with their baby before or after birth. Finally, women falling into Level V may be experiencing mild to severe forms of a particular mental illness and variations in symptom impact. Either way, the impact can be significant to the psychological work involved in developing a mother-child relationship. For example, within this level, there could be a well-supported, very self-aware and psychologically competent woman who has had a history of depressive periods, and there could be a woman who has battled schizophrenia since childhood and therefore never developed a strong network of coping skills and whose attempts at self-exploration only exacerbate her symptoms. The nature of the mental illness differs; however, the impact on the developing mother-child relationship remains the same, as it is not the actual presence of an illness but rather the interference of the symptoms of the illness, such as isolation, dissociation, confusion around reality, or delusions. (See Table 1.1 page. 18)

The majority of women will progress through pregnancy and into motherhood as long as they have a solid support system. So many

TABLE 1.1 LEVEL OF RISK: ISSUES, PROBLEMS, AND INTERVENTIONS

LEVEL	ISSUES	POTENTIAL PROBLEMS	INTERVENTION GUIDELINES
I	Normal or typical developmental tasks of pregnancy and an ordinary transition to motherhood	Normal developmental tasks Emotional changes Increased conflict, isolation, & anxiety Desire for resolution of past issues and relationships	Support Encouragement Discussion Processing Prompting movement through these issues Coaching and guidance
II	Presence of one psychological or psychosocial stressor or risk factor *Physical issue*	Presence of a stressor or risk factor	Support the elimination or modification of the stressor or risk factor Facilitation
III	Experiencing one or more psychological or psychosocial stressors or risk factors	Psychological/ psychosocial stressors Impact of stressors Desire for change	Support Coaching Facilitating Linking Coordinating Introducing Augmenting present resources
IV	History of Trauma & Loss	Reactivation of unresolved issues Ghosts from the Nursery	Therapy Revisiting the past
V	Mental Illness	Exacerbations Changes from old patterns	Therapy Hospitalization Medications

changes occur physically, psychologically, and socially during pregnancy, that having support allows the woman to accommodate these changes and meet the challenges they may bring. A normal developmental progression implies that under usual circumstances, women complete the needed psychological work and progress through this developmental stage with just the amount of struggle necessary to make it meaningful work.

As discussed above, Levels II and III represent those women who are currently experiencing at least one or more psychological or psychosocial stressors or risk factors. While these stressors or risks may be tolerable to the non-pregnant woman, the pregnant woman may feel overwhelmed with what this stressor may mean to her pregnant condition and to the subsequent birth of her child. Some women may have felt competent in dealing with a chronic stressor or risk when it only impacted them and before the idea of having their child also be exposed was introduced.

Risk factors may include things such as poverty, homelessness, domestic violence, age at time of pregnancy, lack of a support system, drug or alcohol abuse, illness, or recent job change. The goal of intervention with women in this category involves directive intervention aimed at helping the woman deal with the stressor(s) or risk factor(s) and to decrease the presence of or impact of the stressor(s) or risk factor(s). It is important to remember that it is not always the stressor or risk factor itself, but how the woman is dealing with it and how it is impacting her life. Some women are incredibly resilient and other women seem to have an ability to protect their children from the potential impact of a stressor or risk even when they have not been able to protect themselves from it.

Interventions for Level IV women will include all those types of interventions found in Levels I through III, as well as processing past issues. Some processing is done informally within certain relationships, specifically those dealing with parent-child relationship issues. For many women, formal pathways to processing and healing the past need to be established and this needs to happen through a therapeutic relationship with a professional therapist. Referrals to an appropriate provider must be made. If resources do not allow for such referrals, many self-help and support groups are available. In the latter case, the woman will not only need encouragement and support to begin attending a group, she may also require the interventionist to help her take the first few steps by attending one or more initial meetings with her.

Level V women obviously require not only support, guidance, and intervention, but they may also require psychological and/or medical treatment such as therapy, medication monitoring, and even hospitalization. The needs of these women frequently go beyond the scope of care available to women in pregnancy support groups, early intervention programs, or even general medical practices. Persons affected by mental illnesses can experience a range of symptoms and needs, which can be life threatening.

Other symptoms frequently seen in relation to mental illness might include refusing to get out of bed, stopping eating, sleeping all the time, refusing to leave the house, confusion around who they are, where they are, or the time period they are living in, major but seemingly unwarranted fears, rapid mood swings, confusion over reality, spacing out, or major anger outbursts. The presence of one or more of these or other symptoms does not necessarily indicate a major mental illness; however, it should warrant further evaluation with a trained mental health professional.

Women identified as having Level V needs will still need assistance with the needs from other levels. Likewise, women with Level IV needs will still need assistance with Levels I through III needs, and so on. A higher level of need does not eliminate the psychological and developmental work required during pregnancy. Sometimes a combination of interventions may be required. These could include medication monitoring for a bipolar disorder, psychotherapy for a long history of abuse and trauma, and intervention for housing needs and education around labor, delivery, and attachment issues. Support and guidance for the normal tasks of pregnancy may also be required.

The Impact of Motivation to Be Pregnant

There are many reasons women and teenagers become pregnant. Each of these reasons is significant in the understanding of the impact of the pregnancy on the pregnant woman, her developing fetus, and her eventual ability to form a nurturing, positive relationship with her child. It is again crucial to remember that several women experiencing similar paths leading to their pregnancies will all experience those paths in their own way, again dependent on their own capacity to deal with life circumstances, their personal psychological and emotional histories, and the support or lack of support they have in place.

As one example, in rural areas of Alaska, it is not uncommon to see teenage girls actively deciding to get pregnant in order to be able to leave their rural villages and towns to come to the city (in rural Alaska women are strongly discouraged from giving birth to their babies in their villages due to the lack of medical resources and the concern for fetal mortality and morbidity). For some girls, this also provided them the chance to separate from their families and to try to achieve personal independence. Other communities throughout the country have also found that women and girls see pregnancy as a rite of passage between childhood and adulthood. With the lack of formal avenues to make this transition, it is understandable that some women may equate the desire to "be an adult" and achieve personal independence with having a child.

Pregnancy can often be viewed as a "safe place" to escape lives more usually filled with abuse. It is not uncommon to find a girl with a chronic history of sexual abuse getting pregnant at a young age in an attempt to protect herself from a perpetrator. Some women find pregnancy to be one of the only times her partner or other members of her family treat her kindly and refrain from hurting her. Still other women find themselves pregnant due to experiences with rape by a stranger or acquaintance.

In many other countries and within certain systems in place in our country, it is not uncommon for pregnancy to be one of the periods when a woman is allowed access to benefits such as free medical care, nutritional programs, and housing facilities. These benefits are often withdrawn at some point following the birth of the child with the expectation the woman can then be self-sufficient. This line of thinking, however, has often been criticized as setting women up in a cycle of repeated pregnancy in order to stay tapped into various systems.

It is not uncommon to hear of women actively choosing to become pregnant in order to try and make their intimate relationship with their partner more secure or even to actually construct an intimate relationship based on the fact they are pregnant. Many marriages have taken place due to an accidental or intentional pregnancy. In addition, accidental or unintentional pregnancies, even without an overt underlying motivation, are extremely common.

Some women make very intentional choices to get pregnant based on the fact their "biological clock is ticking." It is becoming more and more common to see women putting off childbearing in order to focus on their career or because the pressure to be married at a younger age is not as powerful. Other women have often been working with infertility treatments for years, when they finally achieve pregnancy in their late 30's and early 40's. When working with the pregnant mother who has had a lengthy experience with infertility, it is important to evaluate the impact of her experience on her developing relationship with her child, as infertility has been identified as a potential risk factor for some. Along this same kind of physically-motivated pathway are girls and women who get pregnant as a statement of their sexual activity or simply to prove that their reproductive organs work the way they should.

A personal emotional path to pregnancy occurs for many girls and women. This path is usually motivated by very intimate feelings, a few well thought out, others more spontaneous. Certain of these personal motivations can be seen as risk factors, as for instance when girls and women become pregnant with the idea that having a child will help them deal with feelings of loneliness or being unloved. On the other hand, some women have put a lot of thought and emotional energy into deciding when they are most prepared to parent a child and integrate that child into their life. A competent, emotionally prepared woman giving birth to an anticipated and much wanted baby would definitely be seen as a protective factor for that mother and child relationship.

Pregnancy as a Time of Preparation

Much of the work and many of the ideas that underlie the writing of this book and the development of interventions during pregnancy was based on the work and theory of Reva Rubin[26]. Rubin studied what women do during pregnancy to transition into and prepare themselves for motherhood. She believed that in response to being pregnant, the woman searches for the essence and meaning of her relationships. The pregnant woman focuses mainly on her relationships with her parents, primarily her mother, and her partner or spouse. She wants to understand herself better and spends time discovering what is and is not important in her life.

It is important to understand the tasks Rubin identified as critical to successful role attainment. These tasks will be examined in more detail in Chapter 3, but a brief introduction to them seems key to the understanding of the larger picture of the psychological significance of pregnancy.

Rubin identified the four independent tasks in which pregnant woman engage:

1) Seeking safe passage for herself and her child throughout her pregnancy, labor, and delivery

2) Ensuring the acceptance of the child she bears by significant persons in her family

3) Binding-in to her unknown child

4) Learning to give of herself

Briefly, seeking safe passage begins with the woman first worrying about her own safety during the first trimester; in the second trimester, she focuses more and more on the child within her, often becoming more protective and emotional; and, by the third trimester, she becomes unable to separate her needs from her child's, causing her to demonstrate no real separation of the two and making the mother and child together the focus of concern.

The second task, ensuring acceptance, generally finds the mother both securing and assuring that the people important in her life are prepared to accept and care about her baby; in essence, she develops a support network for herself and the baby. This is also a period when she might reconsider the significance of persons in her life and decide to exclude or minimize their involvement.

In the third task, binding-in, the woman begins to think about her baby and herself as a "we." She moves into an emotionally protective place, assuming and practicing some of the roles she will need to take on. Her wishes and fears for the baby become central.

Finally, the fourth task, giving of oneself, begins in the first trimester, with the mother identifying and evaluating the changes she needs to make for her baby, such as stopping drinking or smoking. The child is not yet a reality so this is difficult for many women. As her pregnancy progresses, her ability to identify what she needs either to give up or give to her child changes, according to her balance of self-awareness and awareness of the needs of her fetus. All of these tasks support maternal role attainment, or the acceptance of the idea of becoming a mother and developing a relationship with the child, the beginning of bonding.

A second type of preparation going on in pregnancy is more related to the development of the mother-child relationship than to the development of the maternal role. This preparation involves the idea of images and fantasies. Recent research has demonstrated that the images and fantasies that a parent develops during pregnancy are strongly related to the type of relationship they eventually develop with their infant[27]. A good example of this is the mother who complains her baby in utero "just wants to keep me awake all night" and who, after the baby's birth, states her child cries just to upset her. The idea that the fetus/baby does things to purposely upset or bother the mother remains consistent. The ideas a mother forms about what her baby will be like, how her baby will act, how her baby will respond to her, and how she, herself, will fulfil her idea of what a mother should be like, will all affect the development and quality of the mother-child relationship. Although the images and fantasies developed during pregnancy often have long-term implications for what occurs after birth, these images and fantasies are also occurring during one of the mother's most flexible and vulnerable psychological and emotional times. This is good news for persons intervening with mothers who are creating negative or hurtful images of their babies, as work can be done to help these mothers shift these ideas. The impact of this preparatory work will be examined more closely in Chapter 4, addressing the impact on the developing mother-child relationship.

Summary

Hopefully, it has become clear that pregnancy is a very volatile and vulnerable time for women—physically, psychologically, and emotionally. Many changes occur and much energy goes into preparation for the next stage, that of taking on the role of "mother" and integrating a child into one's life. It is no longer appropriate to think only of a single goal in the period of pregnancy and childbirth. Instead, goals within the physical, psychological, and emotional domains should each be considered. These include:

PHYSICAL

The successful birth of a healthy baby to a healthy mother

PSYCHOLOGICAL

A woman who has successfully developed an idea of herself as a woman in relation to those she holds significant to her life and who feels competent to mother a child, with whom she has developed a beginning relationship and has begun to integrate into her life

EMOTIONAL

A woman who feels prepared to experience a range of feelings towards her baby, herself, and her life, understands these feelings are normal, and knows whom she can depend on to share these feelings

Embedded in these goals are the two different, but equally important, assignments taken on by the pregnant woman. The first of these is *taking on the role of mother* or doing the work necessary to assume the multiple roles required in being a mother. The second is completing the preparation necessary not only to welcome a child into the world, but also to integrate that child into the woman's life, or *developing the mother-child relationship*. The remainder of this book will be devoted to these issues, to the impact of these issues on the developing baby or child, and finally, to ways and means of fully assessing the pregnant woman.

Chapter 1

Points To Remember

The physical course of pregnancy has been the traditional focus of prenatal care in our society. Intervention programs based on maintaining the physical well-being of the pregnant woman and her unborn child have been moderately successful—decreasing teen pregnancy rates, but making little change in neonatal and maternal death rates. Finally, we are realizing that focus solely on the physical well-being of the pregnant woman is not adequate for healthy mother-child outcomes. Prenatal intervention requires a more holistic view, taking into consideration not only the physical realm, but the psychological and emotional realms, as well.

- The transition from a woman without child to a mother is a complete metamorphosis.

- A child's prenatal period and early childhood can have life-long effects.

- The motivation to be pregnant or to have a child can have a significant impact of the course and outcomes of pregnancy.

- Pregnancy should be thought of as a time of preparation.

- There are 5 levels of issues, potential problems, and interventions with regard to pregnant women:

  1. Normal or typical pregnancy

  2. Presence of one risk factor

  3. Presence of multiple risk factors

  4. History of trauma or loss

  5. Mental illness

- Pregnancy involves two central tasks:

    - taking on the role of "mother"

    - establishing the beginning of the mother-child relationship

In every conceivable manner, the family is link to our past, bridge to our future.

ALEX HALEY

2

Transitions

An exploration of the impact of pregnancy on a woman's personal belief system, her relationships with her parents—most specifically her mother—and her spouse or partner, and her body image.

Woman Without Child to Woman With Child

Childhood is often filled with games of fantasy and make-believe. Little girls pretend to be mothers, gently caring for their dolls, feeding them, rocking them, and putting them to bed. At some point, a young girl might help her mother by assisting in caring for the new baby in the family. As the young girl grows up, other opportunities to practice being a mother might occur, such as babysitting younger siblings or a neighbor's children. In adolescence, daydreams of marriage and children are common; for some, the birth of their own child might also take place. Even after a woman has had her first baby, fantasies of what it would be like with two, three, or even four children persist. Thoughts of what it would be like to have a boy, if they gave birth to a girl, or of having a girl, if they had a boy, are also entertained. Of course, this is an idyllic description of the opportunities available in the years from toddlerhood through young womanhood that allow girls to practice being mothers and to begin to develop mothering behaviors and ways of thinking.

When a woman begins planning to have a baby of her own for the first time, or when she discovers she is pregnant, all the input she has stored up over the years about mothering and baby care comes to the surface to be reexamined. The woman needs to pull those ideas out of her memory. She thinks about how they apply to her in the present and to the type of mother she wants to be. She also needs to reconsider the relationships she has had up to now, the impact these relationships have had on her, and what type of impact they may have on her child. Role renegotiations within these relationships are required. The roles once held within specific relationships will inevitably be altered with the addition of a baby. Finally, a transition in physical self-identity needs to occur. This involves incorporating the body changes experienced by the pregnant and postpartum woman into the existing ways the woman views herself.

This process changes little for the woman having her second, third, or any additional children. The actual transition from woman without child to woman with child, which occurs with the first baby, can cause a complete metamorphosis for a woman. However, each additional pregnancy forces a reconfiguration of the mother's life. Each pregnancy is unique, just as each new baby is unique. A woman's ideas of what it is to be a good mother and to mother a child change. Experience with previous children makes an impact, she has a better idea of what to expect, what worked with the last child, and what did not work. Over time, relationships will naturally change. After first babies, women may have developed new connections with other first time mothers, while their interactions with certain single friends became less frequent. Physically, a first baby changes a woman's body in both temporary and permanent ways. She will go into each new pregnancy with a different body than she began with in her previous pregnancies. In addition, the normal aging process will change a woman's body over time, causing her body to respond to each pregnancy in new and different ways.

These three components, reevaluating ideas about motherhood and babies, reevaluating relationships and making role adjustments, and accepting body changes, represent smaller components of the major task of transitioning from woman without child to woman with child. For the woman transitioning to the role of a mother to more than one child, these components are equally important; however, they may occur in more subtle ways and with less intensity. A woman's self identity needs to change to embrace her new baby physically, psychologically, and emotionally.

First time mothers need to be able to accept themselves as mothers and believe they can fulfill the role. Of course, all mothers have days when they feel more competent and successful at mothering than other days, as well as days when they feel absolutely worthless and unable to fulfill the role. These fluctuations are normal and expected; women should be encouraged to discuss both the good days and the bad days without guilt. It is only when the bad days outnumber the good that it becomes an issue of concern.

In this chapter, the process of change in the pregnant woman's ideas and beliefs, relationships, and body will be explored. These sections focus on the first time mother, the woman who is making the greatest transition of woman without child to woman with child. It is important to remember that this process of change occurs with women in each subsequent pregnancy. This process of change, however, tends to be less intense and less dramatic in most women who are already mothers.

Changing Ideas and Beliefs

Changing her ideas and beliefs involves a progression of steps throughout the processes of pregnancy, childbirth, and into motherhood. Women begin to re-evaluate whether what they believed about pregnancy is actually holding true. They begin to incorporate the information they gather from relatives, friends, and professionals.

They compare old ideas to new information. The goal is to develop an understanding and acceptance around what this pregnancy means and how it fits into their lives. For example, a woman who has never been pregnant might hold a belief that pregnancy is a special time where a woman feels at her best. She might anticipate the pregnancy with joy and excitement. When she actually becomes pregnant, if she does feel the best she has ever felt, this will solidify the belief; if her pregnancy is stressful and full of emotional highs and lows, her beliefs may shatter, requiring her to work out a new model to represent her pregnancy.

Most pregnancy beliefs relate to issues like what is best to eat, what types of exercise are most beneficial, and the right amount of sleep to get—all issues of self-care. Regardless of the current medical or professional support for new ideas, many women cling to old beliefs based on their own mothers' experience. Cigarette smoking and alcohol use are prime examples of this. The importance of stopping smoking during pregnancy is well-publicized. The relationship between smoking and low birth weight babies is well-accepted. However, many women reject this idea, since "my mother smoked when she was pregnant with me and I was born healthy."

Similar issues come up over alcohol use during pregnancy. The effects of alcohol use during pregnancy have been well known for years. Yet, many women insist it is safe because, again, their mothers drank and they are fine. As can be seen from these two examples, beliefs rooted in families are often difficult to shake.

The beliefs the woman might hold definitely play a role in how she views her pregnancy, impending birth, and subsequent relationship with her child. More importantly, however, is her ability to reconsider past beliefs and ideas, to let go of things that no longer apply, and to incorporate new information. This ability will be required when the woman has her baby in her arms and needs to balance her beliefs about what her baby would be like with what her real baby is like.

Pregnancy-related beliefs are not the only ones tested and reconsidered. Women also need to examine what was important in their lives and what those things mean now that she has a baby on the way. Having a fancy, fast car may have been a priority for the woman prior to having a baby; now, however, having a safe, reliable car may become the priority. Being able to go out with friends spontaneously may have been a priority; now the woman may see having a warm, comfortable, inviting home as coming first.

The advent of the pregnancy brings on a reconsideration of many of the ideas and beliefs that the woman once held true. She becomes more introspective[1]. The most significant beliefs are those impacting the baby. Many already-established ideas and beliefs may still hold true, some may need to be forgotten, and some may need readjustment. Pregnancy is, indeed, a life-changing event.

Relationships

Relationships with Parents

Pregnancy forces the woman to begin to look at her relationships with her own parents, especially her mother[2]. She begins to ask herself many questions. What was good about my relationship with my mother? What was good about my relationship with my father? What did they do right in raising me? What did they do that was not good? What could they have done better? What do I wish they had done? Why did they do what they did? Pregnant women begin to look deeper into these relationships. They think more about why certain things happened rather than only about what happened. They try to take their parents' views and see them from the parent perspective. They decide what they liked and want to pass on to their children, and they decide what they would like to leave behind and avoid doing to their children. They begin to think about the things they have always taken for granted and re-evaluate them. They think about how, as children, they saw their mothers and how, now as mothers, they want their children to see them.

The woman transitioning into a mother needs to be able to feel she can competently fulfill that role. To do this, she needs her parents' support and acknowledgment. Her parents need to begin to see her as a mother to their grandchild, not simply as their daughter. They need to believe she can be a good mother and that she can make good decisions. In other words, they need to see her as an individual, separate from them, and capable of mothering a child.

The woman also needs to be able to separate from her parents in a way she has not had to in the past. She now has to accept the dependence of this baby she is to have. She has to be the person in charge and responsible. In order to accept this dependency of her child, she needs to feel independent of her parents.

Independence can empower her, making it easier for her to assume and accept the role of mother. In order to understand this idea, it is important to understand exactly how independence is defined. Independence does not mean functioning totally alone or in isolation. It does not mean a loss of connection or closeness. Independence means being responsible for oneself, being able to make independent decisions, and having a strong belief in oneself, while being able to maintain and enjoy close, emotional connections with others. Being truly independent requires social relationships, as it is through these relationships we gain the necessary self-esteem and feedback to support our independence.

This move for separation or independence from her parents, particularly her mother, is difficult and often emotional. Women find themselves in arguments and emotional discussions over what is right and wrong regarding pregnancy, childbirth, and parenting. Women begin to challenge many of their mothers' ideas with more current knowledge they have gained through their medical providers, peers, and their own reading and research. They also need to find a place for the wisdom of experience that the women of their family pass on to each other regarding these same issues. This is a process of back and forth, an attempt to balance things taken from the family and the woman's past with the current knowledge, information, and the woman's desire to be separate.

This process of separation can be seen in women through the way they deal with ideas around pregnancy, childbirth, and parenting. The woman who is more passive allows her own mother to take over, telling her what to buy, how to feed, and what kind of schedule to set up. This indicates that this woman is still quite dependent on her own mother and having difficulty separating. Many teen women fall into this category. They have not yet been able to complete normal teen separation or individuation from their parents, as this is generally a task of adolescence. Consider this case example:

> *A 23-year-old mother was living with her spouse in her*
> *mother's home. Her mother, the grandmother, was in the*
> *medical profession in a very minimal capacity, although she*
> *believed she knew how to manage any situation, especially*
> *involving babies. It became known, however, that this grand-*
> *mother had had involvement with child protective services*
> *when her children were smaller. The mother in this example*
> *allowed her mother to take control of the baby care. She made*
> *no independent decisions; she deferred to the grandmother.*
> *When the baby was four weeks old, the grandmother claimed*
> *she had to "discipline" the baby for not sucking her bottle*
> *correctly (the baby was having difficulty latching on). To*
> *discipline her, the grandmother would yell at the baby and*
> *yank the bottle out of her mouth, telling her to "do it right"*
> *and "you know better." The mother never attempted to argue*
> *or challenge the grandmother's actions or ideas.*

In this example, it is obvious that the grandmother had a great deal of power over the daughter and the baby. What grandma proclaimed as correct was the law. This grandmother protected her power by accompanying the daughter on all her doctor appointments and professional visits regarding the baby. This young mother, while independent in many ways, including being educated, married, and employed, had not been able to separate from her own mother in order to become a woman capable and confident in mothering her new baby.

Other women who have had chaotic or difficult relationships with their own mothers also tend to fall into this category. Their relationships often demonstrate a confusing imbalance between mother and child (where the child often acts as a parent to their own parent, but craves being taken care of by that same parent). The women in these groups do challenge their mothers' input; however, while the challenges are usually quite emotional and intense, the women eventually give in to their mothers (leading to further difficulties around the build up of resentment between the woman and her mother). The women in this group are often the ones whose own mothers seem to take over the mothering role for the new baby a majority of the time, as in the case just described.

The second type of woman demonstrates more ability to balance. She can take in new information, come up with her own ideas and preferences, but still listens to her mother. She incorporates only what makes sense to her and seems to fit into her idea of mothering. While conflict does occur, it is generally temporary and able to be worked through between the woman and her mother. In these cases, the woman's mother is also able to respect her daughter's right to make choices and is able to trust that her daughter will be a good mother, even if she doesn't always agree with her. The women in this group tend be more individuated from their parents, have achieved some level of independence without their parents, and may often have a supportive spouse who can reinforce the woman's decision-making capability.

The third type of woman is the woman who may overcompensate by totally cutting herself off from her parents, particularly her mother. This woman does not accept outside information well; she believes she knows what she wants and how she wants to do it. She may look down on her own parents' abilities and behaviors. She may not want to consider any part of who she is or what she does as tied to her parents. This is often an indicator of a woman who has had relationship difficulties with her parents in the past. She may have good reason to totally separate herself from her parents, perhaps past abuse or trauma. She may be caught up in an unresolved conflict with her parents that she deals with by cutting off contact. Whether for good or bad reasons, the woman who is caught up in her anger and believes she can do it all alone is often setting herself up for failure and disappointment. This, in turn, could lead to relationship difficulties with her child. Bigger problems develop if the woman begins to refuse input of others that could be active and helpful in her life in appropriate ways. These women tend to be quite emotionally dependent on their parents but are able to "pretend" they are not by just physically separating from them. Often these women and their parents will reconnect once the baby is born; however, it is often a volatile connection and usually based on needs (babysitting, money, etc.).

The main task of re-working the parent-child relationships is to begin to let go of merely being their parents' daughter. The woman now has to become her child's mother. This requires, however, that her parents accept her new role and let go of their daughter in yet another way. Even if she has been a successful, independent, professional, long-married woman, the fact she is now becoming a mother gives a whole new dimension to their relationship. The mother's parents need to accept that their daughter is now going to be a mother and they are going to be grandparents. Some women and their parents accept these changes without hesitancy or difficulty, others negotiate and renegotiate these changes until the baby arrives, and still others continue in conflict, often allowing this conflict to enter into the grandparent-mother-child triangle of relationships. Much depends on the social skills of the people involved and the type of relationships that were in place prior to the woman's pregnancy.

One final issue related to parents concerns the mother who has experienced the death of one or both of her parents. Oftentimes, significant life events such as graduation, marriage, and having a baby can reactivate the feelings of loss. The mother-to-be might not even realize why she is feeling sad or fearful. General conversation about relationships with parents could open the door to discussion around the current effects of parent loss.

Relationship with Spouse or Partner

Women with spouses, partners, boyfriends, or significant others also need to adjust their relationships. During pregnancy, psychological defenses are more relaxed, which allows for reworking the relationship between the pregnant woman and her husband[3]. Marital or partnered relationships usually begin as intimate partnerships. They become a couple. Each person of the couple focuses their attention on the other. When decisions are made, they are based on only the needs of the two of them. Many women describe this period of their lives as spontaneous, "we could just decide to go to a movie and dinner any night of the week" and active, "I played every sport I could, so did my husband, we were gone every night." Many women also describe this as a time of dual incomes, which provided them with much more available money to spend on themselves and their goals. The pre-pregnancy period is also described as being filled with intimacy. Their sex lives were spontaneous, and they had energy to expend on each other without the competition of a third person.

When the woman becomes pregnant, this all changes. While pregnancy may be a much-anticipated event, it is also life changing for the woman and her husband or partner. The baby may not be physically in their arms yet, but the idea of a baby is swiftly moving into their everyday lives. Both the woman and her partner watch the woman's body change; these changes trickle down into their sex lives and their ability to be intimate with each other. For some couples, it is a time of surprise and celebration as they become creative and learn new ways to enjoy being with each other. For others, it becomes a period of distaste and rejection. Some men become fearful of "hurting" their pregnant partner or lose interest in her during this period. Some women feel so self-conscious that they begin to reject their partners' attempts to be close to them. These feelings vary from couple to couple.

As a couple, the woman and her partner begin to observe other couples with babies. They may even *borrow* children from others to see what caring for a child will be like. They look at the demands and the responsibilities. They have to deal with how this baby will impact their relationship. For example, one woman shared the way that her husband would playfully tease her, as they were going to sleep, that she needed to get up because it was her turn to get the baby (who was not yet born). He would laugh, and tell her he would do it this time. This little exchange would lead to a discussion around the demands of the baby on the two of them and how they were going to meet these demands. This example also illustrates how couples pretend and try out various pieces of the parent role.

Another significant issue, similar to that of the work a woman does with her mother, is the ability of the man to support his wife or partner in her transition to mother and the new behaviors and beliefs she begins to display. Emotionally, this is extremely difficult work for the woman. She is often not aware of how much she is changing; she only experiences the roller coaster of emotion she is feeling. A supportive partner who is able to listen to the pregnant woman's ideas and feelings can play an important role in both how easily and how successfully the changes are made. An unsupportive partner often leaves the woman with feelings of isolation and frustration. If such feelings continue unresolved, there is a strong likelihood that they can carry over into the beginning relationship with their child.

Integrating Body Changes

Pregnancy means a total transformation of the woman's body. While some of these changes fade away after the baby is born, many changes remain for a long time, or even permanently. Body changes all need to be incorporated into the woman's self-identity, as part of her transition to woman with child. During the pregnancy itself, a woman's body goes through a series of transformations. Her belly begins to swell and her breasts begin to enlarge. For some women, these changes are new, exciting, and welcomed. For others, these changes are overwhelming, hated, and unwelcomed. Still others vacillate between days when the changes are exciting and days when they just want to get back to normal. Some women view these changes as temporary. Some hold onto the belief that when the baby is born their bodies will make some attempts to return to a pre-pregnancy state. Some become frightened their bodies will never be the same again.

For example, a common myth in adolescence, and even into adulthood, is the idea that once a woman births a baby her vaginal structures "become all stretched out," making sexual relations less desirable for men. The belief is that men prefer sex with a tighter vagina and can tell during intercourse whether a woman has given birth to a baby or not. This, of course, is not true. But for the young woman who believes her body will be altered so greatly that her partner will not find sexual intimacy as satisfying or will find her to be inadequate, the impact of the pregnancy changes could be difficult to deal with.

The experience of an increase in breast size can also be viewed as positive or negative. While some women have shared excitement that "when I am pregnant is the only time I have big breasts," others may find themselves uncomfortable with the changes, the effect on their outward appearance, and their partner's response. One woman shared that her husband was so excited over the pregnancy-related growth of her breasts that she feared when they eventually returned to their pre-pregnancy modest size he would no longer find her as desirable. Women dealing with the breastfeeding-related changes after the baby is born can also require transition. Again, these can be found pleasurable or seen as a nuisance.

Permanent changes to the woman's body may include things like stretch marks or scarring from a cesarean section. These marks can be initially very disturbing to women. Once they are able to accept them and integrate them into part of their own self-identity, the fear or worry about how these might alter their lives diminishes.

Specific Body Issues

Any women with issues around their bodies, such as anorexia or other eating disorders and sexual abuse or other bodily traumas, would be considered at a higher risk for accepting body changes related to pregnancy. For the anorexic or bulimic mother, the goal to strive for has been to be thin, often unrealistically and sometimes dangerously thin. The eating-disordered mother may actually be unable to connect the changes in her body with the baby, seeing them only as indicators she is "getting fat." Even if she has had treatment in the past and has stabilized, the jolt of the changes to her body could re-awaken some of those old issues, requiring mental health intervention for the health and safety of both the mother and the baby.

In women who have experienced sexual abuse, rape, or other bodily traumas, the experience of pregnancy and the changes in their bodies may mean many different things. In active incest cases, a pregnancy might temporarily stop the abuse. Men who sexually molest young girls often do so because they are sexually interested in young, child-like bodies. Pregnancy brings about womanly changes, making the young girl undesirable. If this were the case, the pregnancy would be a safety zone for the mother-to-be. In some sexual abuse cases, and in many rape cases, the past trauma done to the body may multiply and intensify anxiety, distress, and fear in many mothers-to-be. If the pregnancy was the result of sexual abuse or trauma, this only increases the difficulty for the mother-to-be and warrants mental health intervention. For some women who may have felt healed around the past traumas to their bodies, the pregnancy can reawaken memories of those negative experiences and feelings. While they might have become successful at accepting their bodies and in feeling okay with the reactions people had toward their bodies, the pregnancy may make people take notice and make comments. This type of reaction could possibly raise the mother-to-be's self-consciousness, causing her discomfort or distress around the new attention being paid to her body. Her feelings of vulnerability increase.

Another body image-related issue involves what the mother perceives the pregnancy to represent to others. For women who are uncomfortable with their sexuality or women who have been trying to keep their sexual activity discrete and hidden, the pregnancy says to others, "this woman has been having sex." This idea can be very uncomfortable and scary for some women. They may believe that others will become judgmental of them and criticize them for their actions. Issues such as being unmarried, very young, or an older mother (over the age of 35) might intensify the worries the woman has around other people's perceptions. Other women may view their pregnancy as representing a miracle created with the one they love, and this may cause them to see others as valuing the pregnancy and seeing it as a positive thing.

High Risk Considerations

Not all women exist in an environment where they have the opportunity to begin to imagine motherhood, to explore their relationships, or to think about the changes a baby will bring to their lives. Their lives may be filled with chaos or trauma that require them to focus their energies on other critical issues. For some, homelessness or poverty-related issues, such as hunger, may focus the woman's attention and energies on survival rather than on self-evaluation and personal growth. Others may have been forced to take on early responsibility for younger siblings or relatives, which may have left them resentful of having to "mother." Finally, there are those individuals who, although they have witnessed and practiced mothering, may not have had good role models or education; they may have developed inadequate or dysfunctional mothering behaviors and attitudes, of which they remain very protective.

In all of these scenarios, it is not that the women or girls do not engage in the psychological work. Much of the work described is not purposely thought about or talked about unless someone brings it up for discussion. It does occur, however. The adequacy of the work is related to the variety of resources and supports available. For many women, the work during pregnancy and the idea that they will be incorporating a child into their lives is often a strong motivator for change both within themselves and within their social world.

Summary

The first-time mother has typically viewed life only in the context of her pre-pregnancy world. This may have included her partner or spouse, her parents, her brothers and sisters, her friends, her work colleagues, her teachers and fellow students, etc. These relationships and her role in them provided a structure within which she would make her decisions about what to do, when to do it, what to try, and what to say no to. Once pregnant, this structure transforms into a new one, usually with both her and her fetus and later her real baby as the center, incorporating others around this new center.

When a woman does not begin to think about her life choices in the context of her child, this should be a red flag to those around her. Unfortunately, in our present society, there is not a lot of support for a pregnant woman making decisions within the context of what is best for her and her child. Consider this case:

> *A 21-year-old, single woman, pregnant with her first baby*
> *was in a financial situation that required her to work as long*

as possible during her pregnancy. She was employed as a teller in a market, which required her to stand for several hours. As her pregnancy progressed, her health became affected. Her doctor advised her not to stress her body by being on her feet for so long. She requested a stool to use to rest upon when she was working at the cash register. Her employer denied her request and refused to reassign her. Her requests were denied a second time, even when she brought in a doctor's note supporting her request.

This, unfortunately, is a common example of our lack of support for pregnant women and parents in our society.

In summary, when a woman becomes pregnant she begins to make a transition from a woman without child to a woman with child. This is a major step in any woman's life. Becoming a woman with child means never again being a woman without child. Even if the pregnancy were to end under tragic circumstances, such as miscarriage or fetal death, the woman would still have made some of the transition to a woman with child. Even in circumstances where the woman may birth a healthy baby but, out of some necessity, her baby cannot remain in her care, she has still transitioned. Becoming pregnant means that the woman has taken an irreversible step in how she views and defines herself. For some women, this step is taken with ease, but for others, it can be overwhelming. The success of this transition depends on the woman's willingness to look at the need to make that transition, the cooperation of those around her, and the woman's own willingness to let go of some things from the past to make room for the new.

Chapter 2

Points To Remember

Beginning as young children, we start to develop an understanding about what mothers do, who mothers are, and how mothers should behave. As we mature, our understanding of a mother changes. For instance, an older child may develop a better understanding of a mother's limitations, while a younger child thinks a mother can "do it all." Pregnancy can also bring our understanding of a *mother* to a new level.

- Fantasy and make-believe are helpful in understanding and "trying on" the role of a mother

- A mother has to reevaluate and integrate new information with each new baby

- Over time, new information we collect reshapes our ideas of a mother

- Our relationships, especially with our parents, are reevaluated with each new baby

- A pregnant woman needs to integrate the idea that she is not only her parents' daughter but also her own child's mother

- A pregnant woman's relationship with her spouse or partner goes through a period of reevaluation

- A woman's body changes as the result of a pregnancy; these changes need to be integrated and accepted

- Risk factors can interfere with the necessary psychological work the pregnant woman needs to work through to ensure a successful transition to the role of mother

Mother, can't you see I've got to live my life the way I feel is right for me, might not be right for you, but it's right for me.

SARAH MCLACHLAN, ELSEWHERE

3

Becoming a Mother

This chapter is a review and discussion of Reva Rubin's four tasks found necessary for successful attainment of the maternal identity. The tasks of Seeking Safe Passage, Ensuring Acceptance of the Child, Binding-In to Her Unborn Child, and Learning to Give of Herself are discussed in terms of how the pregnant woman develops her maternal identity and her future relationship with her baby.

Acceptance of the Maternal Identity

In addition to the psychological and emotional work a woman completes during pregnancy, there are also several tasks she must undertake to see herself as a mother and to welcome her baby into the world. In Rubin's[1] book, *Maternal Identity and the Maternal Experience*, she describes the result of many years of research observing and interviewing pregnant women and mothers following the birth of their babies. As mentioned briefly in Chapter 1, Rubin identified four tasks a pregnant woman completes during her transition from pregnant woman to mother. These are *Seeking Safe Passage, Ensuring Acceptance of the Child, Binding-In to Her Unborn Child,* and *Learning to Give of Herself.* Each of these plays an important role in the success of the woman in assuming the identity of a mother and in developing a relationship with her child.

Seeking Safe Passage

During the first trimester of pregnancy, from the time of conception through her third month, a woman becomes concerned about her own well-being. When she first misses a period or develops symptoms such as breast tenderness, she may believe she is pregnant, but she may also fear that something is wrong with her, perhaps an illness. In spite of the availability of over-the-counter pregnancy tests, many women do not accept the fact that they are pregnant until they hear those words from their medical professional. In addition, over-the-counter types of tests are often expensive, inaccurate if improperly done, and for some, embarrassing to purchase. Women with histories of difficulties with their menstrual cycle or those with infertility issues may have difficulty accepting the idea they have actually become pregnant. Likewise, women with either personal or family histories of various illnesses such as cancer or recurrent infections may initially believe the symptoms of pregnancy to be related to those illnesses or conditions, never even considering that they might be pregnant. During this first trimester of pregnancy, it makes sense that women may become anxious over the changes to their bodies and fear for their own health and safety. Even if they recognize that they are pregnant, some women, especially first time mothers, may fear what pregnancy will do to them and their bodies, as well as fearing for their own survival through the pregnancy. These thoughts are often fleeting or even unspoken and can be very difficult for the practitioner or professional to identify. It is important to realize, however, that these types of reactions do occur and that it is normal and natural for women to pass through a period of increased anxiety over their own health and safety when they are first pregnant.

Sophia's first pregnancy required an emergency cesarean section to save her baby, who was having problems. During this procedure, the anesthesia she received was supposed to be localized to only her pelvic region, so she could remain alert.

Problems developed when the anesthesia medicines spread throughout her body, numbing her ability to feel herself breathe. Although she was actually safe, she felt as if she were suffocating and would die. This was a very traumatic experience for her. When she found she was pregnant with her second child, all of the trauma of this experience returned and she began to panic that the same thing or something worse would happen and she would surely die with this pregnancy. By her second trimester, she was no longer feeling a sense of panic; however, as the delivery neared these issues came up again and required intervention. Having her prepare for the delivery by having specific support people present "to watch the anesthesiologist" helped to decrease her anxiety.

By the second trimester, the fourth through sixth months of pregnancy, the concern of the woman shifts from herself to the safety of her unborn baby. Many things occur that cause this shift. The woman's body may have begun to make noticeable changes, increasing the woman's awareness of the baby inside her. Also, by this time, the woman may have begun to gather and/or receive information on the growth of and possible threats to the safety and well-being of her fetus. As her belly begins to grow, the baby inside her seems to become more vulnerable to insult from the outside world, causing her to want to protect it more and more. She often shies away from others she feels may be hurtful to her baby. She may also modify her behaviors and activities that she now sees as carrying an element of danger and potential harm to the baby, such as skiing or driving fast.

As the woman enters her third trimester of pregnancy, months seven through nine or when birth occurs, she begins to be unable to separate the baby from herself; she thinks of them as a unit. She concerns herself with the safety of herself and the baby—what affects one of them affects the other. She views certain things in her environment as equally dangerous to both of them. The woman often feels an increase in anxiety concerning death—hers, the baby's, or both. As her body begins to grow larger, she may experience a loss of normal function; moving around is not as easy, and completing what she used to do with ease now becomes more of a challenge. She begins to worry about her own body—will she really be able to birth this baby that seems so huge inside of her? She also worries about the baby—will the baby be whole and healthy or will the baby be missing body parts and damaged?

These real and imagined dangers motivate the woman to begin to take some control over her environment and the world around her. She begins to want to lessen or eliminate as much of the danger and threat to herself and her baby as she possibly can. In order to do this, the woman takes multiple pathways. One of the most common of these pathways is to gather as much knowledge as possible. She does this by continuously seeking, accessing, and collecting information from different sources and in various ways. She may read everything she can get her hands on, such as baby books, parenting pamphlets, or magazine articles. She may watch movies or television programs about pregnancy, childbirth, or parenting. She may explore the Internet for information and stories, which help inform her. She may ask about and listen to multiple examples of other women who gave birth successfully, as well as ones who experienced difficulty. She may seek out and interview other experienced mothers. While women usually attempt to find other women in their same age group, they will also want information from other family, friends, or acquaintances. The goal of all these behaviors is to know what is probable, learn about what is possible, and explore different ways of coping and dealing with both the probable and the possible. As with any other life event, the more one knows and the more one prepares, the more competent one will feel in handling anything that comes up.

During this process of gathering information and knowledge, it is inevitable that the woman will discover or hear information about tragic outcomes for babies, mothers, or both. These types of stories often increase the woman's anxiety, her fear, and her feelings of vulnerability. Some stories, especially those of women giving birth to multiple babies, may overwhelm the woman's sense of her own ability and lead to feelings of inadequacy. These types of feelings may be spoken or unspoken. Often, women may be afraid to discuss what they consider negative feelings such as fear or inadequacy. It is important to support the mother-to-be in whatever feelings she is experiencing.

Things once thought of as normal or ordinary may now become potential hazards in the world of the pregnant woman. The potential risks of driving a car, such as accidents from speeding, other's carelessness, or slippery roads, take on a new level of seriousness. Other forms of travel, such as flying in an airplane or sailing on a boat, may seem too risky even to contemplate. Even taking walks in "uncontrolled" areas, such as roadsides, hilly areas, or steep stairways, creates a risk of falling or slipping.

As the woman masters this task of ensuring safe passage for herself and her baby, she will often look to others for support and guidance. Her family and her medical provider will most often be her first choices. Family can be a good choice or a poor choice depending on the quality of the woman's interactions with her family and her family's ability to support her in a healthy and positive manner. Even in the closest families who have always provided support, the timing of this particular pregnancy may not have been the most welcomed of events. Family members may have wanted the woman to finish college first, she may be a young teen mother-to-be, or the family may not like the woman's choice of partners. There could be any combination of circumstances and histories which could adversely affect the ability of the woman to seek out and receive emotional support from her family members.

The woman seeks safe passage for herself and her baby through trying to gain control over all the things she perceives as uncontrollable or threatening. She will seek out information and real life examples to help her make sense of what she feels is threatening and to help her gain some sense of control over the new way she looks at the world around her. When this quest for knowledge fails to provide the needed assurances, the woman will often turn to "luck," superstition, and prayer. Renewing one's faith in religion or a spiritual world often takes on a new significance.

The woman's choice of health care providers will also serve to give her peace of mind throughout her attempts to maintain the safety of herself and her baby. The pregnant woman frequently sees her physician, nurse practitioner, midwife, or the local hospital as a safe haven from all the dangers she feels threaten her or the baby. The woman experiences a heightened sensitivity to physical pains, small spots of vaginal blood seem overwhelming, and fetal movement or lack of movement send off fireworks that there may be a problem. Although others may attempt to tell her these things are "normal," until she actually hears that from a member of her health care team, she will often not accept it. In fact, the woman may become so attached to her health care provider that she will insist on maintaining a relationship with him or her in spite of concerns voiced about that provider's ability to care for patients. Additionally, the change or absence of a woman's health care provider when the delivery of the baby is at hand can be a crisis for the delivering woman. Rationally, she may know the provider's absence is necessary, but emotionally, she may be ill-equipped to deal with the threat to both herself and her baby that the change may represent in her perception.

During this period, the woman may experience life with a new intensity. She may become more aware of her environment, more sensitive to the behaviors of others, or feel more isolated and alone. Disappointments may be experienced with a heightened sense of emotion. Fears of threats to the life of the mother or child, such as stillbirth or premature birth, can be devastating. Other circumstances can bring on severe emotional reactions as well, such as when the sex of the baby does not correspond with the wishes or desires of the mother, or when the baby has different physical attributes than imagined.

The goal of this task is to ensure the safe birth of a healthy infant to a healthy mother in a safe environment. The work for the pregnant woman is to manage real and imagined threats to her well-being, her unborn child, and the mother-child unit. It is important to remember that whether real or imagined, anything perceived by the mother as a threat *is* a threat and should not be dismissed casually by those around her. The concerns of the pregnant woman should be treated with respect and sensitivity. Worry about any of these "threats" helps prepare the woman to keep her baby safe by allowing her to do the emotional and physical work necessary to ensure safe passage. The work of this task is just as important as the outcome. The pregnant woman needs to learn to look at her environment in a different way— she needs to learn how to manage the risks in her environment, and she needs to realize her significance in protecting her child. Hopefully, the work she does during her pregnancy will generalize and allow her to apply the same behaviors and strategies to future situations.

Ensuring Acceptance of the Child

The second task involved in developing the maternal identity is ensuring acceptance of the child-to-be by significant persons. Pregnancy, particularly a first pregnancy, puts a great deal of pressure on the woman to examine how this child she carries will or will not fit in with her current social network. How will her family relate to this baby? Will they accept him? How will her husband feel about the pregnancy? Will she be able to work after she has this baby? Will being pregnant affect how her co-workers relate to her? How will her friends receive the news? Will they still want to include her in their outings and activities? Many questions pass through the mother's mind.

When the woman first learns that she is pregnant, the impact of her pregnancy on her social world may seem overwhelming. This social world, her family, friends, co-workers, and acquaintances, has helped define who she is with regard to others and has helped her determine her personal identity. Any losses, changes, or challenges to this social network can be experienced as an attack on her own person. As the pregnancy progresses and it becomes more and more apparent that she is pregnant, this impact and its consequences intensify. Some women will believe that being pregnant is "not a big deal" and that people around her will adapt and she will remain the same as she always was with them. This is often not true; however, some social relationships are not capable of accepting and integrating the pregnancy of a woman or the added demands of a woman with a child. When rejection occurs, the woman may find herself disillusioned and critical of herself, especially when she is not able to relate the impact of her pregnancy with the rejection by others.

The most significant relationship that is affected is the marital or partner relationship. The closer and more supportive the relationship was prior to the pregnancy, the more easily the pregnancy is accepted by both the mother and father. The couple has to renegotiate how they relate to each other. Pregnancy changes the interests, activities, and intimacy of both partners. Some marriages or partnerships have invested a lot of time and energy in planning the future—when they would buy a house, when they would take that trip, and when a child would best fit in their lives. A surprise or unplanned pregnancy can throw the whole plan out the window. Even with a planned pregnancy, the resulting changes can be more than anticipated. Women often underestimate the impact of a baby on their lives, especially the time they will need to devote to caring for and meeting the needs of their baby. Mothers often say that *no one* could really have prepared them for what really happens when they bring that baby home and find they are the ones ultimately responsible for this little human being!

The woman often spends much time talking to her spouse or partner, trying to ensure that they will welcome the baby and support her role as mother. She often thinks about how she will juggle her focus of attention, how she will balance meeting her needs, the needs of the baby, and those of her partner. She will think about the personal sacrifices she will need to make, and will begin to let go of some of those "couple" activities that once held a great deal of importance to her. Ideally, the spouse or partner will engage in the same work.

Without a closeness and supportiveness between the woman and her mate, the work this task entails can be quite overwhelming for the woman. The single woman considers how potential partners may feel about a woman with a child. She also may begin to spend more time thinking not only about the best type of partner for her but also about the best type of person to be a parent to her child. The absence of a spouse or partner will frequently require the woman to discuss her fears and concerns with friends or family. While this can be helpful, mothers who have done this often report that these others never really seemed to share their concerns. It is not uncommon for friends and family to minimize the impact of being a single mother because they do not want to upset the mother, and they feel that in minimizing the situation they are supporting the mother. The opposite is really true, however; women *need* to process their feelings, fears, and concerns.

If there are other children in the family, the woman will also have to do similar work with them in order to ensure their acceptance of the baby. Siblings typically become jealous, do not understand, or become afraid of losing the attention of their mother. It takes a great deal of talking, supporting, and limit-setting to help children through the process of accepting a new baby brother or sister. The more children or immediate family members living with the pregnant woman, the greater her task will be to balance her interactions with them and prepare them to accept the baby.

The acceptance of the baby by extended family members also becomes a focus for the pregnant woman. She commonly looks to her family for support, motivation, and confidence. If they are not happy with or accepting of her pregnancy, they may withdraw the very things she needs to successfully navigate this pregnancy. Again, how the family relationships functioned before the pregnancy will play a significant role in how they function during and after the pregnancy. A supportive family tends to remain a supportive family; an unsupportive family tends to remain an unsupportive family, unless provided with intervention.

Certain issues will also play a role in the response of the family. The pregnancy of a teenage, single, or divorced woman may be seen as shameful or embarrassing to some families. Others see it as an event not without its challenges, but overall a happy, welcomed, and anticipated event. Some families have histories of chaos, drug and alcohol abuse, domestic violence, and dysfunction. These families may not have the skills to support the pregnant woman or to welcome her baby. In addition, the woman may not see them as safe individuals for her baby to have a relationship with, causing her to separate from her family relationships, or at least to redefine them.

The woman's pregnancy and birth of her child also impact friend-ships. It is generally very important for the woman to have the support and excitement of her friends and peers around her. If they, too, have had babies, she will look to them first for answers as to what she can expect. If her friends are childfree, she will have to evaluate if this is a relationship that can welcome a baby. Some of these friendships may dissolve, while others remain strong or become stronger. Women may also begin to develop more and more relationships with peers and friends who do have children or who are expecting. Regardless of the outcomes of this time of relationship transformation, the pregnant woman needs support and gentle encouragement to think about and evaluate the significance of her relationships and how they will be impacted by her baby-to-be.

Although the social relationships of school, work, and community tend to rank lower in social significance than spouse/partner, family, and friends, they are often the relationships that result in the most significant stress related to the pregnancy. For the teen, the school may or may not be prepared to deal with her pregnancy and her eventual role as a mother. This also occurs with the college-aged woman. One woman just admitted to medical school was surprised to discover she was pregnant with her second child. She expected support and understanding from the school of medicine; however, she received criticism for her poor planning and felt "shunned" by many of her professors. She reported that the support of her peers and spouse was the only thing that got her through her pregnancy feeling good about herself.

Working women may also receive mixed responses. While they may be happy for her as a woman becoming a mother, her employers and fellow employees may not welcome the idea of losing this woman as an employee either during the pregnancy or after she has the baby. They may also fear the impact both the pregnancy and the birth of the child will have on the woman's ability to function in her job. Termi-nating a pregnant woman is not a popular decision, so she may be given jobs that are difficult or impossible to do because of her pregnancy. Failure at these jobs either leads to her quitting or to the employer terminating her for failure to do her job. The following example illustrates these points:

Vivian, who worked as a nurse in the hospital, experienced severe morning sickness. She had been a good employee for ten years and was known for her competent nursing skills. Due to the morning sickness, some of her patient responsibilities, which she had taken on without difficulty in the past, now caused her to become nauseous. She began asking others to do certain procedures. Due to the severe nausea and vomiting, she also missed several days of work, so she could remain at home and care for herself. Her supervisor decided the pregnancy was interfering with this woman's work too much and suggested to others that this nurse was using the pregnancy as an excuse to get out of work. The supervisor "laid" the nurse off, citing the nurse's recent problems in fully performing her duties. This was not only a shock to Vivian concerning her skills as a nurse, but also left her without a much needed income and insurance. Vivian filed a grievance and was given her job back. In addition, she was supported in receiving disability to help compensate for the times she was unable to work due to her pregnancy.

Finally, a woman's community relationships may also be affected by her pregnancy. The impact of this effect will be determined by both the woman's closeness to other members of her community and to the manner in which she interacts or interfaces with her community. The goal of the woman is to ensure that her baby is accepted as a welcomed member of her community. She may do this by sharing information about her pregnancy with those she comes in contact with; for instance, the bank teller, store clerk, or church members. She may also put herself in situations where she will come in contact with others who are either pregnant or have young children, searching among them for someone to welcome her into a group of peers who share her current circumstances. While this may be done initially for the mother's own sense of self, it actually helps secure a place in the community for her baby, one already defined with peers and its own social network.

It is clear that the woman works through many social levels to build a positive support network for her child and to ensure that her baby will be welcomed into a nurturing and emotionally rich world. It is important to remember, however, that not all relationships are eager to accept a new member into them, especially when that new member is a baby. In addition, some relationships are incapable of accepting the changes that result from the pregnancy of one of their members or the birth of a baby. The goal of the woman is to ensure a place for her baby in her world; this may involve celebrating and cementing certain relationships as well as dissolving and letting other relationships go.

Binding-In to Her Unborn Child

Young children playing house or "mom and baby" create a fantasy baby for themselves. These fantasies are not limited to caring for or parenting a baby but may also include playing at actually giving birth to a baby. In fact, it is not uncommon to observe young girls between the ages of four and eight assisting each other in giving birth to their babies from under their shirts and dresses. They may or may not use dolls—even stuffed monkeys and rhinos can be given birth to in play. Regardless, they give birth to or create babies with individual person-alities (usually similar to their own), certain physical features, specific behaviors, and well-defined ways of interacting with themselves as the "mother." Very early in life, children are already watching how to be a mother or father. They practice with their younger siblings, their playmates, their neighbor's baby, their toys, or their pets. The baby and the way of being with that baby begins to take shape at a very young age. As children grow and mature, they receive much more input as to how their baby might look or how they should behave as a mother to that child.

This process continues throughout a woman's childbearing years. Women birth fantasy babies in their minds long before they birth real babies from their wombs. Most imagine an angelic being or the smiling baby on the baby food jars. They think about the hair color, the eye color, and the shape of its head. They wonder if the baby will look like themselves or like their partners. They create pictures in their mind's eye of what this baby will be like and what kinds of interactions they will have. They see themselves feeding their child or going on outings to the park.

The pregnant woman finds that, as the pregnancy progresses and the baby within her becomes more interactive, she begins to add pieces of information offered by the baby to her idealized fantasy. If the baby is active, she begins to shape her fantasy as a potentially athletic child, as in "he's going to be a football player." If the child quiets as the mother listens to calming music, her baby might be a music lover. If her child begins to move about with the sound of music, she may imagine it as a dancer. If the child increases movement at night after the mother ate pizza, she may imagine that he will not like spicy food. If the child settles down after the mother enjoys a cup of tea, he or she might be destined to be a relaxed, quiet child. Whatever the mother associates with a particular trait will often be what she begins to associate with her fantasy baby.

As the birth of the baby gets closer, the idea of this child actually becoming a living being separate from the mother begins to take shape. The child begins to transform from a fantasy to a real child. This happens with each pregnancy. Mothers will commonly comment, "my first one looked just like my husband, so this one will look like me" or "my first one was so active, just like this one, I am sure this one will be the same." Many predictions and judgments are made; some will match up with the real baby, and some will not.

This process of fantasizing and imagining helps the woman begin to see herself in the role of mother and helps her begin to develop a relationship with her child-to-be or to "bind into it." The mother-child relationship is built by these images and fantasies and by the woman's moods and physical experience of pregnancy as well. If her pregnancy goes well and the woman feels great throughout most of it, she will most likely have a better view of the event and of her child; if her pregnancy is filled with emotional turmoil, physical restrictions, and frequent periods of feeling ill, she will most likely feel sadness, depression, or detachment.

The woman's demeanor during her pregnancy also becomes reflected in her social interactions. A woman who feels good, is active, and generally healthy will most often be regarded in a positive, supportive way by others; on the other hand, the woman who is depressed and feeling sick will frequently be isolated. Those whom she depended on for social support before her pregnancy may find they have difficulty adjusting to or tolerating her moods, behaviors, and illnesses. While the woman's demeanor during pregnancy may have prompted a change in her social support, the new changes in her available social support may further impact the way she experiences her pregnancy, as well as her interactions with others. Without intervention, the disruption in social support and the impact on the woman's experience of pregnancy may continue to worsen and lead to the development of the problems in other areas, such as the mother-child relationship.

As the woman moves into her third trimester, she has typically and ideally developed a fairly well-established initial relationship with her child-to-be. As the end of the pregnancy grows nearer, she will tend to increase her protectiveness of her fetus and herself. If she has done the necessary emotional work during her pregnancy, it is most likely that she has accepted the identity of being a pregnant woman and a beginning identity, based on fantasy, as a mother. With the birth of the baby, the mother will need to transition, letting go of being a pregnant woman and immersing herself in the role of being a mother, a real mother. Her fantasies may continue, often enabling her to try on different ways of being with her baby until she finds the one that fits her.

The birth of her baby also forces the mother to transition from binding-in to her fantasy baby to binding-in with her real baby. There are several ways she might respond. For instance, she may quickly integrate her past fantasies with her present baby, all unknowingly, moving quite swiftly into acceptance of this baby and her right to mother him or her. The woman may transition more slowly from fantasy to real baby, needing to work through her disappointments and adjust to her surprises. Still other women may become so disillusioned over the birth of this "infant stranger" that she rejects both the baby and the role of mothering that child.

There are also those women who never seem to fantasize about or develop any obvious ties to their fetus. The reasons behind this can be numerous and may include a past history of loss (particularly the loss of a child), a long history of infertility, a limited or no ability to develop healthy attachments with anyone, a past history of abuse, mental illness, a complete denial of the pregnancy, or possibly the tragic or violent way the child was conceived, as in rape. Some of these women are easy to identify. They refuse to talk about their pregnancy, minimize it, or degrade the fetus. Others are virtually invisible as they never seek help or medical care, isolate themselves, and find ways to disguise or hide their pregnancy. Still others appear to do the work necessary to welcome a baby into the world, and then become cold, distant and detached from the child following the birth.

Binding-in to the child while still in utero paves the way to the later good mother-child relationship. Some believe it is during this stage when feelings of love first develop[2,3]. According to Rubin, binding-in is an unconscious process; however, others disagree[4]. Instead they suggest that many women are not only able to identify the phenomena of binding-in but are also able to identify the processes they go through in doing so with their babies. The work in this task is important and requires women to think actively about the child-to-be. For those women who have difficulty binding-in to their child, support and encouragement to discuss possibilities or predictions can be very helpful. For others, more intense mental health interventions may be necessary.

Binding-in mirrors the concept of fetal attachment that occurs prenatally and involves the concept of mutuality. Mutuality has been determined to be the central factor determining the success of fetal attachment[5]. This concept was originally defined as a factor representing cohesion between family members, which is facilitated by role reciprocity and clear communication[6]. Mutuality was seen as a stabilizing factor leading to flexibility and individuation. Recently, this definition has been extended, saying it "implies a security in family relationships that may foster the inclusion of a new member in the family"[7]. Researchers suggest that when mutuality is already present in the family relationships, there is greater ease and efficiency in extending the sense of intimacy to the fetus by the third trimester of pregnancy.

Learning to Give of Herself

As is evident in this chapter, pregnancy is not an easy road. The mother faces many challenges and obstacles. She has to make many adjustments: physically, to the changes in her body; socially, to the changes in her relationships; emotionally, to the changes in her feelings and beliefs; psychically, to the changes in her self esteem, her idea of who she is and her place in the world. Many of these changes are readily apparent to the pregnant woman, while other changes occur on an unconscious level, unknowingly to her.

Pregnant women also make sacrifices. Many women modify their careers, quit their jobs, or put their work/school lives on hold. Many women have to cut the ties they once had with certain people or with certain activities that will no longer fit into their new lives as mothers. With all the changes, challenges, and sacrifices a woman makes during pregnancy, what does she get in return? The answer, of course, is a child.

The pregnant woman learns throughout her pregnancy what she needs to give up in order to provide a safe place for her baby-to-be. She learns what she has to give to the baby as well, in terms of eating healthier foods, getting rest and exercise, providing shelter, clothing, diapers, and toys. The pregnant woman learns to give of herself in order to provide the best possible future for her baby. This is an ongoing part of the mother-child relationship. The mother gives, she provides, she cares for, she nurtures, she protects, and she loves her child. It is often an unbalanced relationship.

Until the child is able to give back to the mother in a way she can identify with and appreciate, the mother often needs to "get" from others. She needs input for her self-esteem, for her ability to nurture, and for her spirit. Family and friends will often bring gifts for the mother or, more commonly, the baby. The mother values these gifts, not for their immediate worth, but for the meaning behind them. Gifts become symbolic of the things—caring, nurturing, attending to, valuing—that the mother needs from others. Food is an important gift as it often symbolizes all those emotional necessities just mentioned as well as providing a symbol of the past, especially when the foods are those comfort or favorite foods of childhood. Grandma's special chicken dinner or mom's famous oatmeal cookies provide the pregnant woman or new mother with good feelings and connect her to fond memories of nurturing, comforting times when she was cared for. Mothers will often want to pass those special feelings on to their children by recreating the things they remember. For instance, one mother had fond memories of spending summer vacations at a special family cabin. She shared childhood stories of taking baths in a large metal washtub, playing naked on the warm sand, and eating watermelon. This mother also shared how she wanted her child to experience these same things and feel as special and cared for as she did as a child.

For the woman who does not have a well-developed support system or a strong family and friend network, this can be a very lonely part of her pregnancy. In addition, women who have difficult pasts without a lot of pleasurable memories, women who are depressed or tend to isolate themselves, women in poverty, and women with a low sense of self worth often exist in situations where others seldom give anything to them, either objects or emotional support. Little things can make a big difference for these women. The doctor or nurse who calls just to ask how she is doing, the home visitor who brings the mother a lunch of comfort foods, the friend who sends a card just to say "I'm thinking of you," can really make a difference. Many early intervention programs have seen increases in women's participation when they bring the mothers food, baby items, or personal items on their visits. In addition, women may also need support in discovering what they have within themselves that they can share with their babies.

During this task, the pregnant woman not only learns to give of herself at multiple levels and in multiple ways, she also learns to value things given to her by others based on what they symbolize, not on what they are. A phone call, a visit, or a card go a long way in reinforcing for the pregnant woman that she is being thought of and that people care about her and her child.

Strategies Involved

In order to fulfill the tasks of pregnancy that lead to taking on the new maternal identity, the woman uses several strategies or behaviors. These strategies include *replication through mimicry and role-play, fantasy, loosening established boundaries,* and *dedifferentiation.* Just as the tasks overlap in some areas, so do these strategies. For instance, mimicry cannot occur in a meaningful way without the ability to fantasize. In order for the new mother to take on new behaviors and beliefs, dedifferentiation has to occur. This involves loosening some of the ties that hold the mother to her old ideas about who a mother is and what a mother does. Once she has let go of some of her old ideas, she becomes ready to collect as many new ideas about motherhood as she can. She then evaluates these, taking only the ones that work for her and letting go of the others. Each of these strategies provides the pregnant woman with another tool to help her navigate the tasks necessary to assume the identity of a mother.

Replication Through Mimicry and Role-play

A pregnant woman begins the process of replication by reaching out to everything and everyone around her in search of information, behaviors, beliefs, and attitudes that she can relate to the idea of being a mother. There is really little, if any, filtering of all this input, which will eventually fill the woman's inner "information container." This container is the beginning of her maternal identity. In other words, it is her beginning to see and think of herself as a mother. The woman is not always aware of how much of this searching and taking on she is doing; much of it is done outside of her consciousness. She will not really use all of this input to help her accept the idea of being a mother, but she is not yet ready to choose what she wants to include and what she wants to discard. All the while she is going through this replication process of collecting information, she is also processing it and sorting through it by using mimicry and role-play.

Mimicry means the woman mimics or literally copies what she observes in others, specifically how mothers care for their babies or how other pregnant women care for themselves. She will actually practice various behaviors or take on certain ideas and beliefs as her own, sharing them with others as a test of their appropriateness. The symbols she has gathered of what a mother is supposed to be doing are sorted through, for instance wearing maternity clothes or purchasing the newest developmental toy she thinks her baby will need. She tries out things that she feels are adaptive to being pregnant and to mothering. What she discovers, if it is good and adaptive, offers her hope that she can be a successful mother, as other women have been.

The woman looks for this information first from peers, then family, and finally within herself. The woman's own mother or mother-figure often serves as the best model of mothering with whom she can identify. However, if there is overwhelming support for another type of behavior or another belief, the majority often rules in persuading the mother-to-be to adopt that particular behavior or belief. For instance, if the woman's mother and perhaps medical provider support and encourage breast feeding, but the popular thing among her peers is bottle feeding, she will likely choose to bottle feed her infant. Despite facts and evidence to the contrary, the idea that many mothers are choosing a certain behavior and are reporting success with it will go a long way in convincing the woman to adopt that mothering behavior.

Women who have no mother role models active in their lives must often find other types of models. These are often found through the media—television, movies, books, and magazines. *Carol Brady*, the mother from the *Brady Bunch* television program is still a popular ideal of a mother. Because of the reruns of older programs, even teenagers refer to these TV moms. These media-based mother models are not necessarily good models for two main reasons: first, they often act in exaggerated, inappropriate, or impossible ways just for the sake of the programming and second, they are often not examples of mothers actually caring for babies. It can become challenging to help women who do not have any mother models readily available, or those who have poor quality mother models, to find acceptable ones. If this challenge can be met by connecting the woman with seasoned mothers, a mentoring program, or a group for pregnant women or mothers, then the women will have the opportunity to begin to create healthy, appropriate ideas of what a mother is or should be, and of what works for them.

If reality does not match what the woman had prepared for or imagined herself doing, a dissonance is created. This means that there is such a contrast between what was prepared for and reality that the woman feels temporarily shaken, surprised, or overwhelmed. When this occurs, she will often search for an answer as to why the two did not match up. The search is motivated by the need for control, often control through understanding, not the need to assign blame. The woman needs to know "why," and behaves as if there is an answer "out there" that will explain why things did not go according to her plan. For example, women who progress through their pregnancies believing that their babies will be born on the predicted due date often become upset when they pass that due date and their babies have not yet arrived. They will often wonder about the safety of their babies, requesting that their health care providers make sure everything is all right. They talk about a sense of urgency in wanting to have their babies as soon as possible. Having a due date gives women some control over the impending birth; they at least "know" when the baby will arrive or when their bodies will begin to go back to "normal." When this does not happen, they begin to search for answers in order to regain control. Learning that the due date was miscalculated or that the baby has not yet dropped into the birthing position can often give the woman something else to focus on, again giving her the temporary feeling of control: "When the baby drops, then I can expect to go into labor" or "We were off a week on the due date so by next week this baby should come."

Role-play is the second piece of the replication process. This involves trying on various behaviors of motherhood, or trying on the role of being a mother. For instance, the woman may baby-sit and act as if she is the mother of the child. She may use a pet as a baby substitute in practicing to be a mother. Even those mothers who are not first time mothers may use role-playing to see what it is like to have two or more children. While this is a good way of practicing the role of mother, it can also decrease confidence if the object of the practice, whether baby or animal, rejects the woman's attempts to "mother" it. Role-play episodes serve as the rehearsal for the true-life performance.

The end result of mimicry and role-play is the integration of the mothering behaviors and beliefs that the woman evaluates as "best" both for her as a mother and for her baby as the recipient of the mothering. In other words, by using both mimicry and role-play the woman filters the information, keeping the good and tossing out what she believes to be garbage or what does not fit for her. Again, this can have positive or negative results, depending on a variety of factors. If what she keeps is the "popular" behavior, but can actually be harmful to the baby or can lead to later harmful consequences, the results can be poor. For instance, although in some circles the popular thing to do is "not to spoil your newborn by picking him up each time he cries," we know this is an unhealthy belief for both mother and baby and often leads to an increasingly distressed infant and possibly later attachment concerns. On the other hand, the popular movement to breast-feeding, seen as healthy for the baby and supportive of a better mother-child relationship, provides a positive outcome.

Fantasy

Fantasy involves the internalizing or integrating of all of the new information on mothering. This means that the information becomes mixed with all the pieces of the mother-to-be that are already present, such as her thoughts, feelings, memories, and beliefs. They are conscious of some of their fantasies and can share them easily. Other fantasies remain unknown, as they exist on an unconscious level, meaning that the mother is not aware of them. These fantasies are not always within easy reach, even though the impact on the mother may be strong. They may be fantasies that were at one time known to them but are too overwhelming to think about, causing them to recede to the back of mothers' minds.

A known fantasy might be a nighttime dream or a daydream. It could also be a way of imagining what mothering will be like. For instance, a woman may have a fantasy of what it will be like to feed her infant or to dress him. She may imagine herself rocking him to sleep. An unknown fantasy can really only be identified through the woman's words and behaviors, since she herself is not aware it exists. For instance, she may describe her fetus as "hyper" because he is always moving and kicking her; while she is not describing her child in the future as hyper, the fantasy is there that when the child is born, he will behave in a hyperactive manner.

Fantasies can be pleasurable and hopeful, or unpleasurable and ridden with anxiety. The fantasies may recreate in the mother's mind what she liked or experienced as a small child. Other fantasies may create an image of a child being born with tragic consequences. The fantasies may also be the woman's *ideal* wished-for child, one resembling an angelic, contented being; these fantasies are often important to the development of a relationship with or binding-in to the infant. Fantasies serve the purpose of providing the mother-to-be the opportunity to work through some of her fears and hopes before the baby arrives. Fantasies can prepare her, but they can also set her up to be disappointed if the idealized outcome does not materialize.

Loosening Established Boundaries

Loosening established boundaries involves the ability to reevaluate existing relationships, activities, or anything the woman sees as important in her life. Pregnancy is seen as one of the best times to do this work. Many researchers have described pregnancy as the most opportune time to make psychological and emotional changes. Pregnancy has also been called a state of intrapsychic disequilibrium[8]; an altered state of consciousness[9]; and a period of crisis involving intense upheaval of psychological processes[10]. All of these descriptions suggest that pregnancy brings on this state of psychological and emotional futility that is sensitive and vulnerable to change, creating a window of opportunity to strengthen a woman's psychological and emotional well-being.

In this stage, as defined by Rubin, the pregnant woman must decide what in her pre-pregnant life she can carry with her into motherhood, what she needs to modify, and what she needs to leave behind. In order to do this, she must first be able to loosen her boundaries or ties to certain people, activities, or beliefs. She needs to acknowledge the purpose they once served in her life, determine whether the need is still there, and decide if this particular way of satisfying her needs is appropriate. For instance, the woman might have had a "get along" relationship with an alcoholic uncle. Although he is not abusive and can be supportive, he also gets quite wild when he drinks, which occurs almost every time she sees him. While she may love and care for this uncle, exposing her vulnerable pregnant body and self to him might be intolerable. In the same vein, exposing her infant to him might also be unbearable. She may try to set limits, such as visiting only when he is sober. No matter what her decision, her changing attitude toward him and his place in her life illustrates a loosening of the boundaries or ties she once had with him.

Dedifferentiation

The final strategy underlying the mastering of the tasks of maternal role attainment is that of dedifferentiation. This process involves examining all the information the mother has around motherhood and babies. She considers this information and determines what fits for her and what doesn't. The mother evaluates the input based on the way the information fits with her existing sense of self or self-image. She tests the information as she begins to acknowledge her own maternal core and to examine the information in reference to that. The woman's instincts begin to surface, and she begins to make decisions based on what she feels is best, with regard to all the information available. The woman starts to think about what is best for the baby and what is best for her as a mother. This all gives root to the ability to bind-in to the child.

In order to do this successfully, the mother must deal with her losses. She must recognize that *she will never again not be a mother*. Even if her child died, she would still be a mother of a child. Her role as a non-mother is in the past. She must resolve issues around what she was able to do previously, especially her freedom to provide opportunities and satisfaction for herself. Now, her child will have to be considered, and decisions cannot be made for herself alone. Sometimes, the woman believes that the shift to being a mother is only temporary and that she will soon reclaim her pre-mother life. When reality takes shape and she realizes things will never return to that pre-motherhood place, she may experience some confusion around "who am I?" Some women fear they have lost their entire identity; they fear that they are no longer who they were before they had this child and cannot seem to define who they have become. For a period they may just feel *lost*. This process is referred to as identity diffusion. The task for each mother is to let go of her previous identity of woman-without-child and complete a psychological transformation into her new self. This does not mean all of who she was is discarded; instead it means filtering through the different dimensions of her self and the roles she once held. She discards those components that no longer fit with her new role and modifies and integrates those that can and do fit. For example, a woman may have once defined herself as a driven, assertive businesswoman who threw herself into her work twelve to fourteen hours a day, seven days a week. She may discard the part of her that was driven to work so many hours, she may retain her assertiveness or even improve on it as she may need to increase her efficiency when working less, and she may modify her need to be in control and begin delegating so she can concentrate on the most important components of her work. She then integrates all of these changes in her business persona with her newly established role as mother. This period of *feeling lost* or *identity diffusion* can be quite uncomfortable but is necessary to support the permanence around the transition to motherhood and the integration of the maternal identity into the woman's sense of self.

Figure 3.1 illustrates the strategies used in the process of maternal role attainment as identified by Rubin: replication, through mimicry and role play, fantasy, loosening of boundaries and dedifferentiation:

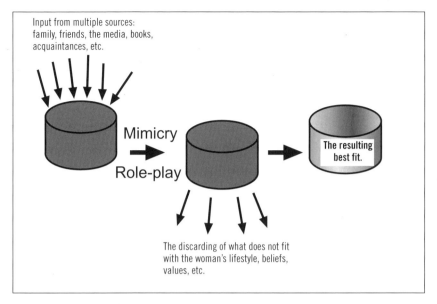

Input from multiple sources: family, friends, the media, books, acquaintances, etc.

Mimicry

Role-play

The resulting best fit.

The discarding of what does not fit with the woman's lifestyle, beliefs, values, etc.

FIGURE 3.1 MATERNAL ROLE ATTAINMENT

Summary

It is important to realize that the development of the maternal identity is gradual, systematic, and extensive. The process takes time; it does not happen overnight. There is a pattern to it; certain things have to happen in order for other things to occur. For example, the information around motherhood cannot be tested until it is collected, and certain things, like the comparison of the fantasized to the real, cannot happen until the baby is born. This process is also extensive, meaning it is not simple, although many mothers make it appear so. Some women move through this process quite rapidly. Others may never be able to accomplish the task of assuming the maternal identity. And still others may just need a little help to get through it, such as being exposed to positive role models or being supported in working through her fears and anxieties.

The four tasks of maternal role attainment identified by Rubin—*ensuring safe passage, ensuring acceptance by others, binding-in to the child, and giving of oneself*—describe the process pregnant women undergo as they work through the transition into the maternal identity and to establish the basis for the development of a relationship with her child. The strategies embedded within these tasks—replication through mimicry and role-play, fantasy, loosening established bonds, and dedifferentiation—assist the pregnant woman to navigate and master the work required for each task, if she is able and willing to use them. Even though this is a simplified account of what a woman progresses through during her pregnancy, these behaviors and strategies provide us with a framework to develop and implement interventions that support and guide the pregnant woman who is reluctant, unwilling, or unable to work through them on her own.

These tasks and strategies apply to first time mothers and to those already having one or more children. Each new pregnancy and new baby finds the woman in a different place in her life. She is older than before, she is perhaps at a different developmental stage herself, the people in her life may have changed, or she may be living in a completely new environment. These tasks are important and, in most cases, will naturally be worked through for each pregnancy a woman experiences. Women experiencing mental health disruptions, multiple stressors, or other issues, may have more difficulty in the navigation and completion of these tasks.

It is important to remember that these tasks and the strategies to accomplish them occur not only in pregnancy but also throughout the mother-child relationship. Fantasies about one's child entering school or going to college persist. Making sure that your child is accepted by his or her peers in preschool or elementary school frequently requires maternal intervention. The continued practice of giving with no guarantee of ever receiving continues throughout the lifetime. Therefore, the work done during pregnancy and in the early postpartum period significantly affects the future of the mother-child relationship and the ways that the relationship unfolds.

Chapter 3

Points To Remember

Reva Rubin identified four tasks pregnant women complete as they transition to motherhood. These include:

- Seeking safe passage
- Ensuring acceptance of the child
- Binding-in to her unborn child
- Learning to give of herself

These strategies help women to complete these tasks:

- Replication through mimicry and role-play
- Fantasy
- Loosening established boundaries
- Dedifferentiation

Making the decision to have a child—it's momentous. It is to decide forever to let your heart go walking outside your body.

ELIZABETH STONE

4

Setting the Stage for the Mother-Child Relationship

This chapter explores the issues related to the development of the mother-child relationship: pregnancy denial, fantasizing, attachment, and bonding.

When does a woman first start imagining what her child will be like? When does a pregnant woman begin to feel connected to the child she carries within her body? When does she begin to think of the fetus as her child? Are there things that occur during pregnancy that help the mother-child relationship after the baby is born? When does this child she carries really feel like *her child*? What needs to occur for the woman to begin to accept that she is going to give birth to a baby and be responsible for the care and welfare of that baby? All of these questions can really be summarized into one central question: "When and how does the pregnant woman begin to develop a relationship with her child-to-be?"

As with any other pregnancy-related issues discussed here, there will always be those who vary from the expected or typical ways that most mothers begin to develop relationships with their babies. These variations are influenced by many of the things that have already been discussed in earlier chapters, such as a woman's history of family relationships, her current relationships and supports, her acceptance of the pregnancy, and her own self-identity and image. The woman will establish some type of relationship with her fetus and later her child, and in doing so, all of the things that affect any relationship will also affect this one.

Many women report feeling connected with their child-to-be as soon as they discover they are pregnant. Some report they felt a connection before they actually knew they were pregnant, suggesting that "they just had a sense." Many women report not even recognizing their pregnancy until they begin to "show" physically through the outward changes in their bodies, and that they do not really feel connected to the fetus until they feel fetal movement. Researchers who have studied this initial connection report similar findings that "showing" of the pregnancy relates to accepting the pregnancy itself, and feeling fetal movement relates to identifying with the fetus.

Some interventions have been shown to increase the connection between the mother and her unborn child. One such intervention involved each woman feeling for the baby's parts and position, describing how her behavior impacted fetal behavior, and receiving encouragement to rub, stroke, or massage her abdomen[1]. Women receiving this "attachment intervention" demonstrated higher levels of maternal behaviors, such as eye contact and touching, than a comparison group receiving no intervention.

Colleen Stainton[2] explored the awareness both parents have about their unborn baby. She found that the process of becoming aware of the unborn baby was an individualized one and seemed to progress through four co-existing levels of sensory and cognitive awareness. These included:

- Level 1: *Awareness of the Unborn as an Idea*

- Level 2: *Awareness of the Unborn Infant's Presence*

- Level 3: *Awareness of the Specific Unborn Infant Behavior*
- Level 4: *Awareness of Infant Interactive Ability*

She concluded that the parents' subjective experiences of fetal behavior played an important role in how they understood and chose to interact with their unborn child. These findings suggest that more attention needs to be focused on these subjective experiences of the parents and how those impact the future parent-child relationships.

Not surprisingly, it is believed that the more aware, excited, and accepting the woman is of her pregnancy, the more likely she is to welcome her actual baby and the easier she will be able to adapt to and relate to that infant. Some intervention programs working with pregnant women have found that the more interaction the woman has with her fetus, such as stroking her abdomen and talking to her fetus, the closer her relationship to her child will be after the baby arrives. It makes sense that women who are able to treat themselves and their fetus or child-to-be in a sensitive, caring, and nurturing manner will tend to do the same with the real child in their arms. It seems clear that much of the work going into the mother-child relationship occurs during the nine months of pregnancy and that there are things that can be done during this period to improve the quality of mother-child relationships following the pregnancy.

Denial of Pregnancy

Although most women accept their pregnancies without difficulty, there are some who struggle and deny their pregnancies. This indicates a high risk for the woman in accepting and relating to her baby. Although it is rare, some women, despite obvious signs and confirmations, can totally deny that they are pregnant[3]. The stories of these women are often depicted in the news as "toilet births," meaning that the women report having gone to the bathroom with abdominal pains thinking they were sick and, to their surprise, delivered a baby into the toilet. In these cases, there has usually been a lot of trauma either around the conception or around the entire idea of being pregnant. In some cases, the woman might have dealt with inability to conceive for so long the idea of being pregnant just becomes too remote to believe. Other times, they are just totally convinced pregnancy cannot occur for them, so they just *never* consider pregnancy as a diagnosis for their physical changes. Consider the following case:

> *A 38-year-old, non-English speaking married woman who reported having had a hysterectomy. She had never conceived despite being married for almost 20 years and never practiced birth control. About a year following this hysterectomy, the woman was cooking dinner for her husband and began to leak fluids from her genital area. She and her husband became very frightened and went to the emergency room where she delivered a 5-pound baby boy. Of course, they saw this as a miracle.*

As unbelievable as this story sounds, it did actually happen. When the woman had surgery, she did have her uterus removed, but she had the very rare condition of having been born with two uteruses. Because there were two, both were underdeveloped. When one was removed, the other was able to mature and gain proper function, and the woman conceived. She had believed, however, that the doctors had removed any chance to become pregnant, and the idea of being pregnant was totally outside the realm of possibility. The baby she carried was quite small, which probably minimized much physical change. The other symptoms of pregnancy were rationalized as indigestion, abdominal pain, and weight gain. This woman did not ever expect to have a child following her surgery as she believed that it was physically impossible.

Another example of a pregnancy in a situation also thought to be impossible is illustrated in the following case:

> *A 34-year-old woman was married to her husband for six years. Her husband had undergone a vasectomy sixteen years earlier, ten years before the marriage. This couple thought conception and pregnancy were totally impossible. Despite obvious signs and symptoms of pregnancy, this woman denied the possibility of pregnancy. She reported that she first*

*believed she was going through early menopause, then she
thought she was gaining weight, and then she became fearful
she had cancer. She refused to see a doctor due to her fear of
bad news. When she was 7 months along in her pregnancy,
she was forced by family and friends to go to the doctor, who
through ultrasound discovered a healthy, normal baby
developing inside her womb.*

This woman was a medical professional, but the idea of pregnancy was
not even considered. When she eventually discovered she was indeed
pregnant, she became hysterical wondering how this could have
happened—as did her husband. A physical examination of her
husband revealed that his sperm had actually created a new "tunnel"
within which to travel. This allowed the husband's sperm to act in a
normal manner, leading to his wife conceiving. Once they accepted
and adjusted to these new ideas, they were able to welcome their new
daughter without any problems.

While rare, these are good examples of how pregnancy denial can
develop. Other situations where a similar denial could occur include
the woman who has had so many years of infertility that the idea of
conceiving is not possible; the older woman, especially one who
believes she has passed childbearing years; or the teenager who is
unsure that she really "had sex" and therefore could never be pregnant.
The most common examples involve women affected by major mental
illness, such as schizophrenia, where their understanding of reality
varies.

Whether the mother is ever able to accept the child she births following denial of pregnancy varies. If the mother had always wanted a
child, as in the examples above, after the initial adjustment, the
mother is usually able to embrace her baby with much affection. For
those mothers who had experienced a great deal of trauma, the
acceptance of the baby by the mother really depends on other factors
such as her own adjustment, her available support, and her belief
systems. Finally, those who have major illnesses such as schizophrenia
that interfere with their acceptance of the pregnancy would most likely
experience similar barriers in accepting and/or parenting the child.

Fantasy Babies

The baby that the mother imagines is one of the most significant influences during pregnancy on the development of a relationship between mother and child. Some women develop fantasies of a beautiful baby and of themselves as adoring mothers. They might imagine their baby to have black hair or blue eyes or their husband's nose. They might imagine their baby to be plump and sturdy. If the baby is quite active in utero, it is not uncommon to hear the mother share a belief that the baby is athletic or full of energy. Some women do not develop such positive images of their child. They may believe the active fetus is just a nuisance and that it is becoming active only to bother or irritate them. One mother, whose fetus seemed to become more active when her husband was speaking, shared with her counselor that she believed the baby hated her and only liked her husband. Other mothers may imagine that their babies carry their own worst traits.

While fantasizing, imagining, and dreaming are all normal and wonderful ways to deal with maternal emotions and prepare emotionally for the baby, these things also play a significant role in the relationship the mother later develops with her child. Research has demonstrated that in a majority of mothers, the ideas they develop about their baby before the birth of the child remain stable until the child is about a year old[4]. This is a powerful finding, suggesting that many of the ideas parents form about their babies occur before the baby is even born. While no research evidence presently exists, it seems likely that these ideas formed during pregnancy could well persist throughout the life of the relationship, unless something outside the relationship intervenes.

Consider the mother who believes her fetus is just doing things to bother her; this would mean that there is a high probability that throughout the child's first year, the mother may interpret the child's normal dependency and neediness as a burden or something the child is doing purposely to annoy her. Sadly, it is not uncommon to hear a mother, of any age, complain that their four-week-old baby is crying just to make them mad. On the other hand, women who describe their children affectionately during their pregnancy would most likely think about their children in the same manner at one year of age as well.

Fantasies seem to provide a psychological bridge between pregnancy and the birth of the child. The power of these images and fantasies provides a wonderful opportunity to intervene. These fantasies help us understand the mother's belief systems and values. They also provide a window of opportunity to help shift problematic beliefs and attitudes. For instance, identifying women who regularly interpret fetal behavior as negative and intervening while these women are still pregnant may go a long way in preventing mother-child relationship problems later on. Prevention, of course, is always better and more effective than intervening after problems have been established.

Even women who have positive fantasies may have some difficulty when the real baby comes. The baby may look like her husband when the woman's fantasy was that the baby would look like her. This may make it difficult for her to accept this baby as hers immediately. Mothers who experienced fantasies of rocking and singing to a contented baby but then have a difficult-to-soothe baby who never sleeps, often have problems matching up their ideal of being a calm and loving mother and the reality of being sleep deprived and overwhelmed. Matching a responsive, contented fantasy baby with an unsoothable, crying real baby is also hard, even traumatic.

Eventually, most mothers find ways to come to terms with reality and let go of their fantasies, although for some women the ideas may persist and may follow the relationship for years. Most mothers still seem to develop a rhythm with their baby. As the baby matures, the relationship is reshaped little by little. Many mothers, however, benefit from some reality testing before the baby arrives, even if only to acknowledge and accept the possibility of what reality might bring. Fantasizing itself is a very important part of adjusting to pregnancy and to the baby once born. It is a behavior that should be encouraged and discussed with enthusiasm and excitement. It is only when the fantasies are unrealistic, highly negative, or completely absent that this becomes a problem in pregnancy. Additional problems that may develop after the birth of the child usually involve a serious mismatch between what was fantasized and expected, and reality.

Attachment and Bonding

Thus far, we have looked at mothers' ideas of when they first felt connected to their babies and how fantasy relates to such a feeling. The connection between the mother or father and the baby is often referred to as bonding or attachment. These terms are often used interchangeably depending on the topic and the author. For the purposes of a clearer understanding, we will differentiate and define each of these terms. It is important for anyone who is interested in or works with family relationships to have a good understanding of both attachment and bonding and how they apply to babies and parents. The following is based on the work of John Bowlby[5-10] and Mary Ainsworth[11]. Although their work in the attachment field has become well accepted and common knowledge, it is important to acknowledge that little of what we understand and operate on today would exist if not for them. Those of you who desire a deeper understanding of attachment in the lives of mothers and children are encouraged to explore their work.

Attachment

Attachment begins as a connection between the baby and the mother (or any person who becomes the primary mother figure). This initial attachment is not a choice; it is a necessary connection to help the baby survive. It has a biological purpose—to sustain life. This drive to survive causes the baby to demonstrate behaviors that help him or her to stay close to the mother. Human babies cannot fend for themselves; they depend on others to feed and care for them. Without someone providing at least basic care for a baby, the baby will die. Therefore, the beginning connection or attachment is "survival based."

Of course, basic care of an infant is not enough to ensure proper growth and development or even long-term survival. This has been known for over 100 years and is based on the knowledge of what happens to babies raised in institutions without a primary mother figure[12,13]. Babies who do not have anyone nurturing them, touching them, holding them, or interacting with them on a regular basis become very delayed in growth, intelligence, movement, and social interactions, despite having food, shelter, and adequate medical care. When this denial of nurturance lasts for long periods of time, the children are at risk for serious developmental delays, mental retardation, or death.

The closeness the baby seeks from the mother and the responses the mother gives to the baby also serve other functions. If the mother responds in a nurturing, supportive way, keeping the baby close, then the baby is more likely to adopt the mother's patterns of regulation. This includes matching her heart rhythms, breathing patterns, sleep/wake cycles, and hunger patterns. Her nurturing behaviors of touching, stroking, soothing, singing, and holding, also help to develop a psychological attachment. That is, they help the baby begin to see him or herself as separate from the caregiver and help the baby develop a firm idea of who they are and that they are good. A baby who is developing along this positive or secure attachment path begins to develop beliefs that his/her mother is:

- Reliable
- Loving
- Caring
- Able to handle my emotions
- A good thing
- Able to keep me safe
- To be trusted
- To be anticipated
- Pleasant
- Always there

The baby begins to associate positive feelings with experiences with mother. It is through this relationship that the baby comes to create personal beliefs such as:

- I am good
- Someone loves me
- I am worthwhile
- I am real
- I am alive
- I am safe
- Others make me feel good
- I can depend on others
- I enjoy being with others
- I am lovable

The baby also comes to see the caregiver as a separate person, as reliable, predictable, and as a good mother. Over time, the baby develops what is termed an internal working model or mental representation of the mother. This is actually an image or thought of the mother that develops in the baby's mind founded on real experience with the mother. Basically, the more loving, available, nurturing, and reliable the mother is, the more stable and clear this model of mother becomes in the baby's mind. This suggests the baby has received enough "good stuff" to begin internalizing the image of his or her mother.

As the model of mother becomes stronger in the baby's mind and as the child develops, the baby will naturally be able to be away from the mother (his security) more and more. It is this mental model that allows this to occur. At first the child will need to be touching the mother in various ways, for example on her lap and later holding onto her leg with one hand while playing with the other. Then the child will begin to move away from the mother, requiring regular physical check-ins. Later, the child will require only visual check-ins and eventually merely verbal confirmations that she is still nearby. Over time, the child begins to venture farther and farther away, until he or she can play for long periods of time without needing to check in with the actual mother. Instead, they depend on this mental model. A stressed or frightened child will commonly revert to an earlier way of interacting until that child again feels secure and safe.

Through the development of this mental model of their mother, babies are able to develop a positive concept of themselves. They are able to see their mothers as secure bases to whom they can always return, which gives them the freedom to venture out into the environment. This, later, develops into a healthy transition to independence. Establishing this "mental mother" within the child's mind enables the child to "take" the mother with him, stay connected emotionally, and continue to feel positive about himself and his abilities. Later, the child will use this model as a guide for behavior when away from caregivers. The child is able to grow and become independent because of a strong sense of personal worth, the ability to depend on others, and emotional connections with others. Relationships are pleasurable; therefore the well-attached or secure child tends to be more social and interactive with friends and others. Thus, this relationship which began as a survival-based dependent relationship matures into an emotionally-connected, balanced relationship. It is this type of relationship that facilitates healthy, optimal growth and the physical, social, emotional, and intellectual development of the child. These relationships are termed "secure attachments."

It is also important to understand how "insecure attachments" develop. When the positive attachment pathway just described is reviewed, several areas where problems can arise become evident. These problems are divided into three general categories including problems with the primary caregiver, problems with the infant, and problems with the parent-child relationship. These are explained in the Table 4.1 on the next page.

These are just a few of the possible scenarios that can affect the development of an attachment between a baby and mother. Even when these issues do exist, a secure attachment can be developed. There may be mitigating factors such as the presence of another individual who is able to respond to the baby in a more nurturing and consistent manner than the primary caretaker, or even a baby who manages to develop ways to compensate for whatever is missing from the mother-child relationship. Sometimes mothers or primary caregivers have the ability to find ways around difficulties or challenges and to figure out unique ways to connect emotionally with their babies through other means.

Insecure attachments develop when babies do not find their primary caregivers as reliable, predictable, and able to meet their needs. These babies may have had caregivers who never or rarely responded to their needs. They may have had caregivers who responded with anger and abuse, creating fear and distrust in the infants. They are often forced to care for themselves in many ways because of the absence, disinterest, or inadequacies of their primary caregivers. These babies may develop some of the following ideas about their caregivers:

TABLE 4.1 FACTORS IMPACTING THE PARENT-CHILD RELATIONSHIP

POTENTIAL PROBLEMS	IMPACT
Primary Caregiver Issues	
• Involvement with drugs or alcohol	Heavy or dependent use of drugs or alcohol can alter the caregiver's state of mind and ability to deliver good, consistent care. Often babies in these circumstances receive intermittent and chaotic care that leads to an inability to connect consistently with caregiver.
• Physical or mental illnesses or conditions which interfere with connecting with or caring for baby	Symptoms of some mental and physical illnesses or conditions can create difficulties in the building of the attachment, such as an inability to get out of bed, lapses in memory that the baby is even there, problems with understanding what the baby needs, barriers in getting to the baby, and issues that require frequent hospitalizations of or separations from the caregiver.
• Personal history of poor relationships and family patterns of insecure relationships	Primary caregivers who had poor relationships with their own caregivers as children are often at risk for developing similar problems with their children. Mothers who were raised by unpredictable and unreliable parents most likely learned to relate to others in the same manner, possibly behaving in a similar way with their own children. Poor relationship experiences also wear down a person's self esteem, leaving little motivation to feel good or positive about any new relationship.
• Domestic violence and chaotic family circumstances	Mothers or other caregivers who need to be focused on their own safety as well as that of their baby often have little energy or opportunity to do many of the things supportive of a secure relationship. Safety comes first; dead, injured, or traumatized individuals are in no shape to make relationships a priority.
• Circumstances around pregnancy	Women who have had traumatic circumstances around their pregnancies, such as a rape, often have difficulty relating to the baby in a way that helps create a secure attachment. Often the mother can reject or even fear the child so much that this interferes with both care and relationship building.
Issues With the Baby	
• Baby illness or health condition	Infants who require major medical care or intervention during the beginning of life are often at high risk for difficulties in attachment development when there is an inability to have mother and child together or when the baby's condition becomes too overwhelming for the mother to deal with.
• Baby behaviors seen or experienced as rejection of others	Difficult-to-manage babies or babies who have various problems often display behaviors which caregivers may interpret as "rejecting." A baby's refusal to nurse or feed for instance can be interpreted as a rejection of the mother, possibly causing the mother to pull back from her child.
Issues With the Relationship	
• Match between mother and child	Sometimes there is simply a poor match between parent and child. A baby displaying difficult behaviors such as frequent crying, difficulty feeding, and poor sleep regulation may be paired with a mother who cannot function well without sleep, is impatient, and disappointed in the baby's inability to feed. The relationship may not be able to develop a balance between the baby's ways of engaging the mother and the mother's ways of soothing the baby. These types of situations can cause the mother and/or baby to withdraw, or can even lead the mother to become more demanding, minimizing the number of interactions conducive to secure attachment.

- She probably won't help me
- Does she love me?
- She can't keep me safe
- She doesn't know I'm here
- Even when she's here, I feel alone

- It doesn't matter if she leaves
- She doesn't want me
- Can't she hear me cry?
- Will she hug me or hurt me?
- Does she know I am here?

The experiences of these infants may lead to the development of certain types of behaviors and strategies—or ways of trying to get their caregivers to respond in ways to meet their needs. Some babies may become avoidant; in other words, they may try to avoid or stay away from their caregivers as much as possible. Some may become clingy and try to keep the caregiver as close to them as possible, often becoming inconsolable if the caregiver leaves them even for a short period of time. Other babies may become so confused with the inconsistency of their caregivers' behaviors that they are not able to find regular ways of interacting and trying to get what they want. Babies with insecure attachments might experience thoughts like these about themselves:

- I am not lovable
- I am not safe
- I don't know what to do
- I have to do it on my own
- I cannot control my emotions

- I cannot depend on others
- I am invisible
- I should be ignored
- I am worthless
- Toys/things are better than people

Children who develop insecure attachments tend to demonstrate more difficulties later in life as compared to those with secure attachments. They tend to have more difficulties in school, with peers, and with general life skills. They have a weaker sense of who they are and are less able to handle things independently. In addition, they tend to lack problem-solving skills. Anything that can be done to improve attachment outcomes between a child and his or her parents can be beneficial for this type of child throughout life.

Bonding

Bonding can be described as the development of a close, affectionate, connection from the caregiver to the child. The person doing the bonding, in this case the mother or other primary caregiver, is not dependent on this relationship to stay alive. She can literally continue to survive physically without this connection—her child. She does, however, take on the dependency needs of her child. She becomes committed to this child and she takes responsibility for the child. She feels genuine affection for the child and can identify and meet the child's needs, often at the expense of not meeting her own needs. The child and the relationship with the child become a priority. The closeness of this relationship is set so deeply that periodic change in feelings towards the baby, such as anger or frustration, does not alter the actual connection.

The beginnings of this bond are thought to occur during pregnancy, when the fetus or child-to-be becomes foremost in the mother's mind. Stories of mothers who insist on continuing with a pregnancy regardless of the consequences to themselves are a good example of putting the welfare of the child first. Mothers who are diagnosed with cancer during their pregnancy, who develop high blood pressure, or whose pregnancies are touch-and-go frequently dismiss the danger to their own lives to ensure that their babies are born into this world. This seems to suggest that some type of bonding, or some piece of bonding, has developed.

The following is an example of a mother who put her baby above her own life:

> Abbey was a 21-year-old woman with a long history of heart problems since childhood. After many years of surgeries and treatments, Abbey underwent a heart transplant at the age of 13. She responded well to the transplant and went on to become a cheerleader (although limited in her participation) and valedictorian of her graduating class at the age of 18. At 19 she married her boyfriend of many years, became em-

*ployed, and settled into a comfortable life. Her heart contin-
ued to work well for her but she was still considered a major
risk for problems to develop at any time. Because of her
health problems, she was advised not to birth children, which
she and her husband understood and accepted. Even so, she
conceived a child during the second year of her marriage. Her
parents and family were terrified of what this would do to
Abbey. They advised her to abort the baby because they could
not bear to lose her. Her husband was willing to support
whatever her decision would be, but agreed with her family.
Her physicians were firmly against the pregnancy. They felt
there was no way this pregnancy would go to term and the
stress on Abbey could definitely be detrimental to her health.
They felt that if she actually tried to deliver the baby, there
was a high probability that Abbey would not survive. Abbey,
however, had never let her heart problems stop her from doing
what she wanted. She reported feeling an instant connection
with her baby, although she, too, was afraid. She would not
be dissuaded, and chose to continue with the pregnancy. She
instructed her husband that if anything happened to her, he
should keep her alive on life support until the baby could be
safely delivered. Abbey cared for herself very carefully, she
talked and sang to her baby in utero, and did everything she
could to make sure the baby in her womb began to know who
she was and to know how important the baby, itself, was. If
she died, she wanted the baby to know something about her
mother. Abbey made it to the end of her eighth month of
pregnancy, when she went into labor. Due to the high risk of
this labor on both the baby and Abbey's heart, a team of
specialists had been previously alerted to this unusual situation and came together to deliver Abbey's baby through
cesarean section. Both Abbey and her new daughter came
through the delivery beautifully. Abbey continues to survive
and live happily with her husband and her daughter, who is
now of elementary school age.*

The period immediately after birth is often referred to as the "critical bonding period"[14]. Many years ago, this period was branded as critical or crucial to a positive relationship between mother and child. The intensity of this claim caused a great deal of fear in mothers who were not able to experience that time with their babies for whatever reason, such as adoption, baby or mother illness, or the interference of medication. Although there was much media attention around this claim, it has never been supported by the many years of research since. This does not mean that the initial period is not important, however. It is merely not *required* for a healthy, secure attachment. This time can be a lovely and important moment for both mother and baby. When possible, mother and baby should be together, skin-to-skin, right after birth. But when circumstances prevent this from happening or when the mothers rejects the idea, a good mother and child relationship is still ultimately possible.

Bonding is a process dependent on many variables. It is out of this affectionate bond that the mother constructs her nurturing behaviors such as soothing, engaging, enjoying, and valuing. The relationship with her baby comes to have special meaning and is rewarding to the mother, regardless of the baby's temperament, disabilities, personality, or appearance. The feelings the mother develops for the child become unconditional. Out of this relationship, the mother is able to support her child in the developmental transitions he or she will make. The mother is able to support the child's need to use her to develop a sense of security, while gently encouraging the child to explore and develop. The mother's response to this desire for security is protection of that child. Most mothers report this experience not as bonding but as falling in love with or loving their child.

Some mothers either do not have the ability to bond or they, for a variety of reasons, do not bond with their child. This is, of course, quite detrimental for the child and his or her subsequent development. These mothers, in general, tend to be less sensitive to their children's needs, are less able to be empathic or understanding with their children, and generally are unable to demonstrate emotion toward their children. Table 4.2 provides examples of behaviors that might be seen with those mothers who have a good ability to bond with their child and in those who do not. These are, of course, two ends of a continuum and many mothers fall somewhere in the middle. The consequences of these interactive behaviors often dictate which children develop secure relationships with their mothers and which develop insecure relationships.

TABLE 4.2 SUPPORTIVE BONDING BEHAVIORS AND NON SUPPORTIVE BEHAVIORS

SUPPORTIVE BONDING BEHAVIORS	NON-SUPPORTIVE BEHAVIORS
Soothing words	Harsh or no words
Showing affection	Abrupt moves
Kissing	Ignoring
Playing	Yelling
Singing	Leaving alone for long periods of time
Holding	Propping bottles
Rocking	No eye contact
Responding to crying	No or little touching
Holding during feedings	Bland environment
Making eye contact	Providing no stimulation
Stroking	Letting the TV keep the baby company
Bathing gently	Hitting
Frequent body-to-body contact	Not responding to crying

Summary

It is during the prenatal period that the mother is thought to begin developing pieces of the larger relationship she will one day have with her child. As mentioned earlier, fetal movement is often related to reported feelings of connection. This is because the baby becomes "real" in a concrete sense. This being inside her has begun to take on human qualities, such as movement. Ultrasound examinations can sometimes increase these feelings of connection. Many mothers and fathers become overjoyed at the ultrasound pictures of their child; some have them framed and others send them out to others who share their excitement. Being able to see the fetus actually coming to re-semble a child, with arms and legs, a head and body, and a beating heart make the baby seem more "real." On the other hand, some women describe being able to develop an affectionate bond with their child without any of these experiences—they say, "it just happened."

A healthy attachment within the mother-child relationship generally means that the mother is comfortable with her ability to care for her infant. She feels genuine affection for her infant. It also means her infant is able to reciprocate in some manner toward her. This provides her with feedback that she is connecting and that the baby is developing a special relationship to her—a relationship she sees as unique from other relationships the baby has. In addition, the mother is able to create a balance between nurturing and keeping her baby near her and giving her baby space to explore, visually, interpersonally, and environmentally.

The mother-child relationship is the result of a process of interactions between mother and baby. How this process unfolds depends on two things: the mother's ability to be emotionally available, sensitive, predictable, and conscious with her infant and the infant's ability to be receptive as well as engaging and rewarding for the mother. This process begins with a baby crying, often from the need to be nourished. The mother responds by either meeting those needs or ignoring the child's attempts to communicate and leaving the needs unmet. If the mother develops a pattern of responding, her baby begins to develop an image that "mom soothes me when I cry and feeds me when I am hungry." If the mother develops a pattern of being unresponsive, the baby begins to develop an image that "my feelings and needs are too big to be managed; I cannot depend on my mom." Each time the mother responds to the baby in a similar manner, the image of the mother becomes more and more solidified; the baby comes to expect, based on the model of his mother he creates in his mind, that because his mother behaves like this then maybe all people behave like this. The baby then begins to develop behavioral strategies to match these internal beliefs. If interventions do not occur as children grow and develop, then they will be likely to become adults who repeat the same interactions with their children. As you can see, the model that is developed from earliest childhood onward becomes a model embedded in the mind that is remarkably persistent and resistant to change and that provides a framework within which the person creates an image of mother or parent that is carried throughout life.

Chapter 4

Points To Remember

- The connections made between mother and child during pregnancy are the beginnings of a lifelong relationship.

- Denial of pregnancy can occur for many reasons, most often because the circumstances preceding the pregnancy ruled out the idea of becoming pregnant.

- Women develop images of the babies they will give birth to; these fantasies help connect the mother and her child emotionally and psychologically.

- Once the baby has arrived, the mother must reconcile her images of the fantasy baby with the real baby in her arms.

- The infant's attachment to his or her mother begins to form out of the relationship between that child and the mother or primary caregiver

- Bonding is the term often used to indicate the connection formed by the mother toward her child.

- Certain maternal behaviors can be considered supportive of a strong mother-child relationship, while others can be considered unsupportive.

If we could give every individual the right amount of

nourishment and exercise, not too little and not too much,

we would have found the safest way to health.

HIPPOCRATES C. 460-377 B.C.

5

The Impact of Maternal Factors on Pregnancy and the Child's Developing Brain

This chapter examines the connections between the prenatal environment within the context of maternal experiences and decisions, fetal brain development, and later child outcomes.

For the past several decades, researchers have studied how the mother's exposure to infections and viruses or her use of medications, drugs, and alcohol can affect the physical development of her fetus. We know that if the fetus is exposed to certain things at specific points during the pregnancy, then the fetus may develop particular physical problems. Less attention, however, has been paid to how the mother's emotional well-being affects her unborn child. In the field of prenatal psychology, researchers are beginning to study the relationships between the mother's emotional experiences during pregnancy and the child's physical, emotional, and psychological well-being later in life [1]. We no longer think of the fetus as lying in storage "waiting to be born." We are beginning to understand that the fetus is vulnerable to more than environmental toxins and drugs. Instead, we now believe that the mother's experience of pregnancy and delivery, as well as the health of her unborn child, can be impacted by the mother's experiences, emotions, behaviors, and thoughts.

It is believed that two-thirds of premature contractions are caused by psychosomatic or psychosocial factors, such as stress[2]. Yet most treatment focuses on the mother's body, not on her emotions or mental health. To reduce premature deliveries and their serious impacts on babies, we need to consider interventions to help mothers deal with emotions and to help them complete the psychological work in pregnancy.

In this chapter, we will look at how nature—the normal course of prenatal development—and nurture—the maternal environment surrounding the unborn child—complement each other and contribute to outcomes in pregnancy, childbirth, and the baby.

Nature: Formation of the Fetal Brain and Nervous System
First Month of Gestation

In the first weeks after conception, cells form three layers: the ectoderm, the endoderm, and the mesoderm. The ectoderm layer consists of cells that will form the baby's hair, skin, brain, and central nervous system, among other body parts. As cell division continues, the cells differentiate. They are carried along networks in the developing fetus to the place where they are needed to grow into necessary structures.

One of these structures formed by specialized ectoderm cells is a thickened wall called the neural plate. As the plate forms, a groove develops and deepens along its surface. Flaps in the side tissues develop, fold over, and join together, forming a neural tube. This eventually becomes the brain and the nervous system. When the front portion of the neural tube becomes the brain, it divides into three sections: forebrain, midbrain, and hindbrain. The rest of the tube becomes the spinal cord.

In normal development, the neural tube closes and protects the structures within it. If something prevents the tube from closing, the brain and/or spinal cord can be exposed to amniotic fluid. This fluid would prevent the structures from growing properly. It could lead to problems such as spina bifida (open spinal cord) or anencephaly (undeveloped or absent brain).

Second and Third Months of Gestation

By the end of the first month of gestation, the neural tube should be closed and the brain should have divided into right and left hemispheres or sides. In the next two months, these sides continue to develop, as does the brain stem, which controls movement, heart rate, breathing, and sleeping. By the end of the ninth week, the fetus should be able to move its arms, legs, head, and body. It will also have some ability to regulate heart rate, sleep cycle, and breathing. By about the tenth week, the fetus will take its first breath in utero. It will also move spontaneously about 14 percent of each 24-hour period.

By the end of three months, the central structures of the brain are laid out. However, they will not completely develop until after birth. In fact, some parts of the brain do not reach maturity until adolescence.

Fourth to Ninth Months of Gestation

During the last six months of pregnancy, connections develop between the nerve cells, or neurons. These brain connections are insulated. After birth, both processes—forming connections and insulating the wires—continue and accelerate.

As the brain and nervous system develop, the fetus gains more abilities and becomes more able to interact with the environment. It can move body parts, sense things in the mother's environment, interact with what is happening, feel emotions, and develop memories. Table 5.1, on the next page, shows the age at which the fetus should be able to do things if the brain and central nervous system develop normally.

TABLE 5.1 FETAL ACTIVITY BY GESTATIIONAL TIME POINT[3]

TRIMESTER	GESTATIONAL TIME POINT	FETAL ACTIVITY
1st Trimester	4th week	Heart begins to beat
	9th week	Spontaneously move extremities, head, and trunk; initial regulation of heart, sleep cycle, and respiration.
	10th week	Takes its first breath; spontaneous movements taking place about 3.5 hours each 24-hour period (14%)
	12th week	Able to grasp, suck, squint, swallow, move tongue
2nd Trimester	14th week	Able to taste
	16th week	Has facial abilities to frown and grimace
	18th week	Gag reflex is operational
	19th week	Active 50% of time
	21st week	Audible crying can be heard with the right apparatus
	22nd week	Has a well developed sense of touch; can differentiate extreme temperatures
	24th week	Hearing structures in place
	25th week	Able to move in rhythm to certain stimulus
	26th week	Is capable of breathing on own (premature infants have a good chance of survival); able to have memories; can discriminate and react to mother's attitudes and feelings; reacts to vibration and loud sound
3rd Trimester	32nd week	REM sleep is occurring (the sleep state of brain activity such as dreams)
	35th week	Visual recognition memory is evident
	36th week	Responds to sound over 80% of time; responds to the sound of the mother's voice with increased movement and heart rate acceleration
	39th week	Fairly mature auditory system; after birth, baby will be able to recognize stories read during gestational period.
	40th week	Breathing becomes more regular and frequent

Nurture: The Environment of the Womb

In the past, we thought the womb could protect the unborn child from environmental harm. The placenta was seen as a barrier, preventing things on the outside from getting inside the womb. It is true that the "placental barrier" does keep out many toxins, drugs, and chemicals that could harm the fetus. However, we now know that the placental barrier does not keep out every harmful substance. The drug, thalidomide, taught us this lesson. Thalidomide was prescribed for pregnant women to prevent morning sickness. Not only did this drug pass through the placental barrier, but depending on the specific time in pregnancy, we discovered it had different effects on the developing fetus. For example, mothers who took thalidomide during the sixth week had infants with missing or deformed arms; mothers who took it closer to the seventh week had babies with missing or deformed legs; mothers who didn't take the drug until after the 50th day of pregnancy had unaffected or normal babies[4].

This experience with thalidomide taught us that drugs taken by the mother can have devastating effects on the unborn child. The influence of the drug on the developing fetus can either be limited or enhanced by the point during pregnancy when the mother uses it. In other words, the risk to the fetus is greater at some times than at others. Much depends on the specific agent—meaning drug, chemical, virus, etc.—and the stage of fetal development.

On the other hand, a fetus can be harmed if a mother lacks vital substances. For instance, folic acid is needed for cell division and DNA synthesis. If the mother doesn't have enough folic acid for her unborn child, cells may not divide properly, structures may not form as needed, and the neural tube may not close. If the neural tube doesn't close, amniotic fluid could harm the brain and spinal cord. To prevent these problems, all women of childbearing age who have even a remote chance of becoming pregnant should have a diet with enough folic acid to support fetal cell growth and division.

Research has shown links between other substances used by mothers and effects on the child. Smoking is linked to low birth weight, alcohol to fetal alcohol syndrome or fetal alcohol effects, and cocaine and crack to effects on the baby's central nervous system. These are tangible substances with specific birth outcomes. We are just beginning to determine links between non-tangible agents and birth outcomes. These non-tangible agents include maternal depression, stress, anxiety, low self-esteem, and low social support. Their effects may go beyond pregnancy and also influence later stages of the child's development.

Maternal Stress and Anxiety

Research shows the most common effects of maternal factors on the baby are low birth weight and preterm labor and delivery[5, 6]. Other researchers have found a relationship between maternal stress and fetal heart rates[7]. When mothers with high anxiety felt stressed, their fetuses had significantly faster heart rates. When low anxiety mothers felt stressed, there were no significant changes in fetal heart rates. These results suggest that a mother's anxiety level, exposure to stress, and ways of handling stress affect her unborn child.

One group of researchers found a link between high anxiety levels in pregnant women and abnormal patterns of blood flow to the uterus[8]. They argue that this may be a reason for a relationship between high maternal anxiety and low birth weight babies. One study measured the psychosocial status—anxiety, stress, self-esteem, and mastery—of 2,593 women during the second trimester of pregnancy and related findings to birth outcomes[9]. After adjustments for substance use and demographics, this study found maternal stress was related to preterm births and low birth weight babies. A Danish study of over three thousand women found that birth weight and head circumference were related to women with high stress and low social network support[10]. These studies support the connection between maternal stress and specific effects on prenatal brain development.

More recent studies have shown the risk of a baby having a cleft palate, cleft lip, or spinal bifida (cranial-neural-crest malformations) if its mother had severe life stress during pregnancy or up to 16 months before becoming pregnant[11]. Severe life stress was defined as the death or first hospitalization of a partner or child due to heart attack or cancer. Other studies showed links between unintended pregnancies and preterm birth[12] and between maternal stress during pregnancy and the child's school grades at age 6[13].

Women who experience high stress in the third trimester have been found to have high levels of stress hormones (ACTH and cortisol) in their plasma[14]. Some stress hormones are suspected of having negative effects on fetal brain development[15]. When stress hormones combine with other hormones produced by the placenta, it may increase the risk of preterm delivery or constrict the flow of blood to the placenta[16]. A study of pregnant adolescents found that high concentrations of cortisol were linked to lower APGAR scores for their infants and a higher need for resuscitation[17].

These studies point out the problems that high levels of maternal stress can have on the baby. On the positive side, a study of African American women found that those with higher self-esteem and more positive self-attitudes were more likely to have babies go full term[18]. They also found a direct correlation between the number of people in the mother's support network and the gestational age of her baby. This points the way to interventions to support the best possible outcomes possible for mother and baby.

Maternal Depression

Overwhelming anxiety can lead to depression. Research has demonstrated that women reporting a high number of depressive symptoms during their third trimester of pregnancy showed elevations of specific neurotransmitters and hormones (norepinephrine, cortisol and dopamine)[19]. It was surprising to find similar patterns of these substances in the infants of these particular mothers just after birth. These findings suggest that these substances pass through the placental barrier and impact the fetus.

Infants of depressed mothers have depression-like behaviors when they are assessed on the Brazelton Neonatal Assessment Scale[20, 21]. High levels of norepinephrine are linked with inferior infant orientation; high levels of prenatal cortisol with abnormal reflexes; and low levels of dopamine with inferior infant excitability and withdrawal scores.

Other Maternal Factors

We often hear teen pregnancies described as "babies having babies." This sometimes leads to problems when mothers don't know how to be mothers. A recent study of teenage mothers found that teens who were adjusted to being parents and who had the support of their mothers were more apt to rear well-adjusted children. The study reported that the best predictor of adjustment for the child was the adjustment of the teen mother[22]. In other words, the mother's adjustment to her new role during pregnancy, her maturity, and her support systems all affect how her child will develop.

Research has explored links between an infant's experiences during pregnancy and birth and later risks of schizophrenia. While the exact mechanisms for the link have not been determined, four possible links have been identified[23]. First, the research reported that congenital infections caused by rubella and some forms of herpes have been linked to schizophrenia. Second, links between poor prenatal nutrition and schizophrenia were found when researchers studied data extracted from a severe Dutch famine in the winter of 1944-45. They argue that just as lack of folic acid may cause neural tube defects, so may the lack of proper diet lead to schizophrenia. Third, there seems to be a high correlation between congenital neural tube defects and schizophrenia. Finally, trauma or obstetric complications at birth have been connected with the later development of schizophrenia.

Some researchers believe there is an environmental link to schizophrenia[24]. If the cause were solely genetic, we would expect one identical twin to develop schizophrenia if the other twin had it. Instead, this happens in only 50 percent of the cases. Not only have infections and malnutrition during pregnancy been suspected as causes but also problems at birth, such as temporary lack of oxygen during a difficult delivery.

Prevention and Intervention

Research has shown that major stress or depression during pregnancy can have serious effects on both the mother and her unborn child. Some stress and anxiety are natural at this time. In fact, they may help the woman do the psychological and emotional work needed to take on the role of mother and welcome her baby into her life and world. However, if the stress and depression become severe, they interfere with the needed work. Intervention can help women early in their pregnancy to find ways to manage their stress. Here are some of the things you can do:

- Discuss symptoms of depression, stress, and anxiety with the mother.
- Help the mother build positive support systems for herself and her baby.
- Have the mother practice relaxation methods to reduce anxiety.
- Support the woman's efforts to avoid drugs, alcohol, chemicals in

certain products, and medications or vitamins not prescribed by her health care provider.*

- Encourage her to eat a healthy diet with nutrients her baby needs.*
- Encourage her to develop an exercise plan with her health care provider to improve her health, reduce the effects of stress, and support optimal blood flow to the uterus.*
- Encourage regular rest periods and getting a good night's sleep.
- Support the pregnant woman in avoiding stressful environments or situations when possible.

Summary

We are only just beginning to understand the complexities of the development of the unborn child. We have only scratched the surface when it comes to understanding the impact the pregnant woman has on her developing baby. We know, for instance, that certain toxins can seriously impact the physical development of the fetus. We do not yet understand, however, how the pregnant woman's emotions impact the development of that same fetus. We now understand that the unborn child is not simply an empty vessel waiting to be filled at birth. We know that unborn child has the ability to hear the outside world, to see and respond to light, to become agitated at the environment, and to respond to touch and pain. The unborn child is already a vessel being filled from the moment of conception.

At this time, we have more questions than answers as to what goes into this vessel and what the unborn child is protected from. For instance, in what ways does a woman experiencing high levels of stress contribute to her unborn child's well-being? Does a woman who feels supported and loved throughout her pregnancy have a better experience giving birth than a woman who feels lonely and abandoned? There are many questions to be answered and many relationships and connections yet to be explored. This chapter has provided a brief introduction to some of these issues.

---

* Activity levels, diet, and medications/vitamins should always be discussed with the primary health care provider before any changes are made.

Chapter 5

Points To Remember

- Psychological factors, such as stress, are now believed to significantly contribute to birth outcomes for baby and mother.

- The natural formation of the fetal brain and nervous system enable the maturing fetus to develop more and more competencies in preparation for birth.

- Toxins and chemicals can have different impacts on the developing fetus, depending on the stage of fetal development when they are introduced.

- Certain substances, such as folic acid, need to be available to the developing fetus or problems may result.

- Maternal anxiety and stress have been linked to problems, such as less optimal uterine blood flow and an increased risk of cranio-neural-crest malformations.

- Maternal depression has been linked to depression-like symptoms in the newborn.

- Prevention and intervention services have been shown to be effective in reducing risks.

- Intervention can help women early in their pregnancy to find ways to manage their stress.

Human relations are built on feeling, not on reason or knowledge. And feeling is not an exact science; like all spiritual qualities, it has the vagueness of greatness about it.

AMELIA E. BARR

6

Issues for Home Visitors/Interventionists

Specific issues identified by home visitors in early intervention pro-grams are explored and discussed. Various approaches to handling these issues are suggested.

Over the course of working with home visitors throughout various early intervention programs, several common issues have been brought up. Home visitors often share similar concerns even though they may work in different programs, with different populations, or in different geographic regions. The most common issues of concern include the following:

1. Not Being a Mother Yourself

2. Visiting an Unclean Home

3. Involving Partners and Spouses

4. Involving Other Family Members

5. Involving Other Children

6. Dealing With Cultural and Religious Issues

7. Dealing With Resistant Mothers: Those Who Do Not Do Their Homework

Each of these issues will be discussed in detail within this chapter.

Not Being a Mother Yourself

During a group supervision session, one interventionist shared that she was feeling hurt and angry with one of her clients who had said to her, "You're not a mother, are you? I can tell you do not have any kids, so you do not know what it is like." The client said this in response to some of the interventionist's suggestions for making things run smoother at home. Through supervision, we explored the interventionist's feelings about this comment, her work with this particular mother, and her struggle to get this client to make any changes in her home life.

Validation for the interventionist's feelings was important. She felt rejected and discounted for her education and knowledge and for her inability to make a positive connection with this family. We explored her goals versus the client's goals. The interventionist wanted the client to organize her day, set better limits with the children she had, and make time for a home visit to discuss what was occurring for the client with her current pregnancy.

The client was seven months pregnant. She had two children under the age of three who both had developmental delays; she was single and had some developmental delays of her own. She also had a long history of relationship trauma, had lived homeless when pregnant with her youngest child, had no car, was dependent on a mediocre bus system, and was being pressured back to work by new public assistance mandates. She wanted to work but had difficulty getting there on time because she had to get her two children to a special daycare. It took two buses to get to the daycare and a third bus to get to work. The morning commute took an hour and a half on a good day, as did the evening commute. When she got home with the children at six p.m., she was tired, the kids were tired and hungry, and motivation for anything was low.

Through supervision, the interventionist was able to look more objectively at the background and current issues of this mom. She was able to develop some empathy for the overwhelming nature of her responsibilities. We explored the mom's response as partly true; the interventionist did not have children. However, as other intervention-ists in the group shared who did have children, they also did not know what it was like to walk in this mother's shoes. They had children with no developmental delays, they had cars, and their husbands or part-ners were supportive and took up some of the responsibility of caring for the home, meals, and children. None of them could say they knew what this mother was going through; they could admit they were not sure how they would handle all of those challenges.

As the interventionist processed her anger and developed more empathy for this particular mother, she was able to generate ideas for how she might deal with this statement of the mother and intervene in a more productive manner. She planned to validate the mother's concern—no, she did not have any children of her own and even if she did, she didn't think she could ever really know what the mother was going through with all she had to take care of by herself. She planned to tell the mother how impressed she was that she was able to get the kids to their special daycare each day and make it to work as well. She would add that she would like to understand better what evenings were like for this mom and would ask to spend an evening just hang-ing out with this mom and her kids and helping with dinner, baths, and bedtime. The interventionist followed through with her plans. She spent an evening with this mother and later reported this mom had so much to do and was so overwhelmed that there was no way she could have really understood that without spending the time with her and experiencing a little of what this mom did every day. This new approach shifted the relationship and the interventionist and the mother developed a good working relationship. The mother's circum-stances changed slowly, but the interventionist was now appreciative of the change no matter how slowly it came.

Several months later, the interventionist shared in supervision that she had just visited the same mother who had her new baby now. The interventionist held the new baby and talked to her. As she held that baby, the mother said to her, "You are going to be a good mom one day." Through her tears, the interventionist shared how moved she was by these words and how she had come to develop an appreciation and special fondness for this mother. She was also able to talk about how the mother had been right with her earlier comments—she did not know what it was really like, but now she felt she could understand it better if she stepped into the mother's shoes even for a short time.

Visiting an Unclean Home

Another common complaint from interventionists is concern about the level of cleanliness in the homes they are visiting. Home visitors have described food left on floors and furniture, baby bottles half full of soured milk poking out from under the couch cushions, discarded dirty diapers on the floor, substances that looked like smeared feces on floors, crumbs and pet hair covering furniture, strong cat box odors, ashtrays overflowing with cigarette butts, cockroaches and other bugs, and so many "things" in the house that there is literally no floor to walk on—forcing them to walk over mattresses, boxes, and other clutter. They reported these homes as smelling so bad it was difficult for the home visitor to stay for long periods of time. The lack of cleanliness in these homes created health and safety concerns for the interventionists.

Interventionists described several tactics for dealing with the problem. Some described bringing cleaning supplies, offering to help clean, trying to force the mother to clean, and calling Child Protective Services (CPS). Sometimes these approaches worked; other times they failed. Many times they put the clients on the defensive and swayed the focus of the meeting to that of the home's cleanliness only.

The lack of success in these situations occurs because the underlying issues of an unclean home are many and complex. There can be an underlying depression, a lack of motivation, a sense of being overwhelmed, a sense of futility, self-punishment, an immobilizing fear, depleted energy, or even a power struggle left over from adolescence (those of you who have ever argued with an adolescent to clean their room will understand this). It is not laziness or a lack of desire to have a clean, comfortable home. The most effective course of handling this is to explore those underlying issues. This can take time with some women.

In the meantime, several interventions can be tried with the pregnant woman. These may help improve the situation or at least make it less stressful on the interventionist. Once you have established a good working relationship with the mother/family, discuss the benefits of having a more organized and tidier home. Some of these are as follows:

1. You are going to be bringing your baby home soon and you want to have things set up in a very positive way for that baby's homecoming as well as your return to home as a mother.

2. Being in a tidy, organized, fresh environment can help make everyone feel better about themselves. It can improve your mood. Feeling better about yourself and your home, especially when pregnant can help a great deal with your changing moods and your adjustment home with the baby.

3. A clean home helps to reduce dust and molds, which have been known to cause asthma and other health conditions. So the cleaner your home is, the healthier you and your baby may be.

4. Regular wiping down of counters, tables, bathrooms, doorknobs, etc., can help reduce the number of colds and respiratory infections you and your baby will be exposed to.

5. Many people, especially in the winter months, spend a great deal of time indoors, so this should be a place that you feel positive about.

6. If other children are present in the home, the less clutter that is present, the more room your children have to play and the more energy they can play off, making it easier for them to fall asleep at bedtime.

If the mother and family decide this is a change they want to make with your assistance, then it would be fine to bring over cleaning supplies. Other ideas include having a cleaning party (which would last longer than a typical session) where you plan a lunch and talk time as well as clean. One of the goals of this approach is to show how cleaning can be made as "fun" as it can possibly be. Play music; make up little games to help you along—try to finish a particular job in so many songs, etc. If other children are present, this is a good time to show how the children may or may not be able to contribute. For example, once children have good control of the grasp and release behaviors, they can begin dropping smaller toys into a box or big bowl. A 2-year-old can also pick up toys as well as help put canned foods in a low cupboard or help push wet clothes into the dryer. A 3-year-old can help carry things between rooms and pick up items on the floor that cannot be vacuumed—larger bits of paper, small toy pieces, crayons, etc. School age children can help with dishes, make beds, sort laundry, and vacuum. You can also take this opportunity to teach the mother and family how helping can benefit the child through practice of physical skills and abilities, practice in social skills, practice in negotiation, improved self esteem for a job well done, a sense of accomplishment, success in responsibility, and a sense of working as a family.

Another suggestion for cleaning up is to make a schedule of what is to be cleaned when. Often when a home becomes very cluttered and untidy, it can feel overwhelming to those living in that home. Instead of looking at cleaning the whole house—which may seem impossible—break things down. For instance, Monday might be the day for the bathroom; Tuesday might be the day for collecting, sorting, and washing the laundry; Wednesday might include cleaning the kitchen; and so on. Help the mother to develop a time schedule as well. Developing a plan where you work on the cleaning task from 9-10 and then take a break may be helpful for the pregnant woman who doesn't have the energy she once had. Breaking cleaning down and practicing a schedule before the baby arrives can also help to show how things can be broken down and spaced based on the baby's initial sleep-wake cycles.

If all of these attempts fail, back off unless the lack of cleanliness is threatening the health and safety of members in that home. You do not want this to become an issue that drives your relationship apart. Do not push the issue. Instead, do things that can make the visiting more comfortable for yourself. Wear an old coat you can lay down on your seat before you sit down. If there are babies or other children you are working with, bring a "special blanket" just for your floor time. Wear clothes that you don't mind getting dirty. Carry an extra set of clothes in your car. One home visitor sat on a sofa that a child had urinated on. She was upset that she sat on the wet spot and it soiled her clothes for the rest of the day. If something like this happens, point it out to the mom politely and constructively, "It seems as though I have sat in a wet spot here. Can I help you clean this up? I have used vinegar in the past to get the smell out and a towel should help absorb the wetness. Maybe we can place this sofa cushion over here while it dries." Keep liquid hand sanitizer in your car to clean up after leaving a home. Finally, when it is nice outside, do outside activities, take walks, sit on porch stairs, or meet at a park.

Unclean homes are not an uncommon problem. They are often delicate to deal with and can bring up many issues of control and boundaries. Think of all the issues that come up with the adolescent's untidy room and a mother's appeal to clean that room. The same types of issues can carry over into your relationship with the women you are working with. It is important not to ignore these problems, but to also understand that what bothers you might not be an issue for other individuals.

Involving Partners and Spouses

When at all possible, it is important to involve the woman's spouse or partner. However, this should never be done without asking the pregnant woman her thoughts on the subject. There may be private issues she wishes to discuss with you. The pregnancy might be generating some confusing thoughts and feelings for her, which she is apprehensive of sharing with anyone else. Do not assume she wants her husband or partner involved. Her relationship with you might be one she cherishes and wants to keep free of other individuals in her life. Her relationship with her spouse or partner might be strained or dysfunctional, and she might be fearful of letting that person in on your work together. If she has a spouse or partner who "takes over," she may not want that person participating because it would leave less for her.

The involvement of a spouse or partner should always be assessed with the pregnant woman. There may be some activities or meetings when you would like him/her involved and there may be others she wants to keep private. It is always helpful at some point to involve the spouse/ partner so you may evaluate that person's ability to deal with the pregnancy issues and to explore the dynamics between that person and the mother. If there are problems, sometimes just having it known there is this real person who is acting as a monitor of the situations can help to improve the couple's relationship. The problem may also come up that the spouse/partner wants to be there, so he/she intrudes on the session. In this case, the home visitor needs to set limits on this intrusiveness. "There are some things I do with pregnant moms and their partners, and there are some things I need to do alone with each mother. This is one of the alone activities, so would it be possible for you to leave us for a few minutes. If you want to come back at the end of our time, we could all talk about what to expect next." If this fails, you may want to conduct your visits elsewhere some of the time to insure privacy for the pregnant woman.

Involving Other Family Members

Other family members present in the home may or may not want to be involved. This involvement can have a positive or negative impact on the work you are doing with the pregnant woman. Limits and arrangements might need to be included just as described for spousal/ partner participation. The most common concern expressed by home visitors is the pregnant woman's mother, the maternal grandmother. Maternal grandmothers have been described as helpful when they have become invested in the work the pregnant woman is doing with her home visitor and when they are supportive of the pregnant

woman's independence and individuality. When the maternal grandmother is intrusive, unsupportive of the pregnant woman, or even
emotionally abusive, two things may need to happen. First, set limits
on the maternal grandmother's participation or choose to have visits
somewhere else, as discussed above. Second, you may need to support
the pregnant woman in her independence and separation. Some of
this work can be done with the interventions that focus on family
relationships. Remember, pregnancy is a time of reworking relationships with mothers and redefining one's self as an independent person
capable of parenting a child. This may be an opportune time to
intervene. Referrals to individual therapy may also be helpful.

Home visitors must be sensitive with issues related to maternal grandmothers and other family members. For some of the pregnant
women, these other family members may be the gatekeepers. In other
words, they may be the persons who allow the pregnant woman to
participate or not. They may also have the ability to support and
endorse your work, adding to the trust between you and the pregnant
woman; or they may discount and sabotage your work, increasing
strain in the relationship and eliminating the possibility to work with
the pregnant woman at all. Each case needs to be looked at individually. Think about what role this family member plays, what kind of
impact they have on the pregnant woman, what role they will fulfill in
the future, and whether the pregnant woman is dependent on this
person for some or all of her own care at this time. If it looks like this
other person is going to be playing a significant role or if it is the only
path through which you can see this woman, you may need to negotiate and find ways to include this other person. If this occurs, care
should be taken to choose activities that would not place the pregnant
woman in an uncomfortable space or make her vulnerable to later
repercussions within the relationship.

On the other end of the continuum, there are times you want another
adult from the family involved with your work with the pregnant
woman. This can come up whenever you have a pregnant woman
who is also dealing with other challenges in her life and who may need
close and constant support. Some of these issues may include (though
not always) developmental problems, problems with drugs or alcohol,

or mental illness that interferes with self-care, safety, and the potential welfare of the baby.

Involving Other Children

When there are already other children in the home, there may be times when their participation would be of benefit to all involved. Children often need some help in preparing for a new brother or sister. They may also need some support to understand what their mother is going through and why things seem to be changing at home. There are many wonderful books and short videos that cover these issues. I encourage you to explore them. For the older child, honest conversation between the pregnant woman and child can be very helpful. How and when to involve other children in the home needs to be at the discretion of the pregnant woman. Her own values and beliefs will guide her decisions, but you can be available to support these decisions.

Dealing With Cultural and Religious Issues

There are two assumptions you must not make when working with any population. First, do not assume that your way is the right way for every person you work with. Second, do not assume that because a particular individual appears to belong to a particular group or claims to belong to a particular cultural or religious group that they will have the same practices and beliefs as other members you have known or worked with from that particular group. There are many, many different ideas and beliefs rooted in different religions and cultures. Everyone develops their own personal way of taking the ideas and beliefs and applying them to their lives. How these ideas are understood will differ. There are differences between groups, and there are differences between members of those groups. In addition, if the women you are working with come from other countries or even other states or communities, they will all be somewhere on the continuum of integrating who they were and how they used to do things with who they are now and how they want to do things.

It is because of this diversity that this handbook was written without information on specific cultures or religions. You need to assess these beliefs as they pertain to each pregnant woman. You will need to assess what she wants and what she needs. This is an important difference. People from other geographic areas have had different options at their disposal than they have in the area where they are living now. There might have been better and more plentiful options or there might have been limited options in both quality and quantity. It is important not to buy into the belief that what you have to offer in your community is better than what others had before. Check it out. What did they like and not like in their previous home and what do they like and not like in their new environment. When specific issues have been discovered, assess what kinds of modifications and choices you can make to create an atmosphere of respect and support.

Dealing With the Resistant Mother: Mothers Who Do Not Do Their Homework

Another common concern raised by interventionists is the uncooperative woman who does not follow through with suggestions, ideas, or important changes. Why does this happen? There are no easy answers and many reasons for this type of response. When you are exploring why this is so for the women you work with, it is best to begin with the basics. Review the following checklist of questions to ask yourself:

Is the Information Being Presented in a Clear and Supportive Manner?

Any mother who is receiving intervention services needs to hear clear and concise information relevant to her life. She also needs to believe that the interventionist is providing this information and asking for specific changes because he or she genuinely cares and wants things to improve. She does not want to feel she is being ordered, shamed, or guilted into doing things or participating in some manner. This type of direction is more apt to shut down communication and cooperation.

Are There Other More Pressing Issues That Need to Be Taken Care of Before the Pregnant Woman Can Concentrate on the Information You Bring Her?

Safety and survival are the priority issues for any human being. You need to be safe and believe you will survive to be able to think about feelings, relationships, dreams, and desires. A woman who is afraid she will not have enough money to pay the rent this month will not be able to pay attention to and grab onto new information no matter how important or significant to her situation it may be. A woman who has no money for food this week or money for gas to get to work is in a similar situation. A woman who has just had a major argument with her spouse or boyfriend who states the baby is not his and he no longer wants a relationship will not be thinking about what she needs to do this week to follow up on your last visit. Check out what other issues might be higher on the priority list at the present time.

Have You Spent Enough Time Establishing a Trusting Relationship?

It takes time to develop and establish a trusting relationship with anyone. Think about which relationships you felt immediately comfortable in and which ones took you a long time to develop. If the women you are working with have had problematic relationships in the past where they have been let down or have had promises broken, it may be even more difficult to establish a trusting relationship. You will have to work harder at being reliable, dependable, and consistent. Some women have had such traumatic pasts that developing a trusting relationship would be extremely difficult. Often these women come and go in programs. For example, they may be able to handle having a relationship with the interventionist for two weeks then disappear for a month, coming back for three weeks, then vanishing again for a period of time. If this happens, you may want to make shorter but more frequent visits so you don't overwhelm her emotionally or psychically with the relationship but make yourself more visible and present in her life. This also enhances predictability and consistency. It is important for you to remember that sometimes just being there for a short period of time can help to shift things tremendously for a woman.

Are You Moving Too Fast or Giving Too Much
Information at Once?

Try to break activities down into shorter and smaller segments. Some
women will only do work you discuss when you are there with them
to discuss it with them. Plan activities that can be done in the time of
your visit only.

Chapter 6

Points To Remember

Home visiting is often challenging for the interventionist. You have to go into another person's home, leaving the safety of your office or organization behind. But, for the women we see, home visiting provides them the safety and familiarity of their home, it eliminates the need for them to travel to get to appointments, and it helps you to understand the way they live. Visiting someone in their home, or anywhere, does not come without problems, however. Several of the problems encountered by home visitors in an early intervention program were discussed in this chapter. There are, most likely, countless other problems and concerns that were not addressed here. While some of the problems addressed here pertained directly to home visiting, others reached beyond that and into the relationship developed between the interventionist and the client.

Remember these important things:

- You will never have the same experiences as the clients with whom you work—but you can try standing in their shoes and really make an investment in what it might be like.

- Empathy can be a direct link to connecting with another person.

- Your safety, as well as the safety of the women you visit, always takes priority. Never go into a home or situation that feels unsafe or that you have concerns about. Know your options, your exits, and who is present in the home before you walk through that door.

Nobody, who has not been in the interior of a family, can say what the difficulties of any individual of that family may be.

JANE AUSTEN

7

Issues in Pregnancy

In this chapter specific issues identified by home visitors in early intervention programs are explored and discussed. Various approaches to handling these issues are suggested.

Pregnancy Loss

Family Planning

Controversy of Ultrasounds

Domestic Violence

Depression During Pregnancy

The Pregnant Woman Above
   Age 35

The Pregnant Adolescent

The Pregnant Woman With
   Disabilities

The Risk of an Imperfect Baby—
   Handicaps, Illness, & Prematurity

The Relinquishing Mother and
   Adoption

Pregnancy Loss

Pregnancy loss includes spontaneous abortion during any of the trimesters of pregnancy, perinatal death of the fetus before birth, stillbirth, and death of the baby within the first several days after delivery. How a woman perceives and makes sense of any of these losses is determined by many factors, such as the meaning of the pregnancy for that woman (for example, an unwanted pregnancy that results in spontaneous abortion might have a different meaning for a woman than the loss of a pregnancy following two years of infertility treatments), the reactions of family and friends, and the support or carc she receives from members of the health care profession. While how a woman perceives and makes sense of the loss of a pregnancy definitely impacts how she immediately deals with the loss, these issues may also contribute to how she deals with later pregnancies, issues related to becoming a mother, and later mother-child relationships.

If the experience of a miscarriage and the loss of the dream child go unresolved, the emotional disturbances may carry over into a subsequent pregnancy. Fears that the subsequent pregnancy will end in the same manner are frequent. Anxiety may be high and may interfere with the psychological work the woman needs to complete during pregnancy. Some research suggests that it is not unusual for women who have experienced pregnancy loss and miscarriage to hold back from binding in to their babies until they know their baby will be safe[1]. This phenomenon is also seen in high-risk pregnancies where the child may be born prematurely and in adoption where the woman does not yet know for sure that she will receive a healthy child. For these women, their dream babies seem to be held captive and cannot become real babies until assurance of safe delivery of a baby who will actually become their child has been made. Intervention needs to take these issues into consideration.

Kristen Swanson[2] studied the experiences of women who miscarried. Through her work with these women, she identified these six experiences: *Coming to know, Losing and gaining, Sharing the loss, Going public, Getting through, and Trying again.*

Coming to know involved the process of coming to the realization that the miscarriage was going to occur or had occurred. Women had to deal with the painful struggle of the loss of their pregnancy and their hopes for a healthy outcome to their pregnancy. *Losing and gaining* involved exploration of what was lost or gained due to the miscarriage. Women searched for meaning in their miscarriage. *Sharing the loss* was the receiving or not receiving of support from others around the miscarriage. It was important that the loss be seen as significant and that others understood this. *Going public* meant re-entering everyday life as a now non-pregnant woman who had to share this news with others and also deal with issues related to other women's continuing pregnancies and babies. *Getting through* happened as everyday life began to have more happy moments than moments tied into grief and loss. Women moved through the physical loss, the pain, and the healing. The final experience was *Trying again.* This involved both the decision of whether or not to try again to become pregnant, as well as the confrontation of fears that a subsequent pregnancy might bring similar challenges. If the woman did become pregnant, this stage also involved getting past the gestational age when her last pregnancy ended in miscarriage.

Swanson's work validated women's experience of miscarriage as a significant loss for many women. This validation and recognition of the impact and significance of miscarriage has not always been evident in either the professional arenas or the general public. Miscarriage was often thought to be something that did not really count, that should just be forgotten as quickly as possible and not talked about. For example, miscarriage and pregnancy loss has been categorized with "pet loss" in some professional literature. Some women may not experience miscarriage as at all traumatic, especially if they had not wanted to become pregnant and did not have a personal investment in having a child at that point in their lives. For others, however, loss through miscarriage has been likened to the loss of any significant person in a woman's life, requiring recognition, grief, and mourning. Miscarriage is not only the physical loss of the fetus; it is the psychological loss of the woman's dream child. The impact of miscarriage is multi-level.

Some of the reactions common to women who experience miscarriage or pregnancy loss include self-blame, depression, anger, stress, anxiety, confusion, loss, emotional disturbances, decreased self-esteem, fear, and guilt. A few mediating factors have been identified. Why the loss occurred is one of these factors. Knowing the reason for the loss of a pregnancy seems to help some women fare better in terms of self-blame[3]. Those who knew why they miscarried reported significantly less self-blame than those women for whom a cause was never established. Levels of anxiety and depression were not significantly different, however. The point in pregnancy at which the miscarriage occurred also impacts the woman's response. The farther along the woman is in her pregnancy, the more significant the impact of the loss seems to be. Finally, younger women who have experienced several miscarriages seem to demonstrate more initial depression than older women following the loss; however, they demonstrate less depression one year past the loss[4].

Two things have been found to enhance healing following miscarriage or pregnancy loss: time and therapeutic caring from others. Time had a significant healing effect in many instances throughout the research literature. This is logical; with any significant loss, time is an important healing factor. Swanson[5] found that using her model of caring to intervene with women who miscarried led to reductions in emotional disturbance, depression, and anger. This model of caring includes five therapeutic processes: Knowing, Being With, Doing For, Enabling, and Maintaining Belief. Each of these processes is explained in the table below.

TABLE 7.1   SWANSON MODEL OF CARING[6]

PROCESS	MEANING
Knowing	Striving or working towards developing an understanding of the woman's experience
Being With	Being present with the woman emotionally, being emotionally available
Doing For	Doing for the woman as she would do for herself if she were psychologically and physically able
Enabling	Facilitating the woman's movement towards resolution of the miscarriage experience through validation and informing
Maintaining Belief	Believing in the woman as someone who can and will get through her miscarriage experience and who will continue forward into a meaningful future

In summary, it is important to keep several things in mind when working with a woman who has miscarried or experienced pregnancy loss:

1) Take this loss seriously, but follow her lead. She will be able to tell you either in words or behaviors whether the loss of her pregnancy has been a significant loss for her or a welcomed answer to desires not to be pregnant.

2) Do not be afraid to bring up the subject or talk about it. If a woman does not want to discuss it, she will let you know; however, most women are grateful that someone will talk about their losses with them.

3) Adopt Swanson's Model of Caring as a framework for responding and supporting women who have experienced miscarriage.

4) Educate others in the woman's social circle, especially family and close friends, that this is a significant loss and should be treated accordingly.

5) Educate other professionals working with women in pregnancy of the significance of this loss for women.

6) Observe for intense emotions and emotional disturbances that may carry over into subsequent pregnancies. If this occurs, the issues needing resolution should be reflected in your treatment goals and plans.

7) When working with a woman who miscarries, it is crucial that you continue to work with her for a period of time following the pregnancy loss. Abandoning her or quickly moving her out of the program because she is now "not pregnant" and no longer fits program criteria is insensitive and a disservice to all women. Build a miscarriage response plan that acknowledges, supports, and honors the woman and her experience.

Family Planning

Working with women in their childbearing years requires attention to family planning. In spite of the availability of several methods of contraception, the number of unintended pregnancies in this country remains high. In one study of almost 1200 pregnant women, 45 percent reported that their first pregnancy was not intended[1]. This percentage of unintended pregnancies is supported by a recent research review that reported about 50 percent of all pregnancies were unintended[2]. It further reported that over one million babies born each year were the result of unintended pregnancies. Little is known about the impact of being "unintended" on the life trajectory of those infants. Research has found that children of ambivalent mothers, or those who initially didn't want to have or keep their babies then later opted to parent, have difficulties in terms of school performance and social relationships[3].

Although the number of family planning options has increased, there is still a lack of availability in certain areas. Issues such as a lack of knowledge around the risks of sexual activity, lack of knowledge of contraception, misconceptions of what prevents pregnancy, fear, embarrassment, shame, and secrecy continue to make it difficult for many women to discuss or seek needed intervention. The relationship between the woman and her partner can also contribute to the lack of contraception and family planning. Protection is often left up to the woman. Male partners do not take responsibility for family planning as often as their female counterparts. Women of all ages have shared stories of male partners refusing to use condoms because they feel unnatural, inhibit sensation, or come in the way of physical closeness. Women are hesitant to insist on the use of a condom because it may be interpreted as rejection or disrespect and suggest a lack of trust. Low assertiveness skills or an immediate need to gratify their own sexual urges can increase the risk for unprotected sexual activity and possibly pregnancy. The sharing of sexually transmitted diseases between partners will also be at an increased risk.

We know that spacing the birth of children can benefit families emotionally, interpersonally, and financially. Families have more time to adjust to each new baby. They have time to nurture and enjoy those early years of each child. There is time to recover financially, and even get ahead a little. Emotionally, these mothers have a lower risk of being overwhelmed by the transition to motherhood and the emotional and psychological changes that occur with each pregnancy. The normal stress with one baby will change and lessen as that child matures. The issues become different. Spacing children allows the mother to divide her energies between each of her children's individual needs. Older children can also support and help out when a new baby arrives. Spacing the birth of children is a form of prevention ensuring optimal mental health in families.

Frank discussion on family planning should be included in the treatment planning of all pregnant women. It will ultimately be her decision as to if or when she decides to follow her present pregnancy with a subsequent one. However, it is the responsibility of the interventionist or practitioner to insure that the pregnant woman (or any woman) has the information necessary to make an informed decision.

The Controversy of Ultrasound

The use of ultrasound has become part of the normal routine of pregnancy for the woman of the 21st century. Rarely do you hear of a pregnant woman who makes a personal decision not to have an ultrasound. Rarer still is frank discussion over the pros and cons of using ultrasound. Is it helpful for women to view their fetus through ultrasound technology? What impact does knowing the sex of the child make for the woman who is developing a relationship with her unborn child? How does the use of ultrasound affect the psychological work pregnant women need to do during pregnancy? We will explore some of these issues in this section.

There can be no argument that the development of the ultrasound has had a most profound effect on pregnancy. We know it has saved the lives of children through early identification of certain birth defects. For some children, this has meant having surgery while still in utero. Ultrasound has brought relief and peace of mind to many parents-to-be fearful of the condition or outcomes of their pregnancies. It has helped to connect fathers to the development of their unborn child in a way never possible before the development of ultrasound technology. Finally, it has allowed some parents having difficulty with the concept of their child-to-be as a real person to begin to acknowledge that at different points in pregnancy the fetus can suck its thumb, open and shut its eyes, and have purposeful movement, just like a real person. In other words, it allows parents to begin to see their child-to-be as a living, interactive human being they can begin to connect with affectionately.

With all the benefits of ultrasound, it is sometimes difficult to take a hard and serious look at the repercussions of ultrasound technology. The routine nature of ultrasound use and the lack of any obvious physically harmful effects on mother or child resulting from the use of ultrasound equipment on the human body have limited both our concerns and our decisions for the need of further exploration of the impact of ultrasound. We assume because it is done on a daily basis throughout medical practices everywhere that it is safe. Let us consider a few of the possible concerns. As discussed earlier, the psychological work of the pregnant woman relies partly on the fantasies and dreams the woman has of her child-to-be. Prior to ultrasound, these dreams and fantasies focused on not only the sex of the unborn child but also on the physical appearance and activity of the baby-to-be. Mothers would also fantasize about their relationship with their babies, how they would hold them, feed them, rock them, talk to them, and play with them. These visions were visions that included a baby, not a fetus. In the sixth month of pregnancy when a woman would feel her baby kick and tumble in her belly, her mind would see an image of a fully developed, healthy baby, not an image of a fetus. T. Berry Brazelton describes three "babies" parents fantasize about: "the perfect four-month-old infant who rewards them with smiles and musical cooing, the impaired baby who changes everyday, and the mysterious real baby whose presence is beginning to be evident in the motions of the fetus."[1] How does seeing the developing fetus during a period of psychological vulnerability affect the pregnant woman? We do not really know. Research and clinical reports vary. Some have reported disturbed fantasies; some a sense of strangeness and separateness[2], and others have reported fantasies that have enhanced the development of the mother-child connection. Many reports have stated that it remains unknown what impact ultrasound and other pregnancy related technologies have on the psychological well-being of the pregnant woman or the subsequent emotional link between the mother and her child.

Other psychological impacts resulting from ultrasound technologies may include the development of fears, such as the pregnant woman who develops an intense fear of birthing her child after she views the size of the baby within her womb[3]. This can bring up psychological fantasies of being physically damaged or destroyed by the fetus. In the case of a malformed fetus, the mother may develop a sense of her body betraying her by allowing a damaged entity to invade and exist within her womb. Some mothers, after viewing the "fetal" being within them, experience an increased sense of separation between their babies and themselves. The fetus can be viewed as a parasite rather than a developing individual they can love. It is not the actual fetus or the actual diagnosis of the fetus but the fantasies, dreams, perceptions, and understandings of the fetus and the status of that fetus that create the most concern. Emotional disturbances can develop and psychological vulnerabilities can be exacerbated. When these things occur, how do they affect the woman's transition into motherhood and the development of her connection to her baby? We do not know.

What happens when the results of an ultrasound indicate a birth defect or other abnormality? Parents, of course, become concerned, fearful, and anxious. The medical professionals order more testing, which will most often include other ultrasounds. As one researcher[4] describes, the identified malformation creates a connection between the parents and the medical professionals. At times, dependence develops where the focus of the entire pregnancy is constantly hinged on the results of the next ultrasound. If the problem actualizes and the baby is born with a defect of some type, then the dependence on the medical personnel and the experiences of fear and anxiety can be justified. There was a real problem and these things helped to prepare for it. What happens if the identified malformation turns out to be nothing? At best, parents would be relieved and embrace their healthy child without any further effects of the misdiagnosis. At worst, the dependence developed on the medical professionals and the heightened emotional state of the parents might have fractured the early emotional and psychological connections between parent and child necessary for a healthy, secure parent-child relationship. The emotional preparation parents go through when expecting an imperfect baby is extensive and traumatizing. With the birth of an imperfect baby, parents receive support from medical and personal sources; with the birth of an unexpectedly healthy baby the parents' intense emotions are expected to turn to immediate relief and gratefulness; however, the emotional charge of trauma does not dissipate easily, especially when there is a lack of support.

A further complication of the prenatal diagnosis of malformations via ultrasound is when the problems are not only realized but are more extensive than earlier identified. Emotional and psychological preparation, as well as medical preparation, for a specific defect can serve as a protective mechanism for both the baby and the parents. When the problems go beyond the expected, the situation quickly turns into an immediate crisis and additional trauma for the parents. Parents can feel let down by themselves, each other, the medical system, and sometimes even their baby. Trust with the health care providers can be jeopardized. This same phenomena occurs when parents were assured everything looked normal and their baby seemed healthy only to discover at the time of birth this "promise of good health" was broken and their baby was experiencing problems. If the reported results of the ultrasound indicated one sex and the baby born was actually of the other sex, the same type of process occurs. Expectations are dashed and a reworking of the imagined relationship with the imagined baby becomes necessary.

An additional complication of the use of ultrasound technologies during pregnancy focuses on the health care providers. The research available suggests that many of those providers doing the ultrasounds, reading the ultrasounds, and sharing ultrasound results with parents do not have adequate training and education in the psychological and emotional work women go through during pregnancy. They do not often have an understanding of either the psychological and emotional work required during pregnancy, the potential disruptions and disturbances that can occur, or the long term effects on the mother-child relationship that may result from ultrasound use. Therefore, it is imperative when an ultrasound is done that those medical persons involved have the necessary education, sensitivity, and awareness of the potential impact on the mother, the father, and the future interpersonal relationships.

We know ultrasound technology can offer security to the majority of pregnant women. We also know some women will be comforted by the results of their ultrasounds, experiencing decreased anxiety and fear. We know that in some cases ultrasounds can provide early identification of problems that lead to early intervention with successful outcomes. We also know that for some women ultrasounds can create problems, emotional letdowns, increased anxiety and fear, and disruptions in the psychological paths leading to the connection between a mother and her unborn child. There are both positive considerations and negative considerations. These need to be examined further to help us understand who is most vulnerable for a negative impact and under what circumstances ultrasound should be conducted. It is important that you consider these ultrasound issues when you are working with the pregnant woman. What would be the benefits of an ultrasound for the woman you are working with? How might she be affected by the identification of a potential abnormality in her child? How is her connection with her unborn child progressing? These are just a few of the questions you should ask yourself.

Domestic Violence

Domestic violence during pregnancy is a problem we like to think does not exist. How could anyone injure a woman with a child in her womb? We see domestic violence as a crime against women, not children. We know that abusive partners represent a full range of social class, occupations, and life styles. We know that domestic violence is a major crime against women, not only harming them physically but also stripping away their sense of self, their power, and their hope for the future. When abusers cross that line to abusing a vulnerable and defenseless unborn child, the crimes become even more heinous. It happens.

The Center for Disease Control[1] reported that domestic violence occurs in up to 8 percent of all pregnant women giving birth to live children. Some researchers, however, have found higher rates in various populations studied. For example, one group of researchers[2] identified 36 percent of the pregnant women they studied experienced domestic violence during pregnancy. Others[3] have examined prevalence rates of domestic violence during pregnancy. They found a range from 7.4 percent to 20.1 percent. The variation in rates was related to the way the violence was measured, the type of population explored, study methods, and point in pregnancy. Asking women more than once during detailed interviews and inquiring during the third trimester tended to demonstrate higher rates of domestic violence reporting. One study[4] of abuse during the year prior to pregnancy and during the current pregnancy with a Swedish population found an overall rate of 24.5 percent of women experienced threats, physical abuse, or sexual abuse. The types of violence included symbolic violence (14.5 percent), threats of mild to serious violence (20.3 percent), actual mild to serious violence (22 percent), and sexual violence (3.3 percent). Yet another study[5] used questionnaires to identify pregnant women experiencing domestic violence. They found a prevalence rate of 6.6 percent; within that group of women, they further found that 63.9 percent reported an increase of violence during pregnancy and that 77.8 percent stayed with their abuser. Furthermore, only 66.7 percent received medical treatment for the abuse, and only one woman ever told her prenatal care provider of the abuse.

Risk factors related to the potential of abuse during pregnancy are just beginning to be identified and understood. In a group of pregnant Latina women, a significant difference in self-esteem was identified, with the battered pregnant women demonstrating lower scores on self-esteem measures[6]. The abused pregnant women also demonstrated a significantly stronger acculturation to the Anglo community than those Latina women who did not report abuse. Three factors have been identified as putting women at increased risk of domestic violence during pregnancy: social instability, unhealthy lifestyle, and physical health problems[7]. Finally, a group of researchers studying a group of pregnant women in a Chinese community found that if the pregnancy was unplanned and if husbands or partners were either unemployed or manual workers, women were at higher risk of domestic violence[8].

Information also exists as to the effects on the mother and the fetus when the mother is involved in domestic violence during pregnancy. The National Center for Chronic Disease Prevention and Health Promotion[9] (NCCDPHP) released the following implications for women and their babies when domestic violence occurs during pregnancy:

- Elevated stress in the mother created by domestic violence may produce poor health outcomes for the baby, such as low birth weight.

- Women in domestic violence situations may delay seeking prenatal care, possibly leading to problems such as poor nutrition. This may, in turn, lead to poor baby outcomes.

- Women exposed to violence may be more vulnerable to high-risk behaviors such as risky sexual behaviors, which may place the unborn child at risk for harm.

- Women exposed to domestic violence more often report unwanted pregnancies or increased unhappiness with being pregnant, which may impact the developing relationship between the mother and her unborn child.

We know domestic violence against women is a significant problem. Many difficulties exist, however, that limit the identification and intervention of domestic violence during pregnancy. Based on the NCCDPHP[10] report, some of these reasons include:

- Low screening rates—we don't ask the right questions

- Lack of effective interventions—we have not developed ways to intervene effectively

- Unavailability of interventions that do exist—domestic violence during pregnancy has not been a large focus of intervention research

- Geographical barriers to appropriate resources—many areas, both rural and urban, lack appropriate resources; connecting with existing resources can be challenging

- Issues around confidentiality—women are afraid to talk about their experiences with domestic violence

- Concern that identification of domestic violence in a woman's life may increase her risk for more violence—fear that identification and attempts at intervention may increase the risk of further violence toward the mother and her unborn child

- Limited numbers of professionals trained in the identification and treatment of domestic violence—few people are trained in working with pregnant women from a psychological, emotional, or relationship perspective; fewer yet are trained in domestic violence with pregnant women

- Lack of effective links between the medical, judicial, and community systems—communication and education between systems is lacking

- Nonexistent or limited prevention services—very few, if any, appropriate services are available

As practitioners and interventionists working with the pregnant mother, it is critical that you ask questions about domestic violence. Little can be done if we do not know a problem exists, and we will not know a problem exists unless it is reported to us. In-person interviews seemed to be the best for facilitating the sharing of information on domestic violence. Questionnaires can also be helpful. Using both a questionnaire and an in-person interview seems to generate the highest rates of identification of the problems [11]. Regardless of the manner of inquiry, questions need to be asked and the answers need to be evaluated if we are to be effective in keeping women and children safe during this very vulnerable time of life.

Little information exists on intervening in the domestic violence of pregnant women. This is an area where both research and clinical practice need to focus in order to facilitate the development of specific, effective interventions. Some guidelines for addressing a pregnant woman who is being battered or abused in a domestic violence situation are listed below:

- Keep communication open.

- Reinforce the idea that every woman has choices over her life.

- Become knowledgeable of the cycle of domestic violence yourself.

- Educate women of the cycle of abuse.

- Understand that leaving an abuser is very difficult and often involves several attempts before one is successful.

- Put safety first. Try to create a safe environment in your practice supporting women and create avenues leading to safe, protected housing for women in abusive partnerships.

- When providing phone numbers for domestic violence referrals, it is most helpful to stay with the woman as she makes her initial call and/or to have a specific name of a person to contact, not just an agency.

- Ask questions with every pregnant client.

- Inquire respectfully about physical injuries.

- Encourage and support the woman to develop a Safety Plan should the threat or occurrence of domestic violence happen again.

- Stock your waiting room with literature regarding domestic violence and numbers to call or provide that information as part of a pregnancy packet to each new client.

- Become knowledgeable about your local shelters, support agencies, and treatment facilities. Know where to refer women in need.

- Prepare a plan of action for your agency or office staff to evaluate domestic violence, referral, and intervention. Lay out emergency procedures that may be implemented immediately to get a woman to safety.

Depression During Pregnancy

The Baby Blues is an expression describing a normal part of the transition to motherhood that generally occurs within the first 10 days following the birth of the baby. A woman experiencing Baby Blues may often feel like crying, experience mood swings, feel depressed, lose her appetite, and have trouble sleeping. These experiences seem to be a normal part of the adjustment and may actually be necessary for some mothers to "reorganize" psychologically in order to assume the mothering role more completely.

When these symptoms do not stop but instead continue or worsen, this becomes postpartum depression. Postpartum depression is as serious as any clinical depression. The symptoms can vary in intensity. Some women will be able to remain functional, while others become totally non-functional in caring for themselves or their babies. Symptoms are consistent with a clinical depression and may include changes in appetite, changes in sleep patterns, depressed mood, a sense of hopelessness, difficulty concentrating, tearfulness or uncontrollable crying, increased anxiety, intrusive thoughts, irritability, a loss of the sense of pleasure in life, and, at times, suicidal thoughts or ideation. Treatment is necessary. The mistake often made is that postpartum depression will resolve in time as it naturally does with the Baby Blues. Women experiencing postpartum depression may need medication, counseling, group support, and possibly hospitalization. Depression needs to be taken as seriously as any other medical illness and treated as aggressively. Postpartum depression interferes with a woman's sense of self-esteem, her transition to motherhood, and her relationship with her baby.

Why are we discussing postpartum depression in a book that is focused on pregnancy? Primarily because we know that the absence of depressive symptoms in the prenatal period often indicate an absence of depressive symptoms in the postpartum period and vice versa; the presence of depressive symptoms in the prenatal period often leads to the presence of depressive symptoms in the postpartum period[1]. This link between prenatal depression and postpartum depression is reported to range from 18-75 percent, depending on the population studied[2]. Research found a significant relationship between prenatal depression and the recurrence of depression at some point during the first postpartum year. Understanding postpartum depression can also help us to look for early signs during pregnancy that may lead to postpartum depression, as well help us to take preventive steps during pregnancy to protect women against postpartum depression.

Depressions that develop during pregnancy can often be overlooked because many of the physical symptoms of depression are naturally present during pregnancy. Symptoms of depression may include loss of appetite, sleep disturbances, constipation or diarrhea, loss of sexual interest, rapid heartbeat, feelings of difficulty swallowing or something interfering with the throat, pain in specific areas of the body, or generalized pain[3]. These symptoms represent the physical half of depression, where the mood changes and depressed feelings represent the emotional half of depression. During pregnancy, many of these symptoms fall within the normal range of experiences for many women. In fact, attempts to measure or evaluate depression during pregnancy are often difficult due to the lack of appropriate depression screening tools. These tools generally have several items that represent somatic symptoms. Because there are so many physical symptoms present for many pregnant women, they tend to score higher on these tools, leading to false positive results. These false positives have suggested to many practitioners that depression is a normal state during pregnancy and therefore should not be intervened with:" it will go away when the baby is born." Due to these beliefs, screening for depression is not always done, preventive measures are not taken, interventions are not made, and many women are left to suffer through their depressions in isolation, often feeling shameful that they do not feel better about being pregnant and having a baby. Unfortunately, the depression that develops prenatally does not tend to resolve with the baby's birth but instead may continue and become a postpartum depression.

In a study exploring the nature of depression during the prenatal period in a group of Japanese pregnant women, three factors of prenatal depression were identified: Cognitive, Affective Symptoms and Insomnia, and Attentional[4]. The Cognitive factor involved hopelessness, personal devaluation, emptiness, and dissatisfaction. Affective Symptoms and Insomnia included depressed affect, crying spells, irritability, and fatigue. The final factor, Attentional, contained confusion, psychomotor retardation, and indecisiveness. Somatic features were excluded due to their natural presence during pregnancy and childbirth. These descriptive factors provide us with a beginning to understand the dimensions specific to prenatal depression.

Treatment for depression during pregnancy has not received much investigative attention. However, in one of the few studies done on the treatment of women with antenatal and postpartum depression, researchers found evidence that short-term individual psychotherapy was effective in impacting the depression[5]. Their treatment schedule began weekly for three months, then bimonthly for a second period of three months. Some women also required medication to treat their depressive symptoms. The study reported that most antenatal and postpartum depressive symptoms responded well after two to three months of treatment.

The use of antidepressant or mood stabilizing medications during the prenatal period is controversial. Little is known about the impact of these drugs on the developing fetus. In women with personal histories of severe depression, medications may have to be considered to ensure her successful navigation of her pregnancy and delivery. Some women who have personal and family histories of depression, particularly postpartum depression, may benefit from prophylactic antidepressant use, beginning immediately after delivery, to try to ward off the development of a postpartum depression. In either of these scenarios, it is important that the woman discuss options with her primary health care provider. The severity and impact of the depressive symptoms need to be weighed carefully against the potential effects of the pharmacological treatment on the mother, her unborn child, and her child after delivery, especially if she is breast-feeding.

Other prophylactic antidepressant measures should be considered throughout pregnancy. Regular exercise has been found to be one of the most effective means to prevent and treat depression. Encouraging the pregnant woman to begin early in her pregnancy to develop an exercise routine that fits into her life and supports her pregnancy is important. Assisting the pregnant woman to develop a solid support system, which can be there not only for her pregnancy-related concerns but also to support her as a woman and a person, is also important. Personal and pregnancy support can be two of the most beneficial services for the pregnant woman.

The Pregnant Woman Above Age 35

Pregnancy is a developmental phase for women. Pregnancy issues are heightened when the woman becomes pregnant at a time in her life when there are other tasks to master in other developmental phases. The optimal childbearing years in this country range from around the age of 19 or 20, up until the age of 35 or 36. While there are many who would argue the validity of this age range, it is well represented throughout the pregnancy literature and will therefore serve as the basis for the information presented here. Women who give birth to their first child in their mid to late thirties have generally held careers or other life interests that involved a great investment of them personally. During this period as they are shifting and preparing to move into their "40's," the developmental focus naturally returns to themselves: what they have accomplished in their lives and their goals and aspirations for the future. Many women begin to change physically; menopause may begin or even be well underway. Traditionally, the late thirties and early forties were not seen as childbearing years. However, with the advent of more and more efficient medical and fertility treatments, pregnancy during this life phase is no longer a rare occurrence; instead it is well received by women and more easily accepted by those around her.

Maternal role attainment is one of the more difficult challenges for the pregnant woman over the age of 35, especially if it is her first baby. For these women, life before the baby was often focused on themselves and their partners. Life could be more spontaneous; a movie after work or a get-together with friends on a whim was possible.

Older mothers have been found to report specific difficulties in the areas of social support, isolation, fatigue/need to heal, and work-career issues[1]. The issue of fatigue was questioned as having been related to the high rate of cesarean births (45 percent) rather than an actual age issue. However, in looking at mothers over the age of 35 who had adopted, problems with fatigue were also commonly reported, suggesting that the fatigue might be more related to the age factor than the birthing factor[2]. Increased stress on the marital relationship and lower maternal confidence has also been linked to becoming a mother later in life[3]. Other issues might include the change in income from dual income to single income or the need to blend returning to work with mothering. Finally, physical changes in the woman's body as she moves into her late thirties and early forties may complicate the actual pregnancy and child birthing process for some women.

As is evident with the information available, care needs to be taken during pregnancy to adequately prepare these women to take on the maternal role with added emphasis on stress reduction, conflicts of career and motherhood, preparation for changes in income, and focus on taking care of self to reduce or limit fatigue. Women over the age of 35 may also need assistance building a positive support system even when it appears they have solid support available to them. These women may have many friends who had babies when they were younger and now those children are in their teen years. In our work at the University of Washington with pregnant and adoptive mothers, mothers often reported having children at times in their lives different from other women in their peer groups. These mothers stated they felt left out and isolated even in the presence of friends; many women reported seeking out a new peer group of women like them who were becoming mothers later in life.

The Pregnant Adolescent

Adolescent pregnancy is often the focus of researchers and clinicians, not so much for the risks it presents to the adolescent body but for the

risks it presents to the adolescent's present psychological and emotional health and the impact of that pregnancy on the adolescent's life
trajectory. One group of researchers found that 60 percent of the
pregnant adolescents they studied experienced some type of major
psychosocial problem that interfered with their daily living[1]. These
problems included a lack of support from family and friends (46
percent), the termination of a relationship with their baby's father (47
percent), homelessness (16 percent), and domestic violence (22
percent). They also found that some pregnant adolescents continued
smoking in their pregnancy (44 percent), drank alcohol (21 percent),
and used illegal drugs (38 percent) including marijuana, solvents, and
heroin. Multidrug use in combination with those drugs just listed
included the addition of benzodiazepines, amphetamines, and LSD.
Another significant finding was the lack of questions asked about
these issues during assessment of the pregnant adolescent. Sadly, it
was found that the "failure to perform an adequate psychosocial
history is often the rule rather than the exception in antenatal care[2]."

A study of pregnant Hispanic adolescents and their mothers found
that becoming a mother was seen as a way to gain freedom and
separation from their parents[3]. The pregnancies seemed to lead to a
decrease in conflict with their own mothers. The adolescents became
better able to tolerate and accept their mothers' supervision of them.
The mothers viewed their daughters' having babies as a move toward
safety, as the girls would most likely stay at home more to care for
their babies rather than be on the streets. In general, family functioning improved for the pregnant adolescent. The pregnancy was related
to decreases in sibling conflict and an increase in cohesiveness with
female family members. Relationships with male family members,
however, became less cohesive and more difficult.

Several factors related to adolescent pregnancy have been identified
when African American and European American teens are viewed as
one group[4]. These factors included being reared in poverty by only
one biological parent, having low educational expectations and low
maternal educational achievement, wanting an ideal number of
children, having lower self esteem and more traditional views of
women's family roles, having a history of more delinquent behavior,

beginning to menstruate at a younger age, and engaging in alcohol usage and sexual behavior at a younger age. When African American teens are evaluated separately from European American teens, it was found that the African American teens engaged in sexual activity earlier than European American teens but that the European American teens engaged in other risky behaviors earlier. It was also found that the negative impact of early pregnancy was less on African American teens. African American adolescents were more likely to stay in school, continue living in their parents' home (providing better access to support and childcare), and delay marriage.

There exists a wealth of data suggesting that adolescent pregnancy may lead to negative outcomes for the adolescents and their babies. It is a widespread problem. In 1990, there were about 1 million teen pregnancies, over half of which ended in live births[5]. The majority of these births were unintended (80 percent). In addition, the Center for Disease Control reports that pregnant teens are more likely to receive inadequate prenatal care than older pregnant women. They also report that pregnant teens tend to experience pregnancy-related hypertension, inadequate weight gain during pregnancy, and maternal anemia. Finally, the babies born to these mothers are at an increased risk of preterm birth, low birth weight, respiratory distress, meconium aspiration, assisted ventilation, and newborn anemia. It is clear from the information available that preventing teen pregnancy is an important goal. However, when teen pregnancies do occur, the focus should be on supporting and maintaining the health of the adolescent through the pregnancy, decreasing risk factors present, and increasing available social support. Finding ways to help the adolescent who chooses to parent to find a way to transition to motherhood with the ability to balance caring for her baby in the most optimal manner, maintaining attention to her own developmental needs, and preparing for the future will be a challenging but important task.

Pregnant Women With Disabilities

It is estimated that there are more than 8 million families in the United States where at least one parent is affected with a disability[1].

Worldwide estimates increase this number many times over. There are many different disabilities, each with its own challenges, risks, and adaptations, such as:

- Multiple sclerosis
- Blindness
- Deafness
- Rheumatoid arthritis
- Spinal cord injuries (paraplegic, quadriplegic)
- Intellectual impairments
- Cognitive deficits
- Spinal bifida
- Dwarfism
- Cerebral palsy
- Chronic illnesses (Crohn's disease, diabetes, lupus, and so on)
- Permanent injuries
- Missing limbs (congenital or through injury or illness)
- Effects of polio (paralysis, and so on)

Women affected by these, and other, disabilities face challenges everyday. Many deal with transportation issues, accommodation issues, prejudice, and stigma. Becoming pregnant often adds to and intensifies the battles they must fight and the challenges they must meet. Pregnancy can be challenging for any woman, with or without a disability. Often, the presence of a disability increases the work needed to adjust to the physical aspects of pregnancy, as well as the traditional psychological and emotional work of pregnancy. For many of these women, their emotional and psychological work often goes unsupported. In fact, many disabled women have reported family, friends, and medical professionals as trying to talk them out of having a child rather than helping them to understand the risks for both mother and baby, learn the best way to minimize these risks, and begin the preparation for the adaptations needed to welcome their child into this world[2,3,4]. Challenges continue when the baby is born, as a woman's disabilities may require specific adaptations to be able to care for the baby in the best possible manner.

Some of the challenges a pregnant woman with a disability may face include:

- A worsening of her symptoms brought on by the pregnancy

- Health care providers unknowledgeable about disabilities

- Health care providers unknowledgeable about the impact of pregnancy on a woman with a disability or her unborn child

- Unfounded assumptions that the presence of a disability means poor outcomes for mom and/or baby[5]

- Lack of the proper equipment in the medical offices to accommodate the disability (for example, a scale that accommodates a woman in a wheelchair)

- Lack of preparation for actual baby care—with or without adaptation needs

- Intensified fears with little or no support to vent or work through feelings

- Pregnancy or baby care information not available in Braille

- Finding balance around taking medications and treatments to manage the disability and protecting the unborn child from the risks of those medications and treatments

- Complications and other health care risks

Working with the pregnant woman with a disability has been described as working in a different culture[6]. As with any culture different from your own, it is important to think about several different issues, such as:

1. Accept the woman for who she is—disability, pregnancy, and all.

2. Remember, it is her choice to become a parent and this choice needs to be respected.

3. Provide clear, factual information about issues that impact both the disability and the pregnancy.

4. Listen to her fears, anxieties, concerns, and celebrate her excitement.

5. Ask questions; it is imperative that you understand her needs, wants, and how she perceives her disability.

6. Advocate for her rights as a woman, a mother-to-be, a patient, and a person.

7. Help her locate disability-friendly services, such as a medical provider who has an accessible examination table.

8. Help to educate those working with the pregnant woman with a disability to understand as much about pregnancy and disability as possible.

9. Encourage her to connect with organizations such as *Through the Looking Glass*, that offer support, education, and advocacy for women with disabilities.

10. Think prevention; it is critical that time is taken in pregnancy to think about how the woman's disability may impact her ability to parent. Does she need assistance? Does she need special equipment? Is she thinking about the adaptations she might have to make?

11. Encourage and support the same "working through" of the emotional and psychological issues of pregnancy—she needs to do this work with or without a disability.

12. Provide support and encouragement of her autonomy and independence. She needs to feel empowered and confident as she transitions out of pregnancy into motherhood.

It is possible for the pregnant woman with a disability to have a normal pregnancy and delivery in many cases. Of course, when the health risks are real for either baby or mother, it is critical that they be addressed and taken care of. The danger is in the assumptions that are made—these limit the opportunities of the pregnant woman with regard to childbirth and whittle away at her self-confidence and sense of control. One study reported the things pregnant women with disabilities felt would have improved their experience[7]. These included primary prevention efforts such as early referrals to physical therapy to help maximize physical function and support exercise efforts, referrals to organizations providing equipment allowing them to do the work of mothers and care for their babies in the best way possible[8,9]; and, personal care assistance in pregnancy and after the birth of the baby as a way to help decrease stress and maintain the family unit.

The Risk of an Imperfect Baby: Handicaps, Illness, and Prematurity

When the risk of having an imperfect baby or medically fragile baby becomes apparent in pregnancy, it changes the nature of the pregnant woman's work. The ideas of risk and threat intensify the stress of the pregnancy. Fears for the baby and herself are no longer diffuse but become real and directly threaten her and her unborn child. The pregnant woman's ability to navigate the tasks and stages of pregnancy becomes challenged. If her identity as a woman is deeply connected to the ideal pregnancy and birth of the ideal baby, the woman may experience negative effects on her self-esteem and self-image. Her psychological view of herself and her capacity to become a mother and to actually mother her child may become threatened, which may, in turn, negatively impact the mother-child relationship[1].

Women react differently when they are posed with a threat to either themselves or their unborn children. Some women may deny the risk or possibility of any harm or adverse outcome, leading to a withdrawing from the medical professionals and the absence of prenatal care necessary for more positive outcomes. If the risk is life threatening and is ignored or minimized, then both mother and child could be placed in even greater danger. It will be important to assess the woman's perception of the risk factors or identified problems and to gauge her view on how to approach these issues.

Some women may latch on to the medical professionals responsible for their care during pregnancy. They may take charge of their circumstances and begin to do everything they could possibly do to minimize the risks and guarantee the safe and healthy birth of their baby. A potential danger in this scenario is the mom who does everything she can possibly do with still no change in outcome. This woman may feel responsible and suffer much guilt and blame. She may feel like a failure to herself and to her child, as well as to those around her. This is especially true when she sees something she has done or a choice she has made as being responsible for the difficulties in the baby. Interventions for these mothers should focus on working through the feelings of guilt and failure as well as the sense of grief and loss that often develop. Many of these mothers will need professional psychotherapy to address their feelings and thoughts. Another goal of therapy would be to ensure that the maternal feelings and reactions do not limit her ability to care for and nurture her baby.

The task of binding into the baby and beginning to develop an attachment to the unborn child becomes a fragile process as the mother is faced with preparing for and relating to a baby that might not actually survive to become the child she has dreamt about and imagined would soon be in her arms. Women experiencing threatened pregnancies were found to still progress through Rubin's stages (see Chapter 3 for a discussion of Rubin's stages); however, the stages became secondary or the background to the well-being of the fetus[2,3]. Uncertainty became and remained in the foreground throughout the high-risk perinatal situation. They experienced an "uncertainty of becoming a mother to this infant." These thoughts dominated the pregnancy and altered the maternal experience and the meanings inherent in it. Mothers reported feelings of no guarantees, fear, not knowing, and helplessness. It will be important when working with mothers in these situations to support their work through the tasks of pregnancy and to focus interventions on supporting the development of a positive mother-child relationship.

The Relinquishing Mother and Adoption

The decision to relinquish a child for adoption often involves a great deal of thought, time, and emotion. No woman easily makes this decision, no matter what her circumstances might be. Some women, of course, will have an easier time than others. Some women may decide very early in their pregnancies, some only when the baby is born, and, others may care for their babies for several weeks or months before they make this decision. Including this section on the relinquishment and adoption came about from our experiences with several different women. Their stories demonstrate the thoughtfulness of their decisions and their commitments to their babies.

> *Katie, age 23, signed up with the program when she was six months pregnant and planning on parenting her child. She worked well in the program and was successful in all that she attempted to do for herself. Only upon the birth of her child did she decide to relinquish. Later, she shared that she had always had it in the back of her mind. She had made phone calls to different agencies to gather information, but had made no commitments or agreements. She stated that through her work in the early intervention program she was able to see what she wanted for herself and for her baby, and realized that although she loved her baby and had a desire to parent, she was not ready to be the mother her child really deserved. She stated that seeing her baby in her arms only reinforced the idea that her baby needed more than she could offer at that point in her life.*

> *Susan, age 19, had made very specific plans on how she was going to care for herself and her newborn. She had been clean and sober for her entire pregnancy, had secured housing, and had tried to create a home for herself and her child. When the baby was about two months old, Susan began to be concerned over her relationship with her baby. She shared that she loved her baby on one hand, but did not feel connected on the other. She described her feelings about being with her baby as being the same as they would be with a stranger. She shared she found little enjoyment in being a mother and felt her baby would be better off with a family that really wanted a baby. Susan was evaluated for postpartum depression, which was*

not an issue for her. She was clearly able to describe her feelings and her desires for herself and her baby. After several weeks of exploring her feelings and options, Susan decided to relinquish her baby through an open adoption, where she could maintain periodic contact with the baby and adoptive family.

Gail was 17 when she became pregnant by her boyfriend of only a few months. Gail had a long history of trauma and loss in her life, beginning with the death of her own mother during Gail's birth. Her father struggled to care for her and her two brothers, often turning to the help of women he would meet, who were usually abusive to the children. Gail and her brothers were eventually removed from their father's care and later adopted into a family. Things went well for a while, but Gail's behavior was difficult to manage; she was angry and aggressive with others. Her adoptive parents eventually placed her in residential treatment in another state. Gail essentially grew up in treatment. She entered at age 9, lived in foster care and was never allowed to return to her adoptive home. When she became pregnant, Gail had fantasies of being the best mother in the world. She had idealized visions of the perfect baby in her arms, cooing and loving her. When the baby was born, she worked hard to care for him. She spent long periods of time watching her baby, thinking about how much she loved him, and wondering what his life would be like. As she looked at him, she would also think about the things she had learned from her home visitor and the things she had discussed with her therapist. Four weeks after her baby was born, Gail decided to place her baby with an adoptive family. She worked out an open adoption where she had regular visitation and was able to still be a part of her son's life. She shared that she wanted her baby to have a good family and she could not give him that, but she also wanted him to know her as the mother who gave birth to him. She also decided she wanted a better life than the one she was living. Following the relinquishment, Gail remained boy-friend-free for three years, finished high school, found a job, moved into her own apartment, and began taking college classes. She also maintained regular contact with her son through his adopted mother, who became a powerful source of support for her.

When the pregnant woman you are working with decides to relinquish her child, your role in intervention takes a different focus. It is important to remember that the decision to relinquish is not an easy decision but may be in the best interest of both the pregnant woman and her child. Most women deciding to adopt their babies out have put a lot of thought into their decisions and have carefully weighed the pros and cons. It will be important not to put down or minimize her decision, but to respect it. Respecting this decision does not mean avoiding discussion of it. It will be important to make sure that the pregnant woman who is relinquishing has connected with a professional who specializes in adoption. If she has not, connecting her with a social worker at the hospital she will deliver at, a specialized therapist, or a local adoption agency will be important. While some women make unshakable decisions, others reevaluate their decisions at various points in the pregnancy or even after the birth of the child.

It will be important to think about ways to discuss the issues of relinquishment without judgment or personal feelings intruding. Comments and questions that are not helpful include:

- Why would you want to do that?
- I could never give my baby to anyone else to raise!
- You will probably change your mind when you see the baby.
- Don't you think you'll be sorry one day?
- I know someone who...

Instead questions and comments should be supportive and aimed at facilitating the pregnant woman to think about and process the issues. Helpful examples include:

- How did you come to this decision?

- Have you discussed your decision with the baby's father?

- Have you discussed your decision with your family or friends?

- What do you hope this decision will mean for the baby's future?

- How do you plan to say good-bye to your baby?

- What made you decide on this family (or agency or process, etc.)?

- You seem to have put a great deal of thought into this decision. Tell me about what that was like for you.

- Do you have someone who can support you through the process?

- Have you discussed your decisions and plans with the hospital and doctor?

Dealing with relinquishment and adoption is a specialized area and requires specialized support, guidance, and intervention. Support women who decide to relinquish by facilitating these specialized services in addition to exploring and respecting her decision. The decision to relinquish is a difficult one but an honorable one. A conscious, well-thought-out choice to place a child for adoption is a beautiful way for some mothers to demonstrate love for their babies. And, again, it may be the best choice for both the woman and the child.

Chapter 7

Points To Remember

Dealing with the physical dimension of pregnancy requires a focus on the here and now—how the pregnant woman's is body responding and how the fetus is developing. Dealing with the emotional and psychological dimensions of pregnancy requires looking beyond the here and now and into the past, and often the future. It also requires looking beyond the physical bodies of the woman and her unborn child and into the woman's thoughts, feelings, fears, stressors, and experiences. In this chapter you have read about several of the different situations during pregnancy that should be considered when they involve one of the women with whom you are working. These issues do not pertain to all women. Nonetheless, these issues are critical for the women they do impact and require your careful consideration and understanding when they do exist.

Section II

Assessment and Intervention During Pregnancy

Pregnant women receiving prenatal care are regularly assessed for weight gain, blood pressure, nutritional status, and body changes. These are important and need to be assessed on a regular basis. It is not as common for a woman's emotional and psychological status to be regularly assessed, and even less common for interventions directly targeted at these issues to be implemented. In this section, the focus will be on the assessment process. You will learn the following:

- What to include in an assessment

- Why it is important

- What types of questions you might ask

- How to identify problem areas

- How to develop goals to deal with these problems

- What types of interventions would be appropriate for your client

This section is divided into three chapters: Assessment, Intervening, and Implementation. The Assessment and Intervening chapters provide the background and understanding for the process of assessing and intervening with the pregnant client. The chapter on Implementation is a resource for the actual implementation of the assessment and interventions.

The Implementation chapter is designed to be used as a tool for assessment, problem identification, goal development, use of specific interventions, and treatment planning using specific actions. It is based on the basic assessment included in Appendix A. There are three major sections: Present Issues, Past History, and Future Visions. In the Present, the topic areas include Current Pregnancy, Pregnancy History, Medical Background, Mental Health, Self Care, Work and Education, Relationships, and Stressors. The Past History section includes Loss and Trauma, Childhood Experiences, and Relationship with Mother. The third section, Future Visions, includes issues around Images of Baby, Images of Becoming a Mother, and the Images of How this Baby Will Change Daily Life.

Each topic area begins with a table that includes areas to be assessed, significance, and typical questions that might be asked. This chart is then followed by potential problems and issues that might come up in the specific areas. Goals for each problem area are identified, specific interventions from the Intervention Units in Section III are identified, and a list of supportive actions and responses is provided.

It is important to note that the information provided in this chapter is to be used as a tool. Each client is an individual. Meeting the needs of some clients may be easily pulled out of the information provided. Other clients, however, might have problems and issues that go beyond the scope of what is provided here. It is always difficult to find the balance between providing ready-made goals and actions and leaving them open enough to fit the needs of each client. It is for this reason that we recommend you use this information as a tool, not as a solution for every client.

Some of the most wonderful people are those who don't fit into boxes.

–Tori Amos

8

Assessment in Pregnancy

This chapter focuses on information on assessment needs unique to pregnancy, including an outline for assessment, tips for observations, and a list of risk factors.

Assessment in pregnancy is called for in a variety of situations. Assessment can be helpful in determining how the woman is dealing with her pregnancy, how it is impacting her life, and how she feels her life will be changed following the baby's birth. Assessment is also indicated when there is the presence of one or more factors that may place the mother, the child, or their relationship at risk. Risk factors include a history of abuse, past involvement with child protective services, or being either a young mother (under the age of 18) or an older mom (over the age of 35). Any present or past mental health illness would also be cause for a detailed assessment. Finally, any woman entering an early intervention program during her pregnancy might require an assessment as part of the protocol for the program. Information gathered from a thorough assessment can be extremely helpful in planning interventions or activities supportive of the mother-to-be.

The assessment described here provides the format for a thorough evaluation of the pregnant woman under any of the circumstances mentioned. It consists of questions aimed at gathering information on the woman's beliefs and feelings about her pregnancy, her history of relationships, and her childhood experiences. All of these questions relate directly to the psychological and emotional work the woman does to prepare to be a mother and to accept her child.

Process of Assessment

A thoughtful assessment generally occurs in a quiet, relaxed setting where interruption is unlikely. The woman should feel free to say anything or discuss any details she feels are relevant in answering the questions. It is important that she understand that the assessment is confidential and that it is used to gather information in order to provide appropriate services in the best possible way.

Assessments are designed to be redundant. This is purposefully done, as different questions about the same or similar things can prompt very different answers. For example, asking someone at the beginning of an interview if they have ever been depressed and asking them the same question following a series of questions on other psychiatric issues can elicit very different responses. With the first question, the woman may say "no," as she is thinking about the pregnancy or feeling anxious about the assessment. With the second question, she may say she experienced depression once when she was young. In this latter example, she has been prepared to think about depression in a different light, prompting her to relate the question more easily to her experience.

Asking the same question in a variety of ways can also be helpful in eliciting the information needed as people think and store their memories in different ways. For instance, using the same depression question, several ways of gathering the information are possible. The questions may be asked in the following ways:

1. Have you ever been depressed?

2. Have you ever had a time in your life when you felt sad or hopeless?

3. Has anything ever happened to you that made you feel overwhelmed? For instance, have you ever felt that you just couldn't deal with things for one more day?

The woman may not associate her behavior or feelings with depression, but she may remember a time when she felt sad or even hopeless. She may not remember a time when she felt especially sad, but she may have felt overwhelmed at a particular time in her life. With any of these questions, it will be important to continue to "prompt" or explore her experiences for more information as to what she recalls. Ask questions such as "What was that like for you?" "How did you deal with it?" "What told you this was depression?" "What kinds of things did you find helpful in feeling better?"

Prompting or exploring is used throughout the assessment to gather more information and more detail about the experience and memories of the woman. People rarely offer much detail when they first answer a question. Providing them several opportunities presented in various ways or asking questions aimed at gathering smaller pieces of information is generally helpful in understanding the woman's experiences and their impact on her life. Developing the "big picture" is necessary in any assessment, but the process of constructing this bigger picture through numerous pieces of rich detail is equally important.

In any assessment, there may be questions you feel have not been answered completely, or you may feel that the person is withholding specific information. Re-asking questions in other areas of the assessment can be helpful. Asking for clarification around certain issues or repeating back what the person has told you can often help clear up inconsistencies as well as prompt the person to rethink what she has shared and restate it in a more complete way. For instance, a woman might claim that throughout her childhood her mother and father never punished her. In another section of the assessment, she may recall how she was always getting in trouble with her friends at school. "Never being punished" and "getting in trouble with friends" suggest that the information she is providing is somewhat contradictory. The following example illustrates how this might be further explored:

> *It sounds like you had quite a group of friends. But I am a*
> *little confused. You said earlier you never got punished, but*
> *actually it sounds like you did get into some trouble with some*
> *of your friends at times…did this trouble you found yourself*
> *in ever involve your parents or anyone else? What kinds of*
> *things happened to you when you got in trouble?*

This line of inquiry allows her to continue to keep private the information she does not yet want to share and it also allows her to provide clarification in a natural way. It is always important to ask questions in a direct but gentle manner, remaining non-judgmental and non-threatening. It is equally important to allow the person being assessed the right to privacy. If they develop trust with you, they will begin to share further information with you at a later date if they feel it is relevant.

Areas of Assessment

The assessment presented here is divided into three general sections: present, past, and future issues. Each section includes several topic areas. Under present issues, these topics include:

- Current Pregnancy
- Self Care
- Pregnancy Background
- Work and Education
- Medical Background
- Relationships
- Mental Health
- Stressors

The section on past history includes these topics:

- Loss and Trauma
- Childhood Experiences
- Relationship with Mother

In the final section, future visions, the following topics are included:

- Image of Baby

- Images of Becoming a Mother

- Images of How This Baby Will Change Daily Life

Chapter 10 provides a detailed explanation of assessment, problem identification, goal development, and plans for implementation. Each assessment section includes topics to be assessed, the significance of each topic, and sample questions. Appendix A is a copy of the assessment questions format described here. Lastly, Appendix B provides a transcript from an actual interview with a pregnant woman. Two topics are discussed: prior pregnancies and issues with her father.

Observation

A well-done assessment always involves some degree of observation. For example, it is important to be aware of the woman, her home (if a home visit), and how she interacts in that environment. The woman's appearance, how she is dressed, her level of cleanliness, her expressions, her way of communicating, and her overall appearance of health are all important indicators of her current state. What would you think of a woman who appears shabbily dressed; has dirty, unwashed hair; maintains a flat, emotionless expression with downcast eyes; answers questions with one- or two-word answers; and appears pale and/or thin? She gives a different impression of how she is feeling and experiencing her environment and pregnancy than one who appears neatly dressed in casual clothing; has clean, well kept hair; seems nervous but is able to show a range of emotion depending on the questions being discussed; maintains occasional eye contact; provides brief but complete answers; and appears alert and awake, often caressing her pregnant belly as she talks about her pregnancy or baby. The first woman described should raise red flags as to her ability to care for herself, her level of depression, and her feelings toward the baby she carries. The second woman might be perceived as functioning fairly well, able to relate well to others, and feeling positive about the baby she carries.

If the second woman functions as described for all of the interview except when she is asked about domestic violence, at which point she becomes quiet, shifts in her chair, and becomes tearful, this might be an emotional issue for her whether or not she shares an experience of domestic violence with the interviewer. Her behavior suggests this is a difficult subject for her. Depending on your relationship with her, you might either gently share your observation that "it seems these questions are really difficult for you" or just make a note of it to be followed up on at a later time.

Note the following observations from a scheduled home visit assessment of a 28-year-old single mother of two children, ages 2 and 4, and currently eight months pregnant with her third child:

> *Patty answered the door after a multiple series of knocks. She was apologetic for the delay and explained she had just gotten out of the shower as she had gotten behind this morning. She presented with wet hair, no make-up (she has always worn carefully applied make-up during previous interactions), and dressed in a T-shirt that came down to the top of her thighs. Upon entering the home, the TV was on, playing the movie "Home Alone," her two-year-old was belted in her highchair, which was scattered with pieces of cheese and cheerios, and her four-year-old was skipping around throwing washcloths he kept grabbing from the laundry pile. Both children appeared unwashed and were still dressed in their pajamas (it was 1 p.m.). The house was cluttered and strewn with garbage, including soiled diapers, dirty bottles (some half filled with milk), McDonald's bags, and dried french fries. Some dried food substance was smeared on the tile floor. No toys or child-like items were visible in the shared living spaces of the living room, kitchen, hallway, or bathroom. Patty appeared to use a lot of physical effort moving from standing to a sitting position, her difficulty seemingly related to her pregnant belly. As she went to sit down it became apparent that she was wearing no underwear. In spite of the apparent chaos, Patty remained calm, cheerful, and seemingly oblivious to what was going on around her.*

Think about what can be ascertained just from this observation. The messy and dirty home could suggest that this mom is quite comfortable because she is accustomed to this type of environment, or it could suggest that her pregnancy might have gotten to the point where it is interfering with her ability to maintain her home without support. Fragments of fast food and empty McDonald's bags could suggest that she is too tired to prepare meals or shop for food, or it could be the way this family normally eats. Either way, if fast food makes up the bulk of her diet, a referral to the nutritionist or her health care provider might be indicated. The lack of any toys for two- and four-year-old children in the home could suggest that they may be limited to certain areas for play such as their room; it could suggest that this mother does not understand children's needs and does not provide play opportunities for her children; it could also mean she got tired of picking them up so she put them all away in a box so she wouldn't have to deal with them (which is what had actually happened). Patty's lack of make-up and wet hair could suggest that she did not have time this particular day to get ready on time or it could suggest that she is able to pull herself together to go out of the house but falls apart when at home.

Another possibility is that she does not allow herself to leave the house without being carefully fixed up, possibly suggesting that she may be isolating herself. The fact that Patty did not have underwear on generally suggests a lack of boundaries with others, as this type of behavior is unusual even with people very comfortable with each other. It could also mean that Patty maintains a freedom around her body and nudity, feeling very comfortable in various stages of dress or undress. The presence of her two-year-old daughter belted in the high chair suggests that she left her there while she showered. The excitedness of her son's behavior suggests he was running free while his mom was showering.

It should be clear from this assessment of the short observation presented above that a great deal of information can be collected merely from watching and observing. These observations can be powerful in providing a greater understanding of the woman's life, in assessing the accuracy of some of the responses to assessment questions, and in providing information for possible interventions. The discussion of the possible meanings of these observations was filled with suggestions, not facts. Observations generate possibilities, not clear-cut facts. Anything observed can potentially have several explanations. While it is important to think about the many possibilities, it is even more important to explore the woman's explanations. Observations are tools that complement the assessment process, as long as you also assess your observations.

Risk Factors

Determining the presence and number of risk factors present in the woman's life is also important. Risk factors generally indicate an increased risk of problems or challenges for the mother. They do not indicate a pre-determined outcome. Not everyone is impacted in the same manner by the same risk factor and not everyone has the same skills, support, or emotional strength to deal effectively with the challenges presented to them. It can be generally assumed that the more risk factors present in the woman's life, the higher the risk of difficulties and challenges to the woman and the less effective her coping skills will be due to over-taxation of her internal resources. The following list provides a number of risk factors to consider and to explore within the context of the woman and her baby-to-be.

Trauma

Loss

Poor attachment history

Poor relationship with mother and
    other primary mothering figures

Poor relationship with father

Poor relationship with spouse

History of miscarriage

History of infertility

Inability to imagine the baby-to-be

History of mental health problems

Poor physical health

Periods of depression

Poverty

Homelessness

Young mother (under age 16)

Older mother (over age 35)

Spouse or partner unsupportive of pregnancy

Domestic violence

History of involvement with
    child protective services

Past or present criminal
    involvement

Suicidal behavior

Recent major move

History of sexual abuse

History of eating disorders

History of physical abuse

History of emotional abuse

Drug and alcohol use

Death of a loved one

Divorce

History of living in foster homes

Recent change or loss of job

Specific cultural issues, such as preference for a son

Summary

Over time and with practice, each person conducting assessments develops his or her own style of assessing, asking questions, and probing for information. If you are new to assessment, it is helpful to do several practice assessments with colleagues, friends, or family in order to begin to develop a comfort level with the questions and the process. If the assessment is in conjunction with an agency, the questions should be adjusted to include only the information that would be helpful for use at that particular agency or with that particular program. It is a burden for both the assessor and the pregnant woman to explore and share information that does not pertain to the current situation or goals. It is also unfair to ask someone to share intimate details of her life without a valid reason. It is equally important to remember that most people being assessed do not regularly volunteer information unless they are specifically asked. For example, if you do not ask "Have you ever felt like hurting or killing yourself?" and "Are you having any of those feelings now?" you will never know the person's current suicidal status. In summary, it is important to ask both open-ended questions when gathering general information and direct questions when gathering specific information. A well-done assessment provides an efficient and supportive way to identify problems and concerns of the pregnant woman and to develop an accurate treatment plan to meet her needs.

Chapter 8

Points To Remember

A thorough assessment can act as a tool for discovering information on who your client is, what her life has been like, and with what she is currently dealing. This same assessment can also act as an intervention. Talking about one's life, troubles, worries, accomplishments, and future plans and dreams can be therapeutic and freeing. In our work at the University of Washington, we asked women who had received prenatal interventions what it was like for them to have someone visit and talk to them about their experiences of pregnancy. They all reported it as a good experience, emphasizing how supportive it was to have someone to talk to about what was going on with them.

Remember that a mental health assessment during pregnancy:

- Is necessary.

- Requires an in-depth examination into the woman's present, past, and future.

- Should be done in a relaxed setting.

- Can be a therapeutic experience for the pregnant woman.

- Has been reported by pregnant women as a positive experience.

- Will provide you with information critical to supporting your client throughout this pregnancy, helping her prepare for the transition to motherhood, and beginning a strong mother-child relationship with her unborn child.

The richness of the human experience

would lose something of rewarding joy

if there were no limitations to overcome.

HELEN KELLER

9

Intervening

In this chapter, we discuss the three stages of a therapeutic relation-ship; the introductory stage, the working stage, and the termination stage. Issues related to personal safety and managing stress are also addressed.

The emotional and psychological work of pregnancy includes preven-tion, intervention, and supportive validation. Prevention serves to stop escalating mental health issues for some women and to help prevent later problems that may interfere with the mother-child relationship. Research and clinical work have shown that paying attention to the emotional and psychological work of pregnancy can improve the mother's overall physical health during pregnancy and can help prevent these problems related to delivery: premature labor, painful delivery, and overdue delivery[1,2]. Through intervention, prob-lems and mental health concerns can be identified and steps can be taken to assist the pregnant woman with these issues. With supportive validation, the pregnant mother can experience a relationship that supports the natural and necessary emotional and psychological changes during pregnancy. This relationship also bears witness to what can be a very wonderful and exciting period in a woman's life. Finally, this relationship validates that the woman is important, her pregnancy is important, her unborn child is important, and the woman's emotions and thoughts about her experience are important.

This chapter will explore how you can work with the pregnant woman on the emotional and psychological work of pregnancy. You will learn about stages of relationship development in the context of helping pregnant women in early intervention programs and practices. You will learn about taking care of yourself by setting appropriate boundaries and receiving support.

Establishing a Therapeutic Relationship

Entering into a relationship with a person whose home you will regularly visit involves three basic stages: introduction, working, and termination. The introductory period involves establishing the relationship, developing trust, agreeing on rules and boundaries, and negotiating a working relationship. The working stage involves the work of completing the tasks that make the relationship necessary or desired. The termination stage is the process the relationship moves through when the work is complete or the services are no longer needed. These stages are each important to a successful home visiting experience for both the pregnant woman and the interventionist.

Introductory Stage

Every relationship begins with an introductory stage. This is the beginning. It usually sets the tone for the relationship. In home visiting, as in any relationship that deals with physical or mental well-being, the client needs to be able to trust the interventionist. Without trust, the relationship will never progress to the working stage. Many factors go into developing and maintaining trust. For the interventionist, these factors include:

Being non-judgmental	Being predictable
Being honest	Accepting client for who she is
Being consistent	Being realistic

Being reliable

Establishing clear expectations

Being courteous

Being calm

Being attentive

Focusing on the client

Not taking anger personally

Keeping your word

Being respectful

Setting clear limits, up front

Being gently persistent

Being sensitive

Making eye contact

Treating client as an adult

Showing a genuine interest in the client

Connecting between contacts

The client also has a part in the development of this relationship. In general, a client would be expected to be equally truthful, reliable, courteous, and consistent. However, not all clients want the intervention services that are often seen as necessary for them. Not everyone feels comfortable with a stranger, even a professional stranger, in an office or their home. They often feel they are being judged and may fear consequences from the judgment. For these individuals, trust is not easily established. Women with histories of abuse, trauma, addiction, poor relationships, vulnerabilities, or mental health issues, may be suspicious and guarded. They may want only a portion of what the intervention program can provide and may be very resistant to the rest. For instance, one mother had heard she could get childcare assistance if she joined an early intervention program, so she signed on. However, she became very hostile and belligerent when she was asked to complete forms or engage in home visit activities.

Some of these problems can be prevented with a thorough explanation of program benefits and client expectations. Completing a detailed assessment, to understand as much of the client's background and current issues as possible, can also help in preventing problems. In addition, defining the role of the home visitor from the very start will go a long way in helping the client understand what is and is not possible. This prevents disappointments and misunderstandings later on. Finally, setting clear and consistent limits is crucial. Safety is first and foremost for both the home visitor and the client; setting limits helps protect this safety. Clients need to know from the beginning what is and is not okay. For instance, if drugs are present, if guns are present, or if individuals known to be violent or threatening are present, the client should know that the home visitor will not come into or remain in the home. Once this limit is set, the home visitor needs to consistently follow it. If the home visitor does not follow the rules established, neither will the client.

Other limits may need to be set as the relationship begins to be established and each member of that relationship is getting to know the other. For instance, the client might want to set a rule that no visits will occur before noon as she works the late shift and likes to sleep late. The home visitor may want to set a limit on not sharing personal information about her family or non-work life. Over time, other issues will come up and rules and limits will need to be set. Establishing the following "rules" has been suggested by experienced home visitors:

- Client being fully dressed during visit
- Three no-show visits and client will be withdrawn from the program (with ability to re-join program at any time)
- No smoking
- Not giving rides in personal car
- Not lending money
- Informing client's husband he was not allowed to belittle the client during visit
- Not providing home phone number
- Not discussing other clients
- Meeting in an alternative area when specific individuals are in the home
- Having client's mother allow the client and home visitor to meet in private
- Turning off the TV
- Being present for visits and not attending to personal tasks such as cleaning house, showering, etc.
- Client's peers should not be present during visit

Not all of these rules or limits need to be established with every client. Sometimes having the client's peers or mother present can be beneficial to the visit, especially when those relationships are supportive or if the client is especially shy or fearful. For some clients the television becomes a comforting sound and eases any tension the visit may create. Some individuals do not respond well to limits; therefore, instead of trying to limit a husband's belittling remarks about his wife during home visits, the visits may have to occur when he is not home or in an alternative location. Some limits and rules need to be individual or situation specific. The needs of one family may not be the same needs in another family. Flexibility, creativity, and quick thinking are all helpful in dealing with problematic family issues.

Working Stage

Once a relationship is established and a sense of trust has been cultivated, the work begins. The working phase of the relationship takes on the tasks of the program and the desires and goals of the client. This is also a negotiated stage. Interventions can be successfully delivered, but only if the client wants them. Interventions mean learning new things and new ways of being; this can be scary and uncomfortable. The client may be resistant to change. This does not mean that if the client initially says no or is apprehensive about trying something then that intervention should be discarded. Some clients needs gentle persistence. An initial refusal may mean a response of "why don't we try this next week after you have had time to think about it." It may mean more education needs to be done: "What else can I explain that might be helpful in making you more comfortable to try this?" It may involve respecting privacy: "Sometimes I find the women I work with like to try this one on their own or in private. Why don't I leave it with you? You can give it a try this week and we can discuss it next Tuesday when I come." When the safety of the woman or her unborn child is at risk, a more direct approach might be necessary: "I know this is hard, but we need to get you ready to have this baby. Let's begin with number one and go through them slowly. We can take a break if it gets too uncomfortable." If a client still refuses, then the issues should be dropped and her right of refusal should be respected: "I understand this is really difficult for you to deal with right now. I will put it away. If you change your mind later, let me know."

Experiences in mental health counseling, psychotherapy, home-visiting, parent-child programs, and early intervention services have been helpful in the development of a group of specific qualities that are helpful during the working phase of the relationship. These qualities seem to support the development of an honest, direct, and open relationship that can be satisfying for both the interventionist and the client. These include:

- Have realistic expectations
- Set clear limits
- Be consistent with limits
- Encourage client to make own choices
- Provide options and alternatives
- Provide genuine feedback
- Be truthful
- Provide factual information
- Focus on positive
- Encourage client to challenge information she disagrees or feels uncomfortable with
- Be attentive and patient
- Use reflective speech
- Encourage client to listen to and trust her instincts
- Normalize feelings
- Respect privacy
- Can tolerate others' feelings
- Comfort with crying and tearfulness
- Do not make promises
- Do not take anger personally
- Avoid sharing personal beliefs and opinions
- Do not argue with the client
- Avoid power struggles
- Do not share personal experiences unless they directly support the client
- Do not talk about yourself; maintain focus on client
- Know your limitations; get assistance or make referrals as necessary
- Develop a support network for yourself to deal with your feelings around the visits and clients
- Expand on client's comments
- Use touch occasionally (i.e., a reassuring pat on the shoulder)
- Comfort with silences
- Do not make assumptions
- Provide feedback based on your observations
- Keep your word
- Use gentle persistence
- Make frequent eye contact
- Accept client for who she is
- Confront or set limits on hurtful or harmful behavior

- Attend to client continuously
- Remain calm and unhurried
- Do not expect or force rapid change
- Encourage ventilation of feelings
- Ask open-ended questions when appropriate
- Ask close-ended questions when appropriate
- Modify visits to meet client needs (i.e., having two short visits a week instead of one long one for the client needing more support)

- Assess and reassess as needed
- Celebrate the small steps
- Maintain good personal boundaries
- Provide contact between visits (a note, phone call, etc.)
- Share concerns directly and honestly
- Provide alternatives for negative behaviors

Each home visitor or interventionist, of course, has her own personality and ways of being with others. This is important to remember, especially during the working stage of the relationship. There needs to be a goodness-of-fit between home visitor and the client. For instance, a very directive home visitor may not be compatible with a client who is very outspoken and likes to do things her way. These ways of being are neither wrong nor right, they are just part of individual personality makeup. Instead of forcing a relationship where the personalities clash, thought should be given to who works well with what type of client. It is a good practice to provide the client with some say in who she works with. For example, the client may be told by the home visitor, "I want to make sure you are comfortable working with me and we do not know yet if our styles are different. So let's try working together for the next three weeks, see how you feel, and then make a decision. I want to make sure this program works for you." Oftentimes, giving the control to the client prevents any problems from developing.

Within the working relationship, it is also important to consider the roles of the home visitor. What is an interventionist or a home visitor? The role that most often comes to mind first is that of *Educator*. The interventionist provides information and educates the client on what may be happening in her body, what might be expected in the future, what kinds of remedies help with problems that come up, and how her choices impact her life.

The interventionist may also wear the hat of *Counselor*. Listening as someone shares feelings, supporting someone who is confused or scared, and encouraging new behaviors and ways of thinking to build self-esteem are all tasks of a *Counselor*.

Manager is another role. The interventionist often helps to manage the many activities, goals, and referrals in a client's life, even if only temporarily.

Sometimes, the interventionist is also a *Mentor,* supporting and encouraging movement and change in the client's life by opening doors and making connections for them.

The clients often see the interventionist as the *Expert*; they see her as the one who has all the answers and who has a sound knowledge base of the issues at hand.

Finally, and perhaps most importantly, the interventionist is a *Model*. She serves as an example the client looks to for guidance and decision-making. An interventionist who is sensitive and respectful of her client sets an example of how to be sensitive and respectful. An interventionist who celebrates, with her client, each step taken toward a larger goal models for the client that each step she takes is important and worth acknowledging.

In the working phase of the relationship, it is important not only to think about how to be in the relationship but also to explore what kind of work will best suit that particular relationship. The nature of a working relationship between an interventionist or home visitor and the client involves some pre-existing or automatically established goals. These may need to be worked on directly, but they are most often embedded within the context of the relationship itself or within other goals needing to be established for that client. These goals need to be measurable and client focused. They might be stated in the following ways:

- The client will demonstrate an increase in active decision making over her life issues.

- The client will describe an increased sense of control over her life.

- The client will demonstrate increased self-confidence as evidenced by regular sharing of her ideas and thoughts.

- The client will express feelings both verbally and nonverbally.

- The client will identify ways of expressing anger and/or hostility in safe and productive ways.

- The client will maintain open communication with the interventionist.

- The client will describe the interventionist as a supportive figure in her life.

Most intervention and health related programs establish goals and a schedule of interventions for each participant in their program. These goals reflect the needs determined by the initial assessment and the desires of the client. Even if a program does not require a plan with goals and interventions, when working with an individual within the context of a helping relationship, it is helpful to develop such a plan. Goals and planned interventions keep the focus on the needs of the client, keep the visits organized and moving in a forward direction, and help the client define the visits in terms of what her responsibilities are and the boundaries set by the interventionist.

Termination Stage

The termination phase ends the relationship due to the request or needs of either the client or interventionist, or because the program is completed. A premature termination, which occurs before completing the program, can occur for a number of reasons. The interventionist may change her job position, she may quit, or she may be terminated by the agency for which she works. The client may move out of the program catchment area, she may become angry or upset with some component of the program, she may feel she has no time or energy to continue in the program, or she may feel the program is not meeting her expectations.

When the interventionist is the one leaving the relationship prematurely, care must be taken to be respectful and supportive of the client. Both the client and the home visitor have invested time, energy, and themselves in the relationship. For the client, a risk was taken to trust and believe that someone would be there for her. She probably shared details of her life, she may have shared her vulnerabilities, and she entered the relationship thinking it would last until the end of the program. While interventionists cannot always stay with clients until the end of their program participation, there are some things that can be done to lessen the impact on the client. Giving as much notice as possible is very important. The client needs time to ask questions and process feelings. Being honest is critical. The interventionist needs to be able to inform the client she is leaving for a new position or another job. If the interventionist quits because she was uncomfortable or upset about the agency or the system, it will be important for her not to share her opinions or complaints. The client may need the program to support her; therefore, she needs to believe in the program and feel comfortable with it. The interventionist must refrain from making promises or agreements to continue a relationship with the client. Even with the best of intentions continuing a relationship with a client cannot work. The relationship already established was a working relationship with the goal of assisting the client. It was not an equal relationship as the client was never there to meet the interventionist's needs. A friendship, or another type of relationship, generally requires some reciprocity or an exchange of support, sharing, and concern. Expecting a client who has been in a relationship focused only on her needs to now express equal care and concern toward the interventionist is unfair to the client and would be disappointing to the interventionist. The present condition of the client, her pregnancy, and her need to focus on herself and her unborn child would further make the idea of continuing an outside relationship at this time taboo.

If a new person is replacing the original interventionist, time should be taken to transition. If at all possible, both the departing and the new interventionist should co-visit for a minimum of two to three visits. This allows the client to adjust to the new person, and it also demonstrates for the client a connection between the two of them. This is often helpful in beginning to build trust between the client and the new interventionist. The new interventionist is able to observe the interaction patterns between the person she is to replace and the client. This can help the incoming person to understand the style of the client and also bring her up to date on the work they have completed, as well as that still in progress.

Sometimes situations occur that preclude any time for good-byes or for transitions: there has been an emergency, a health-related issue, or an employee was terminated from the agency. If this occurs, it would be most appropriate for the immediate supervisor to contact the clients and let them know of the abrupt departure. Some explanation must be given to the clients; otherwise, imaginations can create a wealth of hypotheses. Even if an agency needs to protect specific information, it can explain that an opportunity came up or a personal situation occurred that required the person to leave suddenly. The clients could also be told that just as their confidentiality is always respected and protected, the details of the separation cannot be shared. If at all possible, it would be helpful to have the departing employee write a good-bye note that could be delivered to the client. It is also important for the replacing interventionist to remember that abrupt separations, especially a supportive working relationship during pregnancy, can be difficult to adjust to and may require a period of grief on the part of the client.

If the client prematurely terminates the relationship for any reason, it will be important for her to be left with an open door to return to the program should her circumstances again change. If a client is moving out of the catchment area, she should be given not only referral numbers of related or similar programs but also an actual name to connect with. The client's permission would be needed to share any of her personal information with another agency, but the new agency could be given information that a former client will be moving into their area.

If a client decides that there is no time to participate in the program, it will be important to discuss with the client what has changed in her schedule and explore any options to continue. Occasionally, clients will want to continue in the program but become involved in a wave of change that feels overwhelming. They may have had to begin work, their workload may have increased, they may be having medical complications with the pregnancy that have become the center of their focus, or they may be overwhelmed by the whole idea of being pregnant. Initially, exploring how the program could restructure what is offered and how it is delivered can be helpful. For example, a client who is having difficulty accepting the idea that she is actually going to give birth to a child may busy herself with other tasks in order to make it difficult to participate in the very program she needs to help her deal with the pregnancy. Her pushing away of the program may not be intentional; she may just want to lessen her anxiety. It may be helpful to try these options before terminating: reducing the time of the visit, focusing on the support of the client herself instead of on the pregnancy (refer to activities on *Honoring the Woman,* see page 383), or encouraging the client to vent her feelings of being overwhelmed and frustrated. If the client still insists on leaving the program, it will be important to support her in doing this, reinforce her ability to make decisions to take care of herself, and to remind her the door is always open to return.

If the client is leaving because she feels the program is not meeting her needs or giving her what she wants, examine exactly what she thought she was going to get from the program and which of her needs she feels are not being met. Simple misunderstandings can quickly lead to problems. Some clients take these misunderstandings and problems very personally rather than try to clarify or work them out. The interventionist should gently provide the opportunity to explore with the client where things became problematic. Occasionally clarification, apologizing, or just asking for a fresh start can eliminate the client's need to terminate. It is important not to argue or to say such things as "but I told you...," or "I explained to you that first day...," or get into a power struggle with the client. If the client insists on terminating, support the client in terms of expressing her feelings and stating her needs. Again, leave the door open to return if circumstances change.

The angry client is often the most challenging to work with. Some clients express their anger in very passive-aggressive ways, such as not being home for visits, not answering the door, double booking the visit with another appointment, being asleep, being sick, not talking during the visits, not answering their phone, and even avoiding the interventionist by going to a friend's home for a while. If there is some way to meet the client, it will be important to do so. Sometimes all the excuses and avoidances are actually true, and the client was just overwhelmed by circumstances. If she can be located, she can be asked about what has been happening in her life and if she is still interested in the program. Occasionally, if the client is able to say why she is angry, the problems can be rectified. If the client insists on continuing to ignore and avoid the interventionist, letters can be sent expressing concern over the client's well-being and ways to make contact. If the avoidance persists, it may be necessary for the program to drop the client from the active list. In this case the client should be sent a letter similar to this:

Dear Carol,

I am sorry I have missed you over this past month. I have been concerned about you and I hope you are doing well. It seems that participating in the program is not working for you at this time. I would love to begin meeting with you again and would be glad to schedule a time if you want to give me a call. If I do not hear from you, I will assume that means you need a break or that you have found some other ways to support yourself during this very important time of your life. I will take you off the active list but I will keep your name on hand for any time you decide to begin again. I hope you are doing well and that your pregnancy is going fine. I hope to speak with you soon.

Take care,

Helen

For the client who is outspoken about her anger, several situations may come up. Those clients who do not have good control of their emotions or actions may become belligerent or threatening. The interventionist should set limits on these behaviors: "I will be happy to talk with you about this problem, but it will not be okay to yell at me, call me names, or threaten me. If these things occur, I will leave." If limits are not observed, the interventionist should leave immediately. If the interventionist has any uncomfortable feelings about going into the home or meeting the client alone, another member of the program staff should accompany her on the visit or the visit could be held in either a public place or the agency. Safety should always come first, and gut feelings and intuition should be considered and explored.

For the client who is angry but who has the ability to control her actions and emotions, it will be necessary for the interventionist to allow her to vent her anger and frustrations. Arguing, power struggles, blaming, and excuses should all be avoided. It might be helpful to ask the client if she feels this can be worked out and what might be done to help the situation. If she insists on terminating, the interventionist might state, "I am sorry we could not work things out. If something changes in the future, I would be glad to meet with you. If you change your mind about the program, please let me or my supervisor know."

When termination is not premature, and instead is the result of program completion, it should be celebrated. However, before the celebration, the termination process must begin. Most early intervention programs continue throughout pregnancy and up through the child's third year. In this case at least 1-2 months before the actual termination, the interventionist and the mother should begin talking about accomplishments, how things have changed, how much growth both the mother and the child have gone through, and how the interventionist has felt about working with the mother. The mother should be supported in her plans for the future. Allow plenty of time for finding resources that might be helpful to her. It should be made clear that the interventionist will no longer be available to provide

those services. A celebration focused on the mother's accomplishments should be planned. It is important to acknowledge the mother
and what she has done, as well as her child. Finally, the interventionist
should provide a symbol to the mother of the accomplishment, such
as a certificate, a plaque, a framed picture, or another item that can be
displayed in the client's home (if she so chooses). Final good-byes
should be stated directly from the interventionist to the mother. For
example, she may say "I have really enjoyed our time together. I wish
you good luck" or "Thank you for being in our program. I am always
impressed by the amount of work you did for yourself and your child.
(Child's name) is lucky to have you for a mother. I wish you both the
best."

Everyone says good-bye in his or her own way. Occasionally, saying
good-bye can be a very difficult experience for a client, especially if she
has a background of painful or non-existent good-byes. This can lead
to no-shows at final appointments or in any of the termination visits.
When this happens, the interventionist might clearly state that she
wants to get together to say good-bye. A way to say good-bye can be
negotiated between the mother and interventionist. If this proves
impossible or too uncomfortable for the mother, a letter should be
sent expressing pride over the mother's accomplishments and sadness
that the time together has ended. A token or symbol of accomplishment should also be sent.

A final word on termination regards the timing. As mentioned earlier,
most intervention programs include pregnancy and the child's first
three years of life. Some programs, however, support the pregnancy
period only. If at all possible, pregnancy programs should extend at
least several months into the postpartum period. Abandoning the
woman just as she has her baby is counterproductive and can sabotage
all the work done during pregnancy. If a new interventionist is taking
over near the point of delivery, the transition should begin several
weeks before the birth of the baby with both interventionists present.
This teaming should continue at least a couple weeks into the postpartum period as well.

Self Preservation of the Interventionist

Maintaining and supporting the mental health and well-being of the interventionist is critical to a successful working relationship as well as a successful program or practice. Helping, assisting, caring, supporting, referring, developing, assessing, preventing, intervening, validating, and encouraging are all actions that the interventionist undertakes on behalf of the pregnant woman. As discussed earlier, the client-interventionist relationship is not a balanced relationship. The interventionist is there for the client. The client is supported and encouraged to take charge of her own life and work on her own issues; she is not there to be a friend to, care about, or assist the interventionist in any way. So, how does the interventionist get her needs met and who is responsible for supporting her?

First and foremost, the interventionist is responsible for making sure personal needs are met. This is one responsibility that cannot be delegated. Even if the agency or program does not offer any support, the interventionist must find ways to debrief or, in other words, to review with someone the day's events and release some of the emotion that gets stored up. Therapists, firemen, policemen, emergency response workers, and medical personnel are often expected to "debrief" following a traumatic event or when working with trauma victims. Working with trauma is hard. Many families have had some type of trauma or misfortune that they have had to deal with. When working with these families or individuals, it becomes necessary to bear witness to the trauma through listening to the story of what occurred repeatedly. This helps the victim or traumatized person discharge intense feelings and begin to deal with the events in a more productive manner. For example, individuals who have been in car accidents often tell their story over and over again. Each time they tell it, the emotional impact of the event lessens for them. Another example is childbirth. Although not necessarily traumatic, it is an event of intense emotion. New mothers often tell their birth story over and over again. With time, the intense emotional tone begins to decrease with each telling.

Working with individuals who have experienced traumatic or highly emotionally charged events leaves the person listening or caring for the traumatized person thinking about and sometimes experiencing the same trauma through mental processes. They may wonder:

- "If that happened to me I would...,"
- "What would I have done if that happened to me?"
- "How would it feel to have that happen?"
- "Would I respond in the same way as she did?"

When these questions are being asked, we are not always aware of them, but feelings develop around the answers or potential answers to these questions. If these feelings and the events are not discharged or talked about with others, the feelings can become quite intense, anxiety and fears can develop, and it becomes unclear what is causing this reaction. Talking about it with others is a way to lessen the impact of other people's trauma and misfortune on ourselves, so we can be available and emotionally healthy to be able to continue helping and assisting those in need.

The interventionist can use several avenues to debrief alone or with fellow employees: peer support groups, informal get-togethers (especially if they are regularly scheduled), discussions with one trusted fellow employee, or journaling about the day can be helpful. Other avenues that are helpful but also more costly would include weekly massage, individual therapy, or a consultation group. Any activity that can help in discharging emotion, exploring personal emotional reactions, or refocusing the individual back into their own life can be helpful.

The employing program or agency also bears responsibility to make sure that systems are in place to support and assist the interventionist. Without these systems, burnout can be rapid and staff turnover will be high, which has a negative impact on the quality of the program. Supervision should be established. This is set up with an outside professional mental health provider who has had experience both with supervision and with the population being worked with. This person would be responsible in helping the staff to explore their feelings and their personal reactions to the families they are working with. Discussions in supervision are held in confidence and an outside person is necessary to increase the feelings of safety and trust for the staff and to eliminate fear of one's emotions being mistaken for inabilities or weakness on the job.

Consultation is a separate system, which is designed to review the progression and treatment of individuals and families. Guidance on treatment, activities, or direction with the family is usually discussed. This can be done either with an inside or outside individual, as long as the person providing the consultation has a solid knowledge base on practicing or working with the group of individuals receiving services. For example, a seasoned clinician in adult mental health who has focused on incarcerated males would not be the best choice for consultation on pregnant women or children. This person may be very knowledgeable and have a great deal of insight in general mental health; however, he or she would not know the workings or issues of those individuals being served, nor would they necessarily understand in-home services.

These systems cannot be periodic; they must be regularly scheduled, and staff must be supported and encouraged to attend. At times, these supports may need to be mandated, as dealing with personal feelings, especially intense or overwhelming feelings, can be difficult to do. Avoidance can become an easy alternative for some people. There are many other ways to support staff other than supervision or consultation. These might include staff activities, celebrations, educational classes on issues that come up, and recognition for the hard work done. Any of these activities should be done in addition to, not in replacement of, supervision and consultation. Both supervision and consultation play crucial roles in maintaining the emotional health and the well-being of staff.

Summary

How the working relationship is established can be critical to the success or failure of client recruitment and ongoing participation. Trust must be built and the program representatives must appear reliable and knowledgeable. As the relationship progresses, the interventionist must begin to balance the needs of the pregnant woman, the demands of the program or practice, and the care of herself to prevent burnout. This can often be a delicate balance requiring support and consultation from outside sources. A good working relationship focused on preventing and identifying problems and issues, developing goals for and with the pregnant woman, and intervening in specific, creative, and respectful ways can be satisfying for both the pregnant woman and the interventionist. A good working relationship boasts visits that are not only productive but also fun. They should be anticipated and enjoyed by both members of the relationship.

Chapter 9

Points To Remember

An effective intervention does not begin with how much you know but with how much you care about the individuals you are working with. Think about your own experiences. How have you felt when someone you are seeing for professional services breezes in and out of your appointment? What is it like when the person you are supposed to trust with your most private feelings and fears has to look at your chart to be reminded of your name? On the other hand, how does it feel when your dentist, doctor, nurse, or therapist sits down with you before they begin anything else and just asks, "how are you?" And then, they actually sit calmly, wait for your response, and listen. All of us have had experiences where we have felt invisible, a nuisance, or disregarded by someone we hoped to receive services from. We have also all had experiences where the people we asked for help from treated us like fellow human beings-who had lives, families, triumphs, and tragedies. Remember these things when you go about developing a relationship with the clients you will be working with. Caring makes a difference.

In much knowledge there is also much grief.

QUEEN MARIE OF RUMANIA

10

Implementation Tools

This chapter links together the information provided in Chapter 8 on Assessment and in Chapter 9 on Intervening. More specifically, this chapter provides some tools to implement the following:

> • *Assessment*
>
> • *Problem Identification*
>
> • *Intervention Development*
>
> • *Action Planning*

Assessment

The assessment tool provided in this chapter could be helpful in assessing the emotional and psychological status of the pregnant woman. It is not designed to provide a medical evaluation of pregnancy, which needs to be done through a health care provider of prenatal services. Under some circumstances, certain areas of the assessment might not be relevant and can be left out. In other circumstances, more specific information or additional information not listed here may be required; this can be inserted under the appropriate sections. Many areas throughout the different sections contain similar questions. If these questions have been satisfied earlier in the assessment, then they can be left out; however, if these questions have not been answered or if more detail is needed, it would be important to include them.

Problem Identification

Problems and issues for each assessment area are listed following each section. Some sections will have problems that directly relate to your client's experience. At other times, there may be no identified problem that seems to fit, requiring you to describe the particular problems. In addition, some ways of stating the problems may need to be shaped or adapted to the needs of your client.

Goal Development

The development of goals particular to any identified problems can be a challenging task for even the most seasoned interventionist. Goals should be clearly stated and measurable. "Measurable" means that data can be collected to support the fact that the goal has been met. For example, the goal "the client will make and follow through with a prenatal appointment" is met once the client makes the appointment and goes to the appointment and meets with the health care provider. A goal such as, "client will express feelings related to domestic violence" would be met when the client actually describes her feelings in words to the interventionist. The words can be described in the progress notes and can be measured through counts of feeling descriptors or times feelings were discussed. In this section, many goals for each problem area are listed. At times, goals not listed may be more appropriate for your client.

Goals should be jointly written by the interventionist and the client. It is important to get input from the woman herself as to the goals she wishes to address. Equally important is providing each client with feedback as to the problem areas or issues you see needing attention. It is not uncommon for anyone to elect to ignore difficult topics or issues that may be emotionally painful or challenging. Topics such as domestic violence may not be a client-volunteered topic needing to be addressed, but still may need to be addressed to ensure the safety and well-being of both your client and her unborn child.

Intervention Development

Appropriate interventions for each of the problem areas are also listed within each section. It is important that you be creative in using the tools presented here, the wants and desires of each client, and your expertise in working with the particular group of women you see. For this reason, relevant units of interventions are suggested under "Specific Interventions" rather than individual interventions. The differences in the clients you work with will dictate whether you choose one intervention from a particular unit or all of the interventions from a particular unit. They will also dictate how you focus on one unit over another. In some cases specific issues, such as substance abuse or orientation of person, time, and place, need to be dealt with and resolved or stabilized before any other interventions will be helpful. Some of these issues are noted in each problem area. Other issues, not indicated here, may need to be resolved or stabilized as well, depending on your particular client.

Action Planning

A list of actions follows the specific interventions. These actions are provided to help you plan your strategy in carrying out the interventions for each client. Some of the actions are supportive, some supply encouragement, and some prompt change or action from the client. The appropriate actions will differ in any given situation, based on client skills, needs, strengths, and challenges.

Remember:

You are the expert— the tools provided here are only to help you to use your expertise to develop the best plan of treatment for each client you see.

An index is provided in Table 10.1 to allow you to find specific problems more quickly. It is important that you familiarize yourself with this entire chapter before depending solely on the index, however. Table 10.2 provides an example of how the different sections link together. The example in this table addresses the assessment and treatment planning of a woman experiencing domestic violence in her relationship.

TABLE 10.1 INDEX TO ASSESSMENT TOPICS AND PROBLEM AREAS

	TOPIC AREA	PAGE
1	**PRESENT ISSUES**	**200**
1.1	*Current Pregnancy*	*200*
1.1.1	Pregnancy-related denial	201
1.1.2	Decision making on outcome of this pregnancy (parent vs. adoption vs. abortion)	202
1.1.3	Lack of support	202
1.1.4	Pregnancy related trauma	203
1.1.5	Fear and anxiety related to pregnancy	204
1.1.6	Maternal and/or fetal health	204
1.2	*Pregnancy History*	*205*
1.2.1	History of multiple pregnancies	206
1.2.2	History of pregnancy loss	206
1.2.3	Infertility issues	207
1.2.4	Presence of other children in the home	208
1.3	*Medical Background*	*208*
1.3.1	Prenatal care—limited or nonexistent	209
1.3.2	Substance abuse	209
1.3.3	Genetic risks	210
1.3.4	Health problems	210
1.4	*Mental Health*	*211*
1.4.1	Disorientation	212
1.4.2	Current or history of depressive symptoms	213
1.4.3	Actual or threats of harm to self or others	214
1.4.4	Current or previously diagnosed mental illness	215
1.5	*Self Care*	*216*
1.5.1	Regulation issues	216
1.6	*Work and Education*	*217*
1.6.1	Education	218
1.6.2	Employment	219
1.7	*Relationships*	*220*
1.7.1	Unsafe relationships	220
1.7.2	Relationship with baby's father	221
1.7.3	Extended family	222
1.8	*Stressors*	*223*
1.8.1	Single or multiple stressors	224
2	**PAST HISTORY**	**225**
2.1	*Loss and Trauma*	*225*
2.1.1	Loss issues	225
2.1.2	Trauma issues	227
2.2	*Childhood Experiences*	*228*
2.2.1	Caregiving or caregiver issues	229
2.2.2	Abuse or maltreatment	230
2.2.3	Dysfunctional family	231
2.2.4	Abandonment	231
2.3	*Relationship With Mother*	*232*
2.3.1	Communication	233
2.3.2	Nature of relationship	234
2.3.3	Difficulties in the interaction	235
2.3.4	Lack of support	236
3	**FUTURE VISIONS**	**237**
3.1	*Images of Baby*	*237*
3.1.1	Issues with ability to imagine	237
3.1.2	Emotional issues	238
3.2	*Images of Becoming a Mother*	*239*
3.2.1	Mother role—resistance or denial	240
3.2.2	Lack of preparedness	240
3.3	*Images of How This Baby Will Change Daily Life*	*241*
3.3.1	Lack of preparedness	242
3.3.2	Lack of concern for self	243
3.3.3	Poor attitude concerning baby	244

**TABLE 10. 2 USE OF TOOLS TO DEVELOP A TREATMENT PLAN ON
DOMESTIC VIOLENCE IN A RELATIONSHIP***

Assessment: Present Issues: Relationships (1.7)

Questions Asked

   I: Tell me about your relationship with your husband.

   W: We get along pretty good. I think he is excited about the baby, but he doesn't say much.

   I: How long have you been together?

   W: About two years, we started dating in high school.

   I: Has there ever been any violence in your relationship?

   W: What do you mean by violence?

   I: Has your husband ever hit you or hurt you in any way?

   *W: Not really...well, once when we first got married...I wasn't taking care of the house very
   well. It was always messy and he got really mad one day and started yelling at me and he
   shoved me into the wall.*

   I: Was that the only time or has anything else like that ever happened?

   *W: No, that was the only time he ever shoved me...I don't think it has ever happened again,
   well, except about a month ago. He was mad at me for gaining so much weight with the
   baby. He called me some names and when I started crying, he just got madder. I shouldn't
   have started crying. He hates it when I cry...he always blows up...*

   I: What does he do when he blows up?

   *W: He yells at me and calls me names, tells me I am stupid...sometimes he throws
   things...it's not his fault, I shouldn't cry over everything...I shouldn't have gotten pregnant.
   He has so much to worry about already...he only hits me when I start crying and that was
   only two or three times. I just shouldn't cry. I know it makes him mad...*

Summary of Assessment
   This woman is providing a somewhat disjointed history of domestic violence with her
   spouse. She blames herself for much of the violence in their relationship and minimizes
   her husband's behavior. She appears to be feeling helpless and she tends to look for truth
   in her husband's abusive words-perhaps as a way of making sense of their relationship.
   She states initially that her husband is excited about the baby, but later states she should
   never have gotten pregnant-this seems like a difficult and fragile topic for her.

Problem Identified
   1.7.1 Issues of unsafe relationships: domestic violence.

Goals Identified
   Acknowledge there is violence in her relationship.
   Develop a plan to keep herself and her unborn child safe.
   Connect with support group/shelter for women in domestic violence situations.
   Will acknowledge she does not deserve to be abused—verbally or physically.

Specific Interventions
   Unit 6: Making Space

Intervention Selected
   3. Circle of Safety to begin to evaluate safe and unsafe relationships in her life.

Actions
   Support woman to come to terms with the abuse; work with woman to develop a safety
   plan; provide information on Domestic Violence Shelters, accompany woman to shelter if
   needed and desired; and, assist woman in connecting with a mental health professional
   who specializes in domestic violence.

*Note: this is not an entire treatment plan—only a single problem example

PRESENT ISSUES

1.1 CURRENT PREGNANCY

ISSUES TO BE ASSESSED
- How many weeks pregnant
- Wantedness of pregnancy
- Plans for pregnancy: parenting, adoption, termination of pregnancy
- What the partner or spouse thinks about this pregnancy
- Family and friends' reactions to the pregnancy

- Which task(s) of maternal role attainment is the woman currently involved in [Seeking Safe Passage, Ensuring Acceptance of the Child, Binding Into Her Unborn Child, and/or Learning to Give of Herself]

SIGNIFICANCE
- It is important to get an idea of how the woman feels about this pregnancy. A pregnancy that is looked forward to and planned is experienced differently than an accidental pregnancy resulting from a brief relationship.

- The more support the woman has around her pregnancy, the better she will do dealing with the issues that come up in pregnancy. Not telling anyone about the pregnancy may be part of a plan to get through a certain point in the pregnancy or it may be she is afraid to tell others, as they will be angry or unsupportive. This information is helpful to know.

- As discussed in Chapter 3, pregnant women move through a series of tasks in preparing to assume the role of mother. Knowing where the woman is in relation to the actual work or completion of these tasks would be important to understanding her movement toward maternal role attainment.

TYPICAL QUESTIONS
- Tell me a little bit about this pregnancy. How far along are you?
- Was this pregnancy planned? How are you feeling about it?
- Have you shared the news of your pregnancy with others?
- How does the baby's father feel about this pregnancy? Will he be involved after the birth?
- How are you feeling about this pregnancy? Do you have any concerns about yourself, your baby, or even the two of you together?
- How are you preparing people for the arrival of your baby? How has your pregnancy affected your relationships with your friends, family, co-workers, etc?
- Is being pregnant what you thought it would be like? What did you think it would be like? What do you think about what your baby is like so far? Did you ever think that during your pregnancy your child would act like this? (These questions can also be asked in the future visions section).

• What has changed in your life since you became pregnant? Have you needed to give up certain things in your life? Have you had to make any sacrifices or trade-offs? What has that been like for you? Did you think you would need to do (or change) these things when you became pregnant or had a child?

1.1.1

Issues of pregnancy related denial: refuses to acknowledge pregnancy; refuses to discuss pregnancy; expresses desire not to be pregnant, have a child or be a parent; denies that having a child will impact her life.

GOALS

- Acknowledge the pregnancy
- Acknowledge the growing child in her womb
- Participate in conversations about the pregnancy
- Participate in conversations about self-care

SPECIFIC INTERVENTIONS

The following units provide interventions that address the issues described here:

Unit 1: Entering Motherhood

Unit 2: Connecting With My Baby

Unit 3: Attachment

Unit 4: Relaxation and Well-Being

Note: Specific interventions will be most helpful once the woman has dealt with her denial of pregnancy.

ACTIONS

- Do not rush acceptance of pregnancy; be supportive, understanding, and honest
- Explore denial and refusal: How does she feel about pregnancy? What were her plans for pregnancy? How would a pregnancy impact her life at this time? How might others respond to her becoming pregnant?
- Refer to mental health providers if acceptance of pregnancy does not begin to occur

GOALS

- Explore various ways in which to handle pregnancy
- Acknowledge the potential impact of a baby on her life
- Discuss the potential impact with each option to pregnancy being considered
- Engage in counseling or support groups dealing with issues of abortion, loss, relinquishment, etc.

1.1.2
Issues in deciding how to respond to this pregnancy: parenting vs. adoption vs. abortion.

GOALS
- Explore various ways in which to handle pregnancy
- Acknowledge the potential impact of a baby on her life
- Discuss the potential impact with each option to pregnancy being considered
- Engage in counseling or support groups dealing with issues of abortion, loss, relinquishment, etc.

SPECIFIC INTERVENTIONS
The following units provide interventions that address the issues described here:
- Unit 4: Relaxation and Well-Being
- Unit 5: Honoring the Woman in Me

Note: Specific interventions will be most helpful once the woman has dealt with her ambivalence over the type of relationship she wants with this child.

ACTIONS
- Explore with the woman her options in dealing with the pregnancy, providing discussion of alternatives and supporting her decisions
- Support decisions as to how to handle pregnancy
- Make referrals, as necessary

1.1.3
Issues of lack of support: spouse/boyfriend/partner is upset about pregnancy, does not want to be a parent, and/or does not want to take responsibility for a child; father of baby denies child is his; family unsupportive of pregnancy; friends unsupportive of pregnancy.

GOALS
- Discuss options in dealing with criticism from others
- Express feelings around lack of support
- Identify sources of support that are available to her
- Explore legal rights when the identified father of her child is protesting paternity

SPECIFIC INTERVENTIONS
The following units provide interventions that address the issues described here:

Unit 4: Relaxation and Well-Being

Unit 5: Honoring the Woman in Me

Note: Specific interventions will be most helpful once the woman has developed adequate support with or without the involvement of specific others.

ACTIONS
- Provide information on legal rights (if known) in state of residence or provide appropriate referral, re: paternity, child support
- Provide support around pregnancy issues
- Facilitate the development of alternative support systems

1.1.4
Issues of pregnancy related trauma: pregnancy is a result of rape, incest, or other traumatic event.

GOALS
- Acknowledge the need for counseling and agree to receive a referral
- Engage in counseling or psychotherapy to deal with issues of trauma

SPECIFIC INTERVENTIONS
The following units provide interventions that address the issues described here:

Unit 4: Relaxation and Well-Being

Unit 5: Honoring the Woman in Me

Note: Specific interventions will be most helpful once the woman has dealt with her past trauma.

ACTIONS
- Assist woman in connecting with appropriate therapeutic services designed to deal with trauma
- Set limits on scope of practice, i.e., that you do not have the expertise to deal with trauma and she deserves to connect with someone who does
- Offer therapeutic listening and support when issues are brought up and shared; however, do not delve into details of traumatic events

1.1.5

Issues of fear and anxiety related to the pregnancy: fearful of being pregnant, fearful of course of pregnancy, fear of death, anxiety over the welfare of her baby and/or herself.

GOALS
- Discuss fears, worries, and concerns
- Explore normal course and expectations of pregnancy
- Explore transitions to motherhood
- Experience a decrease in anxiety and fear related to the pregnancy
- Acknowledge ways in which a baby will impact her life

SPECIFIC INTERVENTIONS

The following units provide interventions that address the issues described here:

Unit 4: Relaxation and Well-Being

Unit 5: Honoring the Woman in Me

Note: Specific interventions will be most helpful once the woman has dealt with her fears.

ACTIONS
- Validate factual information regarding pregnancy; dispel myths and incorrect information
- Explore worries, fears, and concerns
- Provide education on pregnancy, changes associated with pregnancy, and impact of the pregnancy
- Explore and normalize anxiety; refer to therapy services in cases of extreme or intrusive anxiety

1.1.6

Issues related to maternal health and/or fetal health: unwilling to make changes to support her own health, refusing to make changes needed to support fetal growth (such as stopping smoking, avoiding alcohol and drugs, etc.).

GOALS
- Demonstrate changes in her behavior and lifestyle conducive with a healthy pregnancy as evidenced by _____ (eating a healthy diet, stopping smoking, eliminating alcohol, avoiding drugs, improving sleep habits, avoiding potentially violent situations, etc.)

SPECIFIC INTERVENTIONS

The following units provide interventions that address the issues described here:

Unit 1: Entering Motherhood

Unit 2: Connecting With My Baby

Unit 3: Attachment

Unit 4: Relaxation and Well-Being

Unit 5: Honoring the Woman in Me

Unit 6: Making Space

Unit 7: Enhancing My Baby's Brain

ACTIONS

- Provide assistance and alternatives for making positive life changes supportive of pregnancy
- Provide positive feedback for even the tiny changes

1.2 PREGNANCY HISTORY

ISSUES TO BE ASSESSED

- Past number of pregnancies, experience of those pregnancies, and the outcomes
- Past miscarriages and/or abortions and circumstances about these
- How many children, her relationship with these children, i.e. birth, adopted, step, foster, their ages and gender
- Time it took to conceive this pregnancy
- Infertility issues and methods of dealing with them
- Previously relinquishing a child for adoption.
- Involvement with CPS or other state agency.

SIGNIFICANCE

- Prior pregnancies and the outcomes of these pregnancies can directly impact the current pregnancy. Multiple miscarriages prior to this pregnancy may cause a lot of anxiety for the woman as she thinks about the risk to this pregnancy.
- Experiences with other children often provide a glimpse of how this woman may parent the child she is currently pregnant with. It is important to look for patterns with prior children: did she do better with newborns but abandon the children when they learned to walk?
- Infertility has often been linked to difficulties in later parenting. The emotional roller coaster people experience dealing with infertility often creates difficulties for women and how they deal with the baby they worked so hard to conceive. Infertility should be considered a risk factor to parenting and should be assessed.

TYPICAL QUESTIONS

- Have you been pregnant before? How did the pregnancy go?
- Have you ever had a miscarriage or have you ever terminated a pregnancy? How was that for you?
- Do you have any children currently living with you? How about not living with you at this time? What is your relationship with each of these children?

- With this current pregnancy, how long did it take you to get pregnant?
- Did this pregnancy just happen or did you use anything to help you conceive?

1.2.1
History of multiple pregnancies or closely spaced pregnancies.

GOALS
- Explore history of past pregnancies
- Explore decision making and problems solving skills
- Examine family planning beliefs and goals
- Increase knowledge of family planning and birth control

SPECIFIC INTERVENTIONS
The following units provide interventions that address the issues described here:

Unit 3: Attachment

Unit 4: Relaxation and Well-Being

Unit 5: Honoring the Woman in Me

ACTIONS
- Encourage exploration of past pregnancies
- Encourage exploration of impact of past pregnancies
- Provide family planning and birth control information
- Provide information on problem solving and decision making skills: describe problem, list possible solutions, evaluate solution options, choose best option, attempt solution, evaluate outcome
- Support attempts at problem solving and independent decision making

1.2.2
Issues of loss: histories of miscarriage, multiple abortions, pregnancy loss, relinquishment, loss of children to protective services, loss of parental rights.

GOALS
- Express feelings around past loss related to pregnancy or children
- Engage in counseling or support groups to deal with loss issues, as appropriate
- Develop a plan on avoiding issues that might have been involved in past avoidable losses, i.e., need for improved parenting skills, avoidance of domestic violence situation, improved nutrition, stop drug usage, etc.

SPECIFIC INTERVENTIONS
The following units provide interventions that address the issues described here:

Unit 3: Attachment

Unit 4: Relaxation and Well-Being

Unit 5: Honoring the Woman in Me

Unit 6: Making Space

Note: Specific interventions will be most helpful once the woman has dealt with her past losses.

ACTIONS

- Encourage discussion of past loss experiences
- Provide referrals for counseling or support groups, as appropriate
- Facilitate problem solving around preventing avoidable loss
- Provide information on strategies to improve self-care and strengthen independent decision making skills
- Facilitate referrals to parenting classes, women's shelters, rehabilitation programs, etc.
- Explore issues that led to involvement with Child Protective Services in past and how these might be avoided in the future.

1.2.3

Issues related to infertility: use of infertility treatments and/or medications, large investment of time, energy, and money into trying to conceive.

GOALS

- Explore feelings related to infertility
- Engage in counseling or support groups to aid in resolution of issues related to infertility
- Discuss concerns over carrying this pregnancy to term (especially where infertility has involved pregnancy loss mid-pregnancy)

SPECIFIC INTERVENTIONS

The following units provide interventions that address the issues described here:

Unit 1: Entering Motherhood

Unit 2: Connecting With My Baby

Unit 3: Attachment

Unit 4: Relaxation and Well-Being

Unit 5: Honoring the Woman in Me

Unit 6: Making Space

Unit 7: Enhancing My Baby's Brain

Note: Specific interventions will be most helpful once the woman has dealt with her the emotional issues related to infertility.

ACTIONS

- Support exploration of feelings related to infertility
- Make referrals to counseling or support groups
- Acknowledge the impact of infertility in a woman's life

1.2.4
Presence of other children in the home.

GOALS
- Discuss how current pregnancy might affect current children
- Discuss how the addition of another child into the family might affect the current children
- Discuss potential impact of a new baby on family functioning

SPECIFIC INTERVENTIONS
The following unit provides interventions that address the issues described here:
Unit 6: Making Space

ACTIONS
- Discuss with woman how the current pregnancy and birth of a new child might affect her current children
- Provide activities that might be helpful in supporting the current children

1.3 MEDICAL BACKGROUND

ISSUES TO BE ASSESSED
- Any current major or minor illnesses
- Any current medications
- Past or current substance use, including street drugs, alcohol, cigarettes, marijuana
- Past relationship with the medical profession
- Current doctor, health care provider, and/or obstetrician
- Presence and nature of disabilities
- Past hospitalizations or surgeries
- Family history of birth defects, genetic diseases, or conditions

SIGNIFICANCE
- The mother's current state of health will have an impact on how she cares for herself, what kind of challenges she faces, and how she deals with medical issues.
- Knowing drug or alcohol usage is important for helping the woman and protecting her baby. Knowing her plans about usage during pregnancy provides an example of how much value she places on her pregnancy. A woman who continues to use and has no plans to stop or makes no attempts to stop suggests someone who is not thinking about the consequences for her baby.
- The woman's experience with the medical system may have an impact on how she welcomes prenatal care or programs aimed at supporting pregnant women.

TYPICAL QUESTIONS

- Are you currently experiencing any illness or problems with your health?
- Are you currently on any medications? Vitamins? Herbal remedies? How often do you use over-the-counter medications, such as Tylenol or aspirin?
- Do you drink alcohol? If so, how often? How much each time? If in the past, are you currently drinking during your pregnancy? Smoke?
- Have you ever used street drugs, such as marijuana, speed, cocaine, acid, heroin, crack, ecstasy, etc.? Currently using? How often? How much? When exactly did you quit? History of detox program?
- How do you feel your disabilities may or may not affect this pregnancy?
- Do you currently have a doctor, midwife, or nurse practitioner? How has this been? Have you felt supported?

1.3.1

Issues of limited or no prenatal care: lack of health care provider, fear of health care providers, avoiding prenatal care.

GOALS

- Engage in prenatal care with a health care provider she feels she can trust
- Engage in discussions on her fears and concerns regarding medical providers

SPECIFIC INTERVENTIONS

The following units provide interventions that address the issues described here:

Unit 1: Entering Motherhood

Unit 4: Relaxation and Well-Being

Unit 5: Honoring the Woman in Me

Unit 6: Making Space

Note: Specific interventions will be most helpful once the woman has established trusted medical care.

ACTIONS

- Assist woman in finding and securing appropriate health care provider and prenatal care
- Encourage discussion of fears and other feelings

1.3.2

Issues of substance abuse, medication abuse, drug abuse, and/or harmful substances: use of substances harmful to woman or fetus, history of substance abuse (currently sober), history of substance abuse (currently active), self-medicating with over-the-counter medications.

GOALS

- Avoid using drugs, alcohol, or other substances harmful to her unborn child

- Engage, re-engage, or continue to engage in systems supporting sobriety
- Avoid any over-the-counter medications not approved by health care provider
- Engage in substance abuse counseling or support groups

SPECIFIC INTERVENTIONS

The following units provide interventions that address the issues described here:

Unit 1: Entering Motherhood

Unit 4: Relaxation and Well-Being

Unit 5: Honoring the Woman in Me

Note: Specific interventions will be most helpful once the woman has attained sobriety or entered into a specific rehabilitation program.

ACTIONS

- Educate woman about the effects of harmful substances on her unborn child
- Provide education on possible effects of over-the-counter medications
- Facilitate appropriate referrals to substance abuse programs, health care providers, and support groups, as needed
- Support the maintenance of sobriety

1.3.3

Issues of genetic risk: family history of genetic related conditions or birth defects, fear of potential genetic effects.

GOALS:

- Engage in discussions on her fears and concerns regarding genetic issues
- Consult genetic counselors or specialists to increase understanding of risks and concerns

SPECIFIC INTERVENTIONS

The following units provide interventions that address the issues described here:

Unit 3: Attachment

Unit 4: Relaxation and Well-Being

Unit 5: Honoring the Woman in Me

ACTIONS

- Support exploration of feelings related to genetic issues
- Make referrals to counseling or support groups
- Acknowledge the impact of genetic issues on the woman's pregnancy

---

1.3.4

History of current or frequent illnesses, hospitalizations, and/or presence of disabilities.

GOALS
- Explore with health care provider her medical history and how to stay healthy during her pregnancy
- Explore with health care provider the potential impact of pre-existing health conditions or disabilities in pregnancy
- Consult with health care provider on ways to support optimal health during pregnancy
- Work with health care providers to maintain appropriate treatment/stabilization of current medical conditions or disabilities

SPECIFIC INTERVENTIONS
The following units provide interventions that address the issues described here:

Unit 1: Entering Motherhood

Unit 2: Connecting With My Baby

Unit 3: Attachment

Unit 4: Relaxation and Well-Being

Unit 5: Honoring the Woman in Me

Unit 6: Making Space

Unit 7: Enhancing My Baby's Brain

Note: Specific interventions will be most helpful once the woman has secured a regular medical provider and addressed her medical concerns.

ACTIONS
- Encourage woman to be forthcoming with her medical provider about medical concerns, conditions, or disabilities

1.4 MENTAL HEALTH

ISSUES TO BE ASSESSED
- General functioning ability: awareness of environment, ability to answer questions, aware of name, date, and location
- Recent changes in appetite, sleep, or activity level (need to differentiate between pregnancy related changes and changes related to possible depressed mood)
- How the person seems to be feeling, i.e., sad, happy, excited, nervous
- Current or past involvement with counseling
- Past hospitalizations for mental health issues
- Current or past experience with depression
- Present or past use of medications, such as antidepressants, and the circumstances around these periods
- Present or past feelings of wanting to hurt self or feeling suicidal

SIGNIFICANCE

- Understanding the mental health of anyone begins with knowing they are thinking clearly and oriented to reality.

- Depression cannot be over-assessed: many people do not view themselves as depressed, although they may be exhibiting symptoms consistent with depression. The impact of depression can cause multiple problems with the woman, those around her, and her child. Often people have become depressed over time and have just forgotten how it was to feel good or normal. Denial can also play a role. Finally, when someone is depressed, their motivation to access help can be quite low.

- People often initially deny being depressed although they have used antidepressant medication in the past. It will be important to get an understanding of their experience.

- Past or present suicidal feelings are important to assess. Asking about these feelings does not cause them. Sometimes people just need to be asked, and asking can save a life.

TYPICAL QUESTIONS

- What is your full name? What city do you live in? What is today's date?

- Have you experienced any recent changes in your appetite, either eating more or a lot less than usual? How about sleeping, about how much do you sleep each night? Is this normal for you? Has your energy level changed at all?

- Affect should be observed. Generally the manner in which the person answers the questions helps determine their mood or present feelings. Note the range of affect, the patterns, and any predominant tone. Ask: Is the mood you are in today pretty typical for you? If so: Tell me what kinds of things might affect your moods. If not: Tell me what your mood might be like on a typical day.

- Have you ever been involved in counseling? What kind? With whom? How was it for you?

- Have you ever been hospitalized for any reason related to mental health, such as depression?

- Are you on any medications like antidepressants? Have you ever been?

- Have you ever had any feelings like you wanted to hurt yourself or kill yourself? Tell me about those times. Are you having any of those feelings today?

1.4.1

Disorientation: unable to correctly state name, date, or present location.

GOALS:

- Become oriented to name, date, present location, and reality.

SPECIFIC INTERVENTIONS

The following units provide interventions that address the issues described here:

Unit 4: Relaxation and Well-Being

Unit 5: Honoring the Woman in Me

Note: Before any interventions can be implemented, orientation must be established.

ACTIONS

- Orient woman to her name, date, present location, and reality.
- If disorientation persists, develop safety plan that could include having someone known and trusted by woman stay with her, escorting woman to a mental health evaluation center, or calling 911 if disorientation is immediately threatening the woman's safety
- Refer to counseling or support groups as appropriate

1.4.2

Issues of depressive symptoms: disturbances in sleep, changes in appetite, lack of energy, no desire to participate in pleasurable activities, isolating from others, flat affect, lack of emotional range, depressed appearance.

GOALS

- Establish an adequate balance of sleep and awake times
- Establish a stabilization of appetite
- Eat a balanced diet of foods nutritionally appropriate for her unborn child and herself
- Experience an increase in energy appropriate with her state of pregnancy
- Take a walk outside for at least 15 minutes each day (check with medical provider before starting any exercise)
- Participate in one social activity each week
- Call a friend or relative at least once each week
- Explore past activity participation and how it fits in with her vision for her life with a baby
- Explore her feelings about herself, her current situation, and her future as a mother
- Display a range of emotions

SPECIFIC INTERVENTIONS

The following units provide interventions that address the issues described here:

Unit 1: Entering Motherhood

Unit 4: Relaxation and Well-Being

Unit 5: Honoring the Woman in Me

Unit 6: Making Space

ACTIONS

- Encourage and monitor regular rest periods throughout the day, as well as sleep during the night
- Encourage and monitor adequate food intake; if food and drink are not

readily available to the woman, she will need to be connected to community resources providing food

- Encourage and monitor a regular exercise schedule appropriate to woman, such as walking, stretching, etc.
- Facilitate the development of a supportive social network
- Encourage connections with supportive people
- Encourage discussion of feelings, concerns, and worries
- Encourage journal writing as a way of processing feelings, concerns, and worries
- Encourage discussion around the future and how baby may or may not impact her life

1.4.3

Issues related to harm to self or others: suicide ideation—thinking about suicide, feeling a desire to kill self, and/or making plans on how to kill self, suicidal threats, threatening to kill self; homicidal threats—threatening to kill or harm others, threats to harm unborn child, behaving in a careless and dangerous fashion that puts herself and her unborn child at risk—engaging in unprotected sexual activity with different partners, entering into potentially violent environments, interacting with potentially dangerous persons.

GOALS

- Report being free of suicidal ideation
- Not harm herself or others
- Report being free from feelings of wanting to hurt herself or others
- Discuss feelings related to impulses and involved others
- Establish a plan to keep self safe and away from dangerous situations
- Explore the impact of her own behaviors on her unborn child
- Evaluate the appropriateness of her choices of activities as it concerns pregnancy safety and the safety of her unborn child

SPECIFIC INTERVENTIONS

The following units provide interventions that address the issues described here:

Unit 2: Connecting With My Baby

Unit 3: Attachment

Unit 4: Relaxation and Well-Being

Unit 5: Honoring the Woman in Me

Unit 7: Enhancing My Baby's Brain

ACTIONS

- Establish a *No Harm Contract* with woman in writing that she will maintain her safety and that of her unborn child for appropriate periods of time (this could range from an hour to a week depending on the stability and progress of the woman)

- Facilitate safety plans
- Provide emergency contact numbers if suicidal ideation persists or increases
- Refer to mental health providers for complete assessment and ongoing therapeutic services
- Contract with mother that she will not act on impulses to hurt others (duration of contract can range from hour to week, depending on woman's ability and presence of other safety measures)
- Explore and encourage discussion on how mother's behaviors may or may not impact her unborn child
- Educate woman that patterns developed during pregnancy with regard to sleep, wake, and activity are often the same after birth; the fetus is an active learner
- Discuss with mother the safety issues of her behaviors and choices and how they impact her unborn child (for instance, hiking many miles over rough terrain during the 9th month of pregnancy is not a safe behavior due to stress on the mother's body and the risk of going into early labor in a remote area).

1.4.4
Issues related to previous or current mental illness: has gone off medication, history of mental illness (currently stabilized, currently decompensating), has received a new diagnosis for a mental illness.

GOALS
- Engage in activities and therapies that are supportive of remaining stable emotionally and psychologically, most importantly those that have been helpful in the past
- Establish and/or maintain connected with medical providers, therapists, and support groups that provide her with the support and care needed to stabilize her mental illness
- Establish healthy patterns of stress reduction

SPECIFIC INTERVENTIONS
The following units provide interventions that address the issues described here:

Unit 4: Relaxation and Well-Being

Unit 5: Honoring the Woman in Me

ACTIONS
- Assist woman in reengaging or maintaining her connections with other agencies and groups that were helpful in providing stability during past exacerbations of her illness: Alcoholics Anonymous, Emotions Anonymous, community support groups, private therapy, contact with health care practitioner.
- Educate woman on stress management techniques
- Use provided intervention exercises on relaxation and the woman in me
- Refer to counseling or support groups as appropriate

1.5 SELF CARE

ISSUES TO BE ASSESSED

- Present sleep pattern
- Meal routines, current appetite
- Any problems with eating disorders such as anorexia, bulimia, or overeating
- Exercise routines, type and amount of exercise, any limitations
- Types of activities, things she does for fun

SIGNIFICANCE

- Knowing about a person's typical day can provide you a baseline of what is normal for that person, making it easier to determine when things may be going wrong or needing intervention.
- Disturbances in sleep or eating patterns may not only signify problems with mood, such as depression, but can also provide an understanding as to how the woman cares for herself and how her behavior might impact her pregnancy.

TYPICAL QUESTIONS

- Tell me about your typical day—when you get up, when you eat, and so on.
- How are you sleeping? When do you usually go to bed? When do you normally wake up? Do you feel like you are getting enough rest? Is this normal for you? How does your current sleep schedule compare to before you became pregnant?
- Tell me about your typical meal schedule? Do you eat three meals at regular times or do you eat several smaller meals throughout the day when you find yourself hungry? Do you snack much? What types of foods do you usually eat in a day?
- Have you ever been diagnosed with an eating disorder? Have you ever thought you might have an eating disorder such as anorexia, bulimia, or overeating? If so, tell me about your experiences? Are these issues still problematic for you? What has been helpful for you around these issues?
- What do you typically do for exercise? Do you exercise daily or weekly? Is your current exercise program new for you or is it something you have done before? Do you have any limitations or challenges?
- What kinds of things do you do for fun? What activities do you participate in? Do you do these things alone or with friends or family?

1.5.1

Issues of regulation: sleep disturbance, not eating a healthy and nutritious diet, lack of or inadequate exercise, inability to relax.

GOALS

- Establish a balance of sleep and activity
- Utilize non-invasive techniques to help promote and maintain sleep

- Establish a nutritiously balanced diet that is healthy for herself and her unborn child
- Re-engage and/or maintain activities that are supportive of healthy eating behaviors
- Develop ways of dealing with stress and anxiety that are not food-related
- Explore and express feelings around self, situation, pregnancy, and motherhood
- Engage in an exercise or activity routine that is appropriate for current stage of pregnancy

SPECIFIC INTERVENTIONS
The following units provide interventions that address the issues described here:

Unit 4: Relaxation and Well-Being

Unit 5: Honoring the Woman in Me

Unit 7: Enhancing My Baby's Brain

ACTIONS
- Teach and encourage relaxation methods, deep breathing, use of soft music, reading, etc., as non-invasive methods of promoting sleep
- Teach and encourage avoidance of caffeine, alcohol, heavy meals, etc., before bed, as they may interfere with sleep
- Provide information on healthy eating during pregnancy
- Encourage positive food choices
- Assist woman in food shopping to teach and support new food choices
- Educate and encourage stress reduction and relaxation techniques, such as guided imagery, deep breathing, exercise, etc.
- Encourage discussion of feelings, worries, and concerns about self, baby, or transitions
- Encourage journal writing as a way to process feelings, worries, and concerns
- Encourage and support participation in exercise routine; encourage woman to discuss with her health care provider what type of exercises would be appropriate for her stage of pregnancy

1.6 WORK AND EDUCATION

ISSUES TO BE ASSESSED
- Level of education completed or currently in progress
- Current place of employment, position, and type of work
- Work history, types of jobs

SIGNIFICANCE
- Current employment and educational status provide information as to how the woman is supporting herself.

- Understanding the demands of the woman's job or daily schedule is important in order to understand how her work might impact her pregnancy.
- Some women make decisions based on what they feel they are expected to do or what they have done in the past. It will be important to understand each woman's process of balancing caring for herself and her unborn child with the expectations of her work.

TYPICAL QUESTIONS
- How are you supporting yourself right now?
- Do you currently have a job? Do you work part time or full time? How many hours do you work in a week?
- What do you do? Do you enjoy it? Is this what you want to be doing, or do you see it as a stepping-stone to other things?
- What are the demands of your current job?
- Are you able to say "no" to certain projects or tasks in your current job?
- How does your employer support women in pregnancy?
- How is being pregnant impacting your current job?
- How much time are you planning on taking off after you are home with your baby?
- How much schooling have you completed?

1.6.1
Issues with education: lack of high school diploma, lack of GED, adolescent still in school, desire to enroll in classes or school, need for training program.

GOALS
- Participate in high school or GED classes
- Continue to work towards completion of high school or GED program
- Explore college courses or training programs
- Enroll in schooling or training supportive of employment goals
- Develop a childcare plan based on the needs of both the child and herself in preparation for the time she will need to return to school

SPECIFIC INTERVENTIONS
The following unit provides interventions that address the issues described here:

Unit 5: Honoring the Woman in Me

ACTIONS
- Refer woman to a program that assists women in exploring and enrolling in school programs or exploring and finding employment
- If needed, assist woman with enrollment in school
- Encourage completion of high school degree or GED
- Encourage engagement in community classes or instruction on resume writing and interviewing skills

- Explore childcare needs and options and preferences if the plan includes returning to school

1.6.2

Issues related to employment: lack of employment, employment type inappropriate during pregnancy, inability to retain employment, inadequate social skills, need for resume and interview skills.

GOALS

- Connect with employment assistance agency or representative to help explore and secure appropriate employment
- Evaluate current employment and the impact on her health and safety, and that of her unborn child
- Connect with agency designed to help prepare resume and interview skills
- Explore difficulties with past employment experiences and how these can be avoided in the future
- Develop a childcare plan based on the needs of both the child and herself in preparation for the time she will need to return to work or school
- Develop a workable budget within the context of her current and projected income sources

SPECIFIC INTERVENTIONS

The following unit provides interventions that address the issues described here:

   Unit 5: Honoring the Woman in Me

ACTIONS

- Refer to a program that assists women in exploring and enrolling in school programs or exploring and finding employment
- If needed, assist with avenues to finding employment
- Encourage woman to engage in community classes or instruction on resume writing and interviewing skills
- Facilitate practice of interviewing skills
- Evaluate and discuss, as needed, the impact of the current job on pregnancy, i.e., standing on feet too long causing swollen legs, climbing up high ladders, etc.
- Support efforts to create a work environment conducive with pregnancy
- Initiate discussion around past problems with employment and how these can be avoided in the future
- Explore with woman her childcare needs and options and preferences if the plan includes returning to work or school
- Support the development of a workable budget

1.7 RELATIONSHIPS

ISSUES TO BE ASSESSED
- Current relationship with spouse or partner
- Any current domestic violence or abuse in the home or in specific relationships
- Any previous marriages or significant relationships
- Current relationship with mother and father
- Relationships with friends
- How all the people in these relationships feel about the pregnancy
- People in her life she feels are supportive of her and her pregnancy
- Participation in any groups or regular get-togethers

SIGNIFICANCE
- Relationship histories help provide a picture of how much support the person receives from her family. Issues of spousal abuse or domestic violence can have serious effects on a pregnant woman and her unborn child. Also, how the person gets along with family members can be an indication of how she might develop similar relationships with her children and spouse.
- Having friends in one's life suggests the ability to share part of one's life with others, outlets for emotion, successful social skills, and access to others outside the family.

TYPICAL QUESTIONS
- What is your relationship like with the father of your baby?
- How long have you been together? How would you describe your relationship? Are you happy with it?
- Has there ever been any violence in your relationship? Have you ever been hurt or threatened? Have you ever been frightened by your partner or anyone else in your home? Are you concerned that anyone might hurt you?
- How is your relationship with your mom and dad? Is this a supportive relationship or are they sometimes difficult to be with?
- Do you have a best friend? How long have you known each other?
- Are you sharing the news of your pregnancy? How are people responding?

1.7.1
Issues of unsafe relationships: domestic violence, emotional, physical or sexual abuse, coerciveness, threats to pregnancy, unspecified dangers (gang exposure).

GOALS
- Acknowledge there is violence in her relationship
- Develop a plan to be able to keep herself and her unborn child safe
- Identify current supportive formal and informal sources

- Be safe
- Connect with support groups or shelters designed to assist women in domestically violent relationships
- Identify those persons in her life who are abusive or violent with her
- Will acknowledge she does not deserve to be abused
- Establish a plan to remain safe from those persons she views as dangerous or a threat to her safety or that of her unborn child
- Develop a network of positive relationships within her neighborhood, school, community, support groups, etc., that can be supportive of her

SPECIFIC INTERVENTIONS
The following units provide interventions that address the issues described here:

Unit 4: Relaxation and Well-Being

Unit 5: Honoring the Woman in Me

Unit 6: Making Space

ACTIONS
- Support the mother to come to terms with the abuse currently occurring within her relationship(s)
- Work with woman to develop a plan to get her immediate needs met (food, shelter) and to stay safe (free from abuse)
- If woman is a minor, report any abuse to Child Protective Services as required by law.
- Establish a safety plan with the woman that pertains to her current issues
- Provide numbers and addresses to local women's shelters dealing with domestic violence
- Accompany woman to shelter if needed
- Support woman's self esteem through positive feedback for each step to taking care of self and getting safe
- Discuss with woman that no one deserves to be hurt or abused
- Discuss types of abuse: verbal, emotional, sexual, physical, and coerciveness or abusive power
- Develop, with woman, a plan to avoid those who may be unsafe for her or her unborn baby
- Develop secondary plans on how to handle unexpected situations where abusive persons are present
- Encourage and support woman in finding individuals, groups, or contacts who are safe and can be trusted

1.7.2
Issues in the relationship with baby's father: estranged, potentially violent relationship, denial of paternity, history of drug or alcohol abuse, pattern of criminal activity, creates unsafe situations for woman.

GOALS

- Assess the strengths, challenges, and concerns of current relationship with baby's father or other partners
- Explore her relationship with the baby's father and how she wants to define this relationship
- Set limits and boundaries as necessary with those persons in her life she sees as intrusive, hurtful, or unhealthy
- Establish a plan to keep herself and her unborn child safe in volatile circumstances
- Establish a plan to avoid and remain free of relationships that can be hurtful
- See section 1.1.3 regarding paternity issues

SPECIFIC INTERVENTIONS

The following units provide interventions that address the issues described here:

Unit 4: Relaxation and Well-Being

Unit 5: Honoring the Woman in Me

Unit 6: Making Space

ACTIONS

- Support woman's self-esteem through positive feedback for each step to taking care of self and getting safe
- Support attempts to set boundaries with others
- Discuss concerns for baby; for example, what kind of environment is wanted for this child
- Encourage discussion of woman's feelings about her baby's father, type of relationship she wants with him, type of relationship she wants for baby, desires of the father, and potential legal rights and options
- Support attempts to break free from dysfunctional relationships, as needed
- Make referrals as necessary to legal clinics and groups who can educate and support woman on her legal options.

1.7.3

Issues with extended family: no extended family available; relationships involving high conflict; unsupportive, dysfunctional extended family members involved in drugs, alcohol abuse, gangs, criminal activity, etc.; turbulent relationships with extended family members; lack of support for pregnancy.

GOALS

- Assess the strengths, challenges, and concerns of current relationships
- Explore how relationships with different extended family members will affect life with a new baby
- Set limits and boundaries as necessary with those persons in her life she sees as intrusive, hurtful, or unhealthy

- Establish a plan to keep herself and her unborn child safe in volatile circumstances
- Establish a plan to avoid and remain free of relationships that can be hurtful
- Develop a working support system in the absence of a supportive extended family
- Explore which personal needs are being met by relationships with extended family members

SPECIFIC INTERVENTIONS

The following units provide interventions that address the issues described here:

Unit 5: Honoring the Woman in Me

Unit 6: Making Space

Unit 7: Enhancing My Baby's Brain

ACTIONS

- Support woman's self-esteem through positive feedback for each step to taking care of self and getting safe
- Support attempts to set boundaries with others
- Discuss concerns for baby; for example, what kind of environment is wanted for this child
- Support attempts to break free from dysfunctional relationships, as needed
- Make referrals as necessary to counseling and support groups focusing on relationships
- Encourage evaluation of each relationship of concern in terms of impact on mother and impact on baby

1.8 STRESSORS

ISSUES TO BE ASSESSED

- Current stressors the woman can identify in her life
- Impact of these stressors
- Current ways of dealing with these stressors

SIGNIFICANCE

- Pregnancy itself can be a stressful time for both the woman and others in her life. Having other stresses in her life can easily become overwhelming. How the woman deals with stress provides an idea of both her ability to deal with stress and of some strategies for dealing with stress, which can be integrated into interventions for this woman. For example, if a woman has a history of de-stressing with exercise, an intervention involving taking daily walks might have a greater chance of success.

TYPICAL QUESTIONS

- What types of things are stressful to you right now?
- What kinds of things are stressful to you in general?
- Do you ever get upset about different things that happen in your life? How do you usually deal with these stressors?

1.8.1
Single or multiple stressors interfering with optimal functioning: overwhelmed, immobilized, interference with appropriate functioning, lack of knowledge as to how to decrease or modify stress.

GOALS
- Identify the current stressors in her life
- Develop new problem-solving skills, such as prioritizing, letting go, delegating, relaxation, time management, engaging in exercise, guided imagery, etc.
- Utilize problem-solving methods to eliminate, decrease, or modify stressors to lessen their impact on her life
- Increase knowledge of various relaxation methods used to decrease the impact of stress
- Describe ways to modify her responses to the stressors in her life in order to maintain appropriate daily functioning
- Develop network that can listen and support her during times of overwhelming stress

SPECIFIC INTERVENTIONS
The following units provide interventions that address the issues described here:

Unit 2: Connecting With My Baby

Unit 3: Attachment

Unit 4: Relaxation and Well-Being

Unit 5: Honoring the Woman in Me

Unit 6: Making Space

ACTIONS
- Support woman in making a list of the current stressors in her life
- Explore the types of things the woman has tried in the past to deal with stress
- Educate on different types of stress reduction methods, including regular exercise, prioritizing, relaxation, guided imagery, etc.
- Educate on problem-solving skills, including how to identify problem, identify alternatives for dealing with problem, prioritizing the alternatives, choosing one, and putting it into action
- Teach relaxation methods, such as deep breathing, meditation, yoga, exercise, quiet house, soft music, bubble baths, etc.
- Encourage woman to ask herself questions, such as, How important is this problem? Is it in my control to change things? What can I do to help myself to feel better? Who can I ask for help with this problem?
- Assist her in developing a list of support persons

PAST HISTORY

2.1 LOSS AND TRAUMA

ISSUES TO BE ASSESSED
- Loss of significant people in her life, circumstances around loss, and impact on her
- Things in her past she feels were traumatic and the impact of these
- History of abuse, including sexual, physical, and emotional abuse
- History of domestic violence

SIGNIFICANCE
- Loss and trauma can have a major impact on one's self esteem, behavior, relationships, decision-making, and parenting. Histories of abuse can also have a direct impact. In some cases, long abuse histories can be a risk factor in later abuse of the child.
- Trauma can impact the woman and her child in many ways. One case example involved a woman who had accidentally killed two children with her car when she was eighteen (not her fault). When she got pregnant herself at 24, she was so afraid that God would punish her for killing the two children that she was sure her daughter would die shortly after birth. Her fear prevented her from developing any kind of relationship with her child. She felt if she allowed herself to get close to her child, God would take her even quicker. Only professional therapy around the trauma was helpful in impacting this mother and child.

TYPICAL QUESTIONS
- Has anyone in your family or close to you passed away or died? Tell me a little bit about what happened. How did this death change your life?
- Have you ever been through something in your life you would consider traumatic? How did this impact you?
- Have you ever been abused? Have you ever been sexually abused? Physically abused? Emotionally abused? Tell me a little about how old you were and how this impacted your life.
- Have you ever been involved in domestic violence of any kind? Were your parents ever violent with each other? How about you and your partner or spouse?

2.1.1
Significant loss issues: loss of a parent or other primary caregiver, loss of close relative or friend, loss of a child, pregnancy loss, abortions, miscarriages, long-term separations from significant family or friends, severed family relationships, unresolved loss, impending loss, perceived losses, multiple losses.

GOALS

- Acknowledge and discuss the loss of those significant in her life
- Identify ways which are most helpful in supporting her working through her grief
- Develop productive ways of dealing with grief, such as journal writing, letter writing, support groups, etc.
- Develop an awareness of the normal stages of grief: denial, anger, bargaining, acknowledgment, and acceptance
- Develop ways to deal with extreme feelings related to past issues that support reconciliation of feelings and are supportive of maintaining normal daily living

SPECIFIC INTERVENTIONS

The following units provide interventions that address the issues described here:

Unit 1: Entering Motherhood

Unit 3: Attachment

Unit 4: Relaxation and Well-Being

Unit 5: Honoring the Woman in Me

Unit 6: Making Space

ACTIONS

- Refer woman to a professional therapist who specializes in loss, as needed
- Approach loss issues with the understanding that all people respond to loss in their own way and that different losses impact each person in different ways, i.e., some women may be devastated by a past miscarriage; others may not see it as an issue
- Encourage expression of feelings about the loss, whether past loss, present loss, or impending loss
- Identify the woman's strengths and integrate these into assisting her in developing skills for coping with loss
- Listen in a calm, non-judgmental way to the woman's story of her loss
- Use reflective speech (it sounds like that was difficult for you; can you tell me more about..); do NOT respond with statements like "I know how you feel" and refrain from telling personal stories
- Assist woman in developing a positive support system she can contact when difficult feelings or memories surface
- If loss is recent, refrain from placing excess demands on woman; her energy will be needed to deal with the loss
- Treat feelings about past losses with equal respect and sensitivity as recent events
- Listen attentively and demonstrate interest in stories of past loss through asking for specifics about events and feelings
- Support crying by respecting silences, through touch, and validating the need and normalcy of the tears

- Be knowledgeable about the stages of grief: denial, anger, bargaining, acknowledgment, and acceptance; be aware of current stage and provide guidance for what typically comes next
- Encourage day-by-day living when feelings are overwhelming and intrusive into daily life
- Educate on various methods of dealing with grief, such as journal writing, support groups, art, exercise, etc.
- Take care of self through debriefing or sharing with colleagues or through consultation
- Following a visit or session dealing with loss, take time to separate from the issues through personal relaxation, writing, deep breathing, exercising, etc.
- Use provided intervention exercises on maternal role attainment, making space for baby, and acknowledging baby

2.1.2
Issues related to trauma: unresolved trauma, childhood trauma, recent trauma, relationship trauma, medical trauma, history of sexual, physical, and/or emotional abuse, history of witnessing or experiencing domestic violence, violent trauma.

GOALS
- Acknowledge and identify the traumas of the past
- Explore and express feelings related to the traumas
- Explore and express feelings related to past abuse
- Explore and express feelings related to past domestic violence
- Develop ways to deal with extreme feelings related to past issues that support reconciliation of feelings and are supportive of maintaining normal daily living

SPECIFIC INTERVENTIONS
The following units provide interventions that address the issues described here:

Unit 3: Attachment

Unit 4: Relaxation and Well-Being

Unit 5: Honoring the Woman in Me

Unit 6: Making Space

ACTIONS
- Refer woman to a professional therapist who specializes in trauma, as needed
- Acknowledge that it is the person's perception of an experience that determines the traumatic nature rather than our perceptions or expectations
- Identify the woman's strengths and integrate these into assisting her in developing skills for coping with trauma
- Listen in a calm, non-judgmental way to the woman's story of her trauma

- Use reflective speech (it sounds like that was difficult for you; can you tell me more about...), do NOT respond with statements like "I know how you feel" and refrain from telling personal stories
- Provide reality-based assessment of the events: as a child you had no power over your uncle's behavior. He was bigger and more powerful. It is not your fault.
- Assist woman in developing a positive support system she can contact when difficult feelings or memories surface
- If trauma is recent, refrain from placing excess demands on woman; her energy will be needed to deal with the loss or trauma
- Treat feelings about past traumas with equal respect and sensitivity as recent events
- Listen attentively and demonstrate interest in stories of past abuse, domestic violence, or trauma through asking for specifics about events and feelings
- Support crying by respecting silences, through touch, and validating the need and normalcy of the tears
- Encourage day-to-day living when feelings are overwhelming and intrusive into daily life
- Educate on various methods in dealing with post-trauma experiences, such as journal writing, support groups, art, exercise, etc.
- Take care of self through debriefing or sharing with colleagues or through consultation
- Following a visit or session dealing with trauma take time to separate from the issues through personal relaxation, writing, deep breathing, exercising, etc.

2.2 CHILDHOOD EXPERIENCES

ISSUES TO BE ASSESSED
- Who raised her
- Who was in her family, including any stepparents, foster parents, and grandparents
- How she was disciplined
- How she got along with her mother, father, brothers, sisters, and/or other significant people
- Who would take care of her when she was sick or if she was hurt and how they cared for her
- What her family did for fun
- How she played when she was a child
- What her childhood friends were like
- How her family handled holidays, birthdays, etc.

SIGNIFICANCE
- Knowing family history provides a good picture of the woman's general family structure as well as the level of stability throughout her childhood.

Stability and predictability often relate to more successful functioning in families.

- How the woman might have been nurtured may provide information about how the woman thinks about nurturing her own child. If her childhood had been low in nurturance, developing interventions to teach the mother the significance of nurturing and ways to nurture her child could be very helpful.

TYPICAL QUESTIONS
- Tell me a little about who raised you.
- Who was in your family as you were growing up? Were your grandparents very involved?
- How did your parents discipline you? Did you get disciplined often?
- How would you say you got along with your mother? Your father? Your brothers? Sisters?
- Who was responsible for taking care of you when you were sick?

2.2.1

Issues related to caregiving or caregivers: multiple caregivers, raised by sibling, foster care, inadequate caregiving, adoption, placed in care of strangers, left to care for self and/or siblings, divorce of parents, multiple stepparents.

GOALS
- Acknowledge all the people who functioned as significant caregivers and explore what role they actually played in her life
- Discuss feelings related to caregiving or caregiver issues
- Explore how she wished her caregiving experiences would have been
- Explore how caregiving or caregiver experiences will impact her ability to mother her child
- Explore what she learned from her childhood experiences and how these have shaped who she is
- Discuss feelings around the divorce(s) of her parents, including how it felt then, how it feels now, and what she does to handle the situation
- Establish a working plan on how she will achieve her desires for her child

SPECIFIC INTERVENTIONS
The following units provide interventions that address the issues described here:

Unit 3: Attachment

Unit 4: Relaxation and Well-Being

Unit 5: Honoring the Woman in Me

Unit 6: Making Space

ACTIONS
- Encourage discussion around caretakers throughout childhood, how they contributed to her life (good and bad), and how she sees them relating to her life in the present

- Encourage discussion and exploration around how the woman felt having different caretakers and how she would have liked it to be
- Support examination of past experiences and their impact on the present
- Explore issues and feelings related to parental divorce

2.2.2

Issues of abuse and/or maltreatment: child maltreatment, neglect, abandonment, physical punishment, sexual abuse, emotional abuse, physical abuse, witnessing abuse of siblings, witnessing domestic violence, forced to use drugs or alcohol, forced to participate in behavior inappropriate for children.

GOALS

- Discuss and explore feelings related to involvement with agencies dealing with child abuse and neglect, abuse history, or maltreatment
- Explore how her childhood experiences have shaped who she is
- Engage in and participate in counseling or support groups, as needed
- Explore how her childhood experiences might impact her child
- Explore discipline history in terms of the balance between safety/security and the ability to explore/individuate
- Explore what types of decisions she has made for disciplining her own child
- Discuss how the woman plans to provide different experiences for her child and keep the child safe from the dangers she might have experienced as a child
- Establish a working plan on how she will achieve her desires for her child

SPECIFIC INTERVENTIONS:

The following units provide interventions that address the issues described here:

    Unit 1: Entering Motherhood

    Unit 3: Attachment

    Unit 5: Honoring the Woman in Me

    Unit 6: Making Space

Note: Specific interventions will be most helpful once the woman has dealt with issues of abuse and maltreatment, preferably through professional mental health services.

ACTIONS

- Encourage exploration and discussion around involvement with agencies dealing with child abuse and neglect
- Explore discipline experiences during childhood and the impact they have on her now in terms of the types of feelings they create in her now and how she plans to discipline her child.

- Refer to counseling or support groups as needed to deal with abuse or maltreatment
- See 2.1.2 for additional interventions related to trauma and abuse

2.2.3
Dysfunctional family issues: alcoholic or drug abusing family system, enmeshed family system, dependent family members, history of family problems related to the major mental illness of one or more members.

GOALS
- Explore how growing up in an alcoholic family system shaped who she is
- Explore how this family system may or may not impact her baby
- Evaluate the safeness of the family and determine boundaries as needed to maintain safety for herself and her baby

SPECIFIC INTERVENTIONS
The following units provide interventions that address the issues described here:

Unit 1: Entering Motherhood

Unit 3: Attachment

Unit 4: Relaxation and Well-Being

Unit 5: Honoring the Woman in Me

Unit 6: Making Space

Unit 7: Enhancing My Baby's Brain

ACTIONS
- Support exploration of family systems and impact on present
- Encourage and support the establishment of boundaries and limits on family members as needed
- Encourage consideration of family factors that may impact mother and baby
- Refer to support groups such as AlAnon

2.2.4
Issues of abandonment, rejection or isolation: left to care for self, feelings of rejection in childhood, isolation from peers, isolated from others, rejected by peers.

GOALS
- Explore feelings of rejection and abandonment
- Explore how these experiences shaped who she is now
- Explore the differences between her childhood experiences and those she imagines for her child

- Discuss feelings related to prevention of play or other normal childhood activities
- Make a plan for how to experience some of those "missed experiences" of childhood in a safe and effective manner

SPECIFIC INTERVENTIONS

The following units provide interventions that address the issues described here:

Unit 3: Attachment

Unit 5: Honoring the Woman in Me

Unit 6: Making Space

ACTIONS

- Explore play history, who she played with, what that experience was like, what she wished could have happened, and how her experiences affected her
- Explore ways she can incorporate fun and play into her life as an adult
- Explore her knowledge base of baby play and educate around issues of gaining child's interest, stimulation through play, and relationship benefits of play
- Support self exploration, making referrals to counseling or support groups as needed

2.3 RELATIONSHIP WITH MOTHER

ISSUES TO BE ASSESSED

- Quality of this relationship
- Presence of her mother or others she considered mothers to her at some time
- Problems her mother may have faced, such as mental illness or alcoholism
- Ability to communicate well with her mother
- Ability to express her feelings
- Present closeness to her mother
- What her mother did best as a mother
- What her mother did not do so well or the mistakes she made
- How her mother's behavior impacts her ideas for how she will mother her child—how much influence her mother has on her
- Whether the mother's influence on the pregnant woman will be helpful and supportive or critical and intrusive

SIGNIFICANCE

- Pregnancy often results in the woman rethinking her relationship with her mother. This relationship becomes extremely important to the woman, requiring her to explore the good and bad parts of it. Assessing her relationship with her mother provides two benefits. First, it can provide an opportunity to talk about her thoughts around her mother instead of just thinking about it. Second, it can provide an idea of what the woman is dealing with and what she will need to explore.

- Knowing how much influence the woman's mother has on her can provide an indication of the pregnant woman's ability to think independently. It can also provide a window into what their relationship is like in the context of this pregnancy.
- It is important to understand the impact the mother has on the pregnant woman, both through your observations and from her perspective.

TYPICAL QUESTIONS

- Tell me more about your relationship with your mother? What kind of a mother was she? How would you describe her?
- Were there others you felt also might have mothered you? Any stepmothers, aunts, grandmothers, older sisters?
- Did your mother ever have any major problems she had to deal with as you grew up?
- Were you able to talk to your mom about your life or how you felt about things? Can you still do this?
- Has your mother shared with you what her pregnancy with you was like? Has she talked about the first few weeks after you were born and what that was like? How does it feel to hear those things? How do you think your experience may be the same or different from your mother's?
- What do you think your mother did really well as a mother when she was raising you? Do you plan to do these same things with your child?
- What were her mistakes as a mother? How do you think you might do things differently?
- Does your mother offer you advice on your pregnancy and the baby? What do you think of this advice? Is it helpful or does it interfere with your relationship?

2.3.1

Issues related to communication: lack of communication, mother providing invalid or harmful information about pregnancy or care, poor communication.

GOALS:

- Explore problems with communication she has with her mother.
- Evaluate information coming from mother with other sources, i.e., medical provider
- Establish connections with supportive others as needed

SPECIFIC INTERVENTIONS

The following units provide interventions that address the issues described here:

Unit 3: Attachment

Unit 5: Honoring the Woman in Me

Unit 6: Making Space

ACTIONS
- Encourage expression of feelings about woman's communication efforts with her mother
- Encourage exploration of communication problems.
- Assist woman in evaluating reasons for no or poor communication, if this works for her (in terms of safety, protection, avoidance of abuse, etc.).
- If warranted, support woman in problem solving communication issues
- Encourage discussion and questioning of new information
- Teach limit setting behaviors

2.3.2

Issues related to nature of relationship: rejection by mother, emotional dependence on mother, financial dependence on mother, unable to make decisions independent of mother, mother physically present but emotionally unavailable, client is a minor and is required to remain with her mother, dependent on mother for future caregiving responsibilities of baby, dependent on mother for basic survival needs.

GOALS
- Discuss her feelings about her relationship with her mother
- Establish a plan to increase independence from mother
- Explore the positive and negative features of her relationship with her mother
- Establish a plan on how to develop in herself the positive qualities she wants to take from her own mother
- Establish a plan on how to avoid repeating her mother's mistakes
- Identify people in her life she has felt offered her things mothers usually offer to their daughters
- Discuss feelings related to rejection
- Begin to grieve the things she has never gotten from her mother
- Develop ways to mother herself in the ways she needs (for example, if she believes mothers should celebrate their children's birthdays, she could develop a way to celebrate her birthday and honor herself)
- Begin to take responsibility for her life decisions
- Make decisions on her own

SPECIFIC INTERVENTIONS
The following units provide interventions that address the issues described here:

Unit 1: Entering Motherhood

Unit 3: Attachment

Unit 5: Honoring the Woman in Me

Unit 6: Making Space

ACTIONS
- Encourage expression of feelings about a woman's relationship with her mother
- Encourage exploration of the relationship in terms of positives, negatives, what she wishes it could be like, what she feels she is missing in that relationship
- Assist woman in exploring those persons in her life who have offered her maternal support and what they have been able to offer her. Discuss feelings about her relationships with these people
- Encourage exploration of feelings about past or present abuse by mother
- Encourage discussion of feelings of rejection
- Support self-esteem
- Educate and assist woman in developing ways she can honor herself and provide herself with the things she craves
- Encourage acknowledgment that not getting what you needed from your mother or not having a mother is something that could and should be grieved
- Encourage expression of grief and movement through the stages of grief
- Encourage and reward any attempts and/or successes in making own decisions and in taking responsibility for her own actions
- Provide referrals and alternatives that are supportive of independent living.
- Teach limit setting behaviors.
- Assist in developing a shared parenting plan.

2.3.3

Issues related to interaction difficulty: maternal mental illness or addictions interfering with healthy mother-daughter relationship, maternal physical or medical illness, abusive relationship, conflict.

GOALS
- Discuss her feelings about her relationship with her mother
- Explore the positive and negative features of her relationship with her mother
- Establish a plan to develop in herself the positive qualities she wants to take from her own mother
- Establish a plan to avoid repeating her own mother's mistakes
- Discuss feelings about mother's mental illness or addictions and how those have affected their relationship
- Discuss feelings resulting from experienced abuse by mother
- Begin to grieve the things she has never gotten from her mother
- Develop ways to mother herself in the ways she needs (for example, if she believes mothers should celebrate their children's birthdays, she could develop a way to celebrate her birthday and honor herself)
- Explore methods of dealing with conflict

SPECIFIC INTERVENTIONS

The following units provide interventions that address the issues described here:

Unit 1: Entering Motherhood

Unit 3: Attachment

Unit 5: Honoring the Woman in Me

Unit 6: Making Space

ACTIONS

- Encourage expression of feelings about woman's relationship with her mother.
- Encourage exploration of the relationship in terms of positives, negatives, what she wishes it could be like, what she feels she is missing in that relationship
- Support self-esteem
- Educate and assist woman in developing ways she can honor herself and provide herself with the things she craves
- Teach limit setting behaviors
- Encourage acknowledgment of grief over her mother's inabilities related to interfering factors such as illness

2.3.4

Issues related to lack of support: lack of maternal support, maternal disapproval of pregnancy and/or baby's father.

GOALS

- Discuss feelings related to lack of support of pregnancy
- Design ways to gather support from others
- Explore methods of dealing with conflict

SPECIFIC INTERVENTIONS

The following units provide interventions that address the issues described here:

Unit 1: Entering Motherhood

Unit 3: Attachment

Unit 5: Honoring the Woman in Me

Unit 6: Making Space

ACTIONS

- Assist woman in exploring those persons in her life who have offered her maternal support and what they have been able to offer her. Discuss feelings about her relationships with these people
- Explore other options for gaining support
- Encourage patience in dealing with her mother, allowing time to adjust to the pregnancy and/or who the baby's father is
- Support self-esteem
- Provide education on dealing with conflict

FUTURE VISIONS

3.1 IMAGES OF BABY

ISSUES TO BE ASSESSED
- When did she first have a sense she was pregnant
- What does she imagine this baby to be like
- What will this baby look like
- Has she thought of names
- What does she hope for her child as he or she grows

SIGNIFICANCE
- Some women are more sensitive and intuitive about both their bodies and the babies they carry. It is important to know when the woman first sensed or felt she was with child and when she first felt connected with that child.
- Research suggests that the ideas and images a woman develops during pregnancy have a strong relationship to how she thinks about her child after birth. Exploring these images can provide an idea of how the mother is thinking about her baby and how she might interact with the baby after birth.

TYPICAL QUESTIONS
- When did you first sense you were pregnant?
- When did you first sense your child?
- What was that like for you? Does your child seem real to you yet?
- Have you thought about what your child will look like? Tell me about what you imagine? Do you have any other fantasies about your baby?
- Do you know the sex of your baby?
- Is there anything that makes it difficult to imagine your child? Do you ever have concerns about your baby?
- Have you dreamed about your baby yet?
- Have you thought of any names yet? If so, how did you choose that name?
- What do you hope for your child as he or she grows up? What kind of adult do you think your child will become?
- What three wishes would you make for your child?

3.1.1
Issues with images: lack of images of baby, inability to imagine baby, refusal to imagine baby, scary images of baby.

GOALS
- Describe what she thinks or imagines her baby to look or be like
- Journal and discuss any dreams of her unborn child

- Discuss her anxiety or apprehension about imagining her baby
- Draw or create a symbol or picture of what her baby will look or be like
- Discuss the impact of her own activities and life style on her baby
- Discuss her ideas and beliefs for what kind of life her child will lead in terms of people in her life, education, relationships, personality, etc.

SPECIFIC INTERVENTIONS
The following units provide interventions that address the issues described here:

Unit 1: Entering Motherhood

Unit 2: Connecting With My Baby

Unit 3: Attachment

Unit 6: Making Space

Unit 7: Enhancing My Baby's Brain

ACTIONS
- Encourage woman to describe ideas or images of her baby
- Make comments about what the baby will be like (I bet he will have black hair like you; I imagine your baby will grow up to be organized like you; I can tell by how your baby moves around he will like music...etc.)
- Encourage nonverbal exploration of images, symbols, pictures, etc., of baby
- Assist the pregnant woman in keeping a dream journal of her dreams of her baby; encourage discussion and exploration of these dreams
- Encourage woman to discuss how she does and does not want her baby to be like her (or like baby's father, or other significant person.)

3.1.2

Issues with emotions related to baby: denial of any emotional connection to baby, fearful of allowing feelings toward baby to surface, inability to hold an image or idea of baby in her heart or mind.

GOALS
- Discuss feelings of fear, apprehension, worry, or anxiety
- Practice developing an image of her child in her mind and holding it there for several seconds at a time
- Journal and discuss her dreams and fears of her unborn child
- Draw or create a symbol or picture of what her baby will look or be like.
- Describe three wishes she has for her child in the future
- Describe what her child might be like in 20 years
- Explore how the baby will fit into the woman's own future plans

SPECIFIC INTERVENTIONS
The following units provide interventions that address the issues described here:

Unit 1: Entering Motherhood

Unit 2: Connecting With My Baby

Unit 3: Attachment

Unit 5: Honoring the Woman in Me

Unit 6: Making Space

Unit 7: Enhancing My Baby's Brain

ACTIONS

- Encourage nonverbal exploration of images, symbols, pictures, etc., of baby
- Explore with woman how her life choices and circumstances have affected her and her decisions
- Assist the pregnant woman in keeping a journal of her feelings of her baby as they come up; encourage her to write about what was happening when those feelings came up and what happened after that; encourage discussion and exploration of these feelings
- Reality test the safety of various life decisions; for example, allowing the baby to be in areas where there is a history of violence (intentional or accidental)
- Refer to counseling as needed

3.2 IMAGES OF BECOMING A MOTHER

ISSUES TO BE ASSESSED

- What it will be like to be a mother to this particular child
- How she plans to raise this child
- Who will be involved with this child's life
- How does she plan to discipline this child
- How will this child impact her life
- Idea of being a mother

SIGNIFICANCE

- The adjustment to motherhood can be a challenge. It is important to know how the woman plans to make the transition and meet those challenges. How she believes her mothering behaviors and decisions will impact her child is an important indication of how she views that connection.
- Exploring the value the woman places on motherhood is significant to her acceptance of the role.

TYPICAL QUESTIONS

- How will it be for you to become a mother to this child?
- What kinds of new things do you think you will need to learn, as you become a mother?
- How do you think you will be different as the mother of a child than you were as a woman without a child?
- How do you plan on raising your child?
- Who will be involved in your child's life?

• Is there anyone you know you would not want involved in your child's life? Why?
• How will you discipline this child?
• How do you think the way you raise your child will affect him/her?
• What does being a mother to this child mean to you?

3.2.1
Issues related to resistance to or denial of acceptance of mothering role: unable to imagine what it will be like to be mother, refusing to discuss issues, minimizing impact, denying current plans for how she will take on that role.

GOALS
• Identify and discuss three things a mother does or is responsible for
• Identify three mothers she knows and admires
• Identify and discuss a mother she does not think behaves like a good mother
• Identify her fears or worries about becoming a mother
• Engage in counseling, if denial or refusal continues without change

SPECIFIC INTERVENTIONS
The following units provide interventions that address the issues described here:

Unit 1: Entering Motherhood

Unit 2: Connecting With My Baby

Unit 3: Attachment

Unit 5: Honoring the Woman in Me

Unit 6: Making Space

ACTIONS
• Assist the woman in identifying and then discussing the various roles that are involved in motherhood
• Encourage expression of feelings, including worries and fears.
• Provide materials that illustrate the roles and responsibilities of a mother
• Explore how she expects to care for her baby
• Refer to counseling if denial or resistance persist

3.2.2
Issues related to lack of preparedness for taking on the mothering role: has unrealistic expectation, denies need for changes in her life, is unable to share ideas for how she will care for or raise baby.

GOALS
• Identify her fears or worries about becoming a mother
• Identify and discuss three things she believes are important in raising a child
• List three ways a baby might require her to make changes in her life

- Describe two things she intends to do to meet baby's needs without making any adjustments in her life (i.e. how she will feed the baby at night if she does not change her sleeping schedule)
- Explore who might be available to help her in meeting her baby's needs

SPECIFIC INTERVENTIONS
The following units provide interventions that address the issues described here:

Unit 1: Entering Motherhood

Unit 2: Connecting With My Baby

Unit 3: Attachment

Unit 5: Honoring the Woman in Me

Unit 6: Making Space

Unit 7: Enhancing My Baby's Brain

ACTIONS
- Encourage expression of feelings, including worries and fears
- Assess knowledge base woman has in terms of caring for and raising a child
- Educate and discuss different ways of raising children and rationale behind these choices
- Encourage thought about how babies impact their parents' lives
- Reality test the woman's predictions the baby will have little or no impact on her life
- Assist woman to make a realistic evaluation and plan on the impact babies have on parents' lives
- Reality test how woman will balance her needs with baby needs
- Assist in making a plan on how to meet baby's needs and woman's needs in the most appropriate way, as well as how to prioritize the needs of each

3.3 IMAGES OF HOW THIS BABY WILL CHANGE DAILY LIFE

ISSUES TO BE ASSESSED
- Plans for initial weeks after the birth of the child
- Ideas on how bonding might progress
- Plan on how she will feed baby
- Plans for daycare
- Plans for returning to work or school
- Ways she might get emotional support

SIGNIFICANCE
- It is important to get an idea about how the woman views the impact of this child on her life and how she has prepared for this impact.
- Does the woman take bonding for granted, does she feel it will be automatic, is she concerned about bonding or attachment issues?

- Does the woman feel the baby will quickly adapt to the mother's schedule so she can return to her pre-baby life, or does she anticipate the changes she will need to make and that her life will be forever changed?

TYPICAL QUESTIONS
- How do you plan to handle those first few weeks after the baby is born? Will you have any help at home?
- How do you think it will be to see your baby for the first time? Have you thought about how you will show your baby you love him or her? What do you think you will do to become close to your baby? Do you think this will be easy or difficult? How do you think it will go for you?
- How will it be to establish a relationship with your baby?
- How will you be feeding your baby? (Breast, bottle, combination)
- Are you planning to use day care at some point? What age do you think you will start?
- When will you be returning to work/school?
- Who will be there to give you "pep talks"? Who will be there to help you with being a mother 24 hours a day?

3.3.1
Issues of unpreparedness for baby: no home preparations, no feeding plan, has not purchased baby items, no place for baby to sleep, no plan on how to support baby, no plan on who will care for baby when mom has to return to work or school.

GOALS
- Begin to acquire items necessary for baby, such as crib or cradle, diapers, clothing, etc.
- Enroll and participate in a baby care class
- Ensure that adequate supplies are available
- Identify a place where baby will sleep that is safe and protected
- Explore feeding options and think about what is right for both mother and baby
- Discuss her care plans for the baby
- Become educated in infant CPR

SPECIFIC INTERVENTIONS
The following units provide interventions that address the issues described here:

Unit 1: Entering Motherhood
Unit 2: Connecting With My Baby
Unit 3: Attachment
Unit 5: Honoring the Woman in Me
Unit 6: Making Space

ACTIONS
- Assist in locating free or low cost supplies for those women with limited funds
- Encourage participation in a baby care class
- Explore options with woman as to where the baby could sleep that is safe and protected, and where she can monitor baby and get to baby quickly
- Provide information on feeding alternatives
- Make referrals as necessary for feeding issues, WIC, group support, use of a doula, or counseling
- Provide information and educate woman on the various things a baby needs in terms of items and personal care
- Assist woman in obtaining infant CPR certification

3.3.2

Issues of lack of concern for self: has not created a support system for self, denies baby will impact her.

GOALS
- Identify two people who could be called if help was needed once the baby is home
- Demonstrate knowledge of contact numbers for agencies and individuals who can offer assistance as needed
- Demonstrate a working plan on who to call and where to go when there is an emergency situation that threatens the baby
- Establish procedures in case of emergency
- Develop a plan on obtaining available help for the transition into the home with the baby

SPECIFIC INTERVENTIONS
The following units provide interventions that address the issues described here:

Unit 1: Entering Motherhood

Unit 2: Connecting With My Baby

Unit 3: Attachment

Unit 4: Relaxation and Well-Being

Unit 5: Honoring the Woman in Me

Unit 6: Making Space

Unit 7: Enhancing My Baby's Brain

ACTIONS
- Assist the woman in identifying persons in her community, church, neighborhood, school, place of employment, etc., who could act as supports and emergency contacts

- Provide detailed referral source information, including phone numbers, addresses, and the name of a contact person
- Assist in creating an emergency plan that keeps both baby and mother safe

3.3.3
Issues of poor attitude concerning baby: attitude of indifference, negative or hostile attitudes about baby, refusal to consider bonding or developing a relationship with her baby.

GOALS
- Discuss feelings for baby
- Identify three things babies depend on their mothers for; explore how she will provide these things
- Discuss the concept of bonding with her baby
- List five things that help to promote healthy bonding and attachment between mother and child
- Engage in counseling if problems persist

SPECIFIC INTERVENTIONS
The following units provide interventions that address the issues described here:

Unit 1: Entering Motherhood

Unit 2: Connecting With My Baby

Unit 3: Attachment

Unit 4: Relaxation and Well-Being

Unit 5: Honoring the Woman in Me

Unit 6: Making Space

Unit 7: Enhancing My Baby's Brain

ACTIONS
- Make referrals for group support or counseling, as needed
- Provide education and information on healthy bonding and attachment between mother and child
- Educate on the things that help promote a better relationship

Chapter 10

Points To Remember

This chapter simply provides you with several tools—identified problems, goals, actions, and interventions—that you can use to prepare the plan of treatment most appropriate for the clients with whom you work. It is the combination of these tools, your creativity, and your understanding of your client that completes the formula for an appropriate intervention. There are several things to remember:

- This chapter provides only a starting list of problems, goals, actions, and interventions—no matter how complete the list, there will be always be others completely different than anything here or with their own unique twist.

- Use your creativity and flexibility—fit the intervention plan to your client, not your client to your intervention plan!

- Choose as few as one or as many as three goals to work on at any given time, depending on your client's needs, wants, and abilities.

- Safety first—always prioritize goals regarding the safety of your client at the top of the list! If your mind is focused on staying safe and secure there will be little energy left to deal with feelings and relating to others.

- Choose goals based on what your client wants to work on but also choose goals based on what you see your client really needs to deal with. While a client-based practice can be helpful and effective, it is also important to address issues that are uncomfortable, that have been ignored, or that have been kept secret. Your client may need your direction and gentle guidance to delve into these issues—rather than collusion to keep them alive but unaddressed.

Section III

Pregnancy Interventions

Using These Interventions

This section contains 56 interventions designed to support the pregnant woman's mental health, maternal role attainment, and her course of connecting and relating to her baby. The interventions are grouped into seven units, which include *Entering Motherhood, Connecting With My Baby, Attachment, Relaxation and Well-Being, Honoring the Woman in Me, Making Space, and Enhancing My Baby's Brain and Development*. Within each of these units are eight different interventions. These interventions were developed to be as basic as possible and to allow the interventionist to style the interventions for the particular pregnant woman or population being served. To achieve this end, we used the factors listed below:

Time Required

Each intervention was designed to be completed or introduced within a time frame of fifteen minutes to an hour. Some interventions can easily be completed during an office or home visit.

Other interventions depend on the follow-through of the pregnant woman. Some can be divided over several sessions.

Level of Complexity

These interventions vary in terms of the level of simplicity or complexity. In our work with different populations, we have found that some women do better with simple, straightforward interventions with one or two steps. They do not want anything that calls upon them to complete more "work" over a number of hours or days. On the other end of the continuum are the women with advanced skills and a wealth of motivation. These women seem to thrive on doing intervention after intervention, they seem to prefer complexity, and they have a high degree of self-determination that supports their need to learn more and more. Most women fall somewhere in the middle. For this reason, some interventions have been designed to be simple and straightforward, while other interventions require the women to think about the intervention and complete work over specific time periods. The latter interventions tend to be more complex and will tap into more self-examination.

Level of Intimacy

As with the levels of complexity, these interventions reflect varying levels of intimacy. Some interventions are designed to be supportive only, while others ask the woman to think about and discuss personal issues. A final group of interventions asks the woman to delve into her emotions, her intimate behaviors, and her personal relationships. A woman's comfort with intimacy is often part of her personality; however, it can also be mediated by her comfort and trust with the interventionist, the significance of the subject to her, her motivation for personal examination and growth, and her feelings of self-worth and well-being on any particular day.

Point in Pregnancy

The majority of these interventions are designed to be done at any point in pregnancy. The exceptions would include certain interventions that can only occur with specific conditions of pregnancy. For example, an intervention dealing with the movement of the unborn child would not work early in pregnancy before the baby's movement can be felt and would not easily work later in pregnancy as the baby's movement slows down in the weeks before birth.

Cultural Variations

In our work with clinics and early intervention programs, we have seen a great number of different cultures served. In some communities, there were as many as fifteen languages spoken within the same program catchment area. Trying to tailor each intervention to the infinite number of cultures that exist would prove impossible. Instead, we decided that the interventionists know their communities and cultures better than anyone else and would know how to do the tailoring needed to make the interventions appropriate for the women they serve. The one culture that was kept in mind as these interventions were written was the culture of poverty that is often shared by many early intervention programs (living in poverty often serves as the criterion for entrance into programs). Our research with women in poverty and other high-risk situations helped guide the format and levels of complexity of the interventions. In summary, it will be important for you to keep in mind that the content in these interventions was written from a white middle class perspective and will require personalization for the clients you work with based on culture, geographic area, level of income, language spoken, and individual belief systems.

Number of Interventions

There are 56 different interventions listed throughout the following units. It is not expected that any pregnant woman would be able to complete all of the possible interventions nor would it be expected that the interventions chosen for one woman would be the same interventions needed by another woman. The number of interventions and their variety make it possible for you to tailor a specific set of appropriate interventions for the pregnant woman or group with whom you may be working. You know your clients better than anyone else; you know what they need to learn, what they have the capacity to do, what scares them away, what they need to be successful, what their weaknesses and strengths are, and what they want. You will need to decide, based on your knowledge of your clients and on the assessments you make, which interventions would be best.

Sequencing the Interventions

To make these interventions as useful and universal as possible, no defined sequencing was designed into the interventions. This was done for several reasons:

1. You may begin working with women at different points in pregnancy.

2. Women's abilities and skills will differ in terms of what they may or may not be able to do or tolerate.

3. There are no guarantees how many visits you will get with particular women.

4. Women's needs differ depending on their circumstances and individual make-up, which cannot be reflected in a prescribed sequence or set of interventions.

Repetition

As you go through the interventions, you will notice that there is some crossover and repetition of content and themes. This is important for two reasons. First, repetition is one of the best learning strategies. It can be especially effective if the repetition of information occurs through various avenues. Second, the content and themes naturally cross over. Many of the interventions could be included in a number of areas. This flexibility allows specific information to be introduced in a variety of ways. For example, a pregnant woman may feel very comfortable dealing with a specific issue when it falls under the area of relaxation but may be fearful and apprehensive of dealing with the same issue when it is considered a step toward connecting with her baby. The crossover and repetition allow for more flexibility in how you design the intervention schedule best for the pregnant women you work with.

Individual Versus Group

All of these interventions are written based on working with an individual client. However, all interventions can easily be adapted for work with a group. The appropriateness of an intervention for a group format will need to be determined by the group leader(s). Many things need to be considered:

1. The balance of personalities in the group—the blend of talkative, outgoing individuals and quiet, more reserved individuals.

2. How advanced in her pregnancy each woman is—you want some commonality between women so they can easily share personal experiences, but you also want diversity of experience so they can learn different things from each other.

3. The motivation of the group members—a balance of those who want to be there, those who are willing to give it a try, and those who need to or are mandated to be there (due to court order, etc.)

4. The trust they have with each other—a level of trust and respect for each other must be developed to make the group work.

5. Their ability to take risks sharing personal information with each other—the development of a feeling that people will not be judged by each other or the group leaders for their feelings and thoughts.

Other factors such as the length of time the group runs, the number of members, and the budget you have to work with, are also important.

Level of Knowledge

The interventions were designed to be used with individuals who have a basic level of knowledge about pregnancy. In reality, women will vary greatly in their knowledge and experience related to pregnancy. This fact needs to be taken into consideration, as these interventions are being chosen and used. There are five main questions you need to be asking to choose and complete the appropriate interventions for each individual pregnant woman. These include:

- What does this woman already know about pregnancy?

- What does this woman already know about this specific topic area and/or this intervention?

- What are the past experiences of this woman with respect to pregnancy and this particular intervention?

- What does this woman want to work on or know?

- What does this woman need to work on or know?

It will be important that you assess each of these questions with respect to each individual client. Being respectful of what they do know and what they can share and contribute is extremely helpful in maintaining openness for learning new information, ideas, or interventions.

Focus on Pregnancy

There is no direct link to an intervention for every issue that can be extracted from the assessment and intervention planning for any particular woman. Such a book would have been overwhelming. The interventions listed in this book are designed to target issues related to mental well-being during pregnancy, taking on the maternal role, and supporting that connection and beginning relationship with the baby. Other mental health issues, specific individual needs, physical issues, safety, and other specific issues need to be taken in consideration when choosing the interventions for a particular pregnant woman. Issues not related to the focus of this program need to be dealt with directly through the use of other written materials, referrals, and available supportive programs.

Materials Required

The materials required for any particular intervention vary, but they generally include paper, worksheets, and materials for writing or drawing. Camera-ready worksheets that can be copied are a component of this program. You are encouraged to be creative, design your own worksheets, or have the pregnant women you work with design what may work best for them. A few interventions require special items like a stethoscope for listening to the baby's heart tones, but the need for special items was kept to a minimum. Appendix C lists where to find these special items.

Introducing the Interventions

Each intervention begins with a section called "About the Intervention." This section explains the background and importance of the intervention. If you are comfortable with that guidance, use your own words to start the exercise. If you need more help getting started, use the suggested script that follows in the section that follows, "Introducing This Intervention." As you and the mothers-to-be become more at ease with the exercises, you can switch from the suggested script to the natural give-and-take of your conversation.

Including Others

While these interventions were designed for the pregnant woman, some can easily be adapted to include spouses, the woman's parents, or even her friends. Encourage the pregnant woman to include others if she wishes, but insist that inclusion means supporting and participating, not just observing. Some women have spouses or supportive partners; some are single and alone—the variations are many. This should be a factor in the interventions you choose for the women with whom you work.

Summary

The interventions provided in the following units are a beginning to the program you choose to develop with the women with whom you are working. You will know the individuals you work with better than anyone else, so you should decide what will work best for them. Begin by asking the women what they think they need to work on or what they think will benefit them most. Assess the women you are working with. Although they may have ideas on what they need, they may not be objective about their needs. You may see things they don't. You may understand an issue better. This allows you to discover areas where they could use some support and an intervention that may lead to a more satisfying pregnancy and a better start to their relationship with their babies.

Think about the budget you have to work with, the time you have with each woman, the point in pregnancy, the cultural issues, your level of creativity, the level of trust you have developed with each woman, and the woman's individual abilities with regard to reading, motivation, emotional vulnerability, and sense of fun and adventure. You are the expert.

For those of you who want a suggested set of interventions to work from, we have included a set for working with the individual and a set for working with a group in Appendix D and E. Because we do not know the infinite number of variations represented by the populations you serve, we based these suggested sets on basic knowledge. If you choose to use these sets, adjust them to the specific needs of your individual or group. In addition, Appendix F contains some specific information helpful in organizing and running group interventions.

List of Intervention Units and Pregnancy Interventions

"Trust yourself. You know more than you think you do."

DR. BENJAMIN SPOCK

Unit 1

Entering Motherhood

KEY CONCEPT

Maternal role attainment has been identified as a significant step in the transition from being a woman without a child to a woman with a child. Understanding what the maternal role involves, and the expectations and responsibilities that role brings with it, helps to support the woman in her transition to being the mother of a child.

OUTCOME GOAL

The mother-to-be will be able to discuss the various roles that come with the transition into motherhood.

EXERCISES

1. Other Mothers

2. Parenting Observation

3. Motherhood Myths

4. The Many Hats of Motherhood

5. Balancing Needs—Mother's and Baby's

6. Mother Interview

7. Celebrating the Transition

8. Taking the Good (no worksheet/handout)

INTERVENTION 1

Other Mothers

TASK
To explore different mothers, what they do, how they do it, what is good, and what changes might be needed.

OPTIONAL MATERIALS
VCR, video clips or movie

REFERENCE
Chapter 3

ABOUT THIS INTERVENTION
Every woman approaches motherhood in her own unique way. Some mothers integrate motherhood and career, others transition leaving their careers behind them and focus solely on mothering, some are taken by surprise by motherhood, and other have spent years preparing themselves to be mothers. Each woman has had her own unique experiences with mothering. Some have babysat, some have been the older sister, some have had no opportunities to practice caring for children, and some have purposely avoided any situation where young children might be dependent on them. Some women have had great mothers themselves while others have struggled to find one person to fulfill that role in their life. Many children grow up promising themselves never to repeat certain things their own mothers did with them; others try their hardest to be like their mothers. Each woman needs to find her own way to mothering. In this intervention, different mothers and different mothering behaviors will be explored.

INTRODUCING THIS INTERVENTION
All mothers are different. They have different strengths and challenges. For instance, a woman who stays home with her baby may have more time with her baby. However, she may have less money to spend on things for her baby or she may feel cooped up and begin to miss adult conversation and activities. On the other hand, a woman who works outside the home may feel guilty or cheated about missing her baby's first word or first step or other first achievement. There is no ideal situation, so every mother has to figure out how she can make the best life for herself and her baby.

One way to do this is to learn from the successes and problems of other mothers. Think of all the women you know—your mother, other family members, neighbors, friends, women at school and work, women in stores, offices, banks, and doctors' offices. How many of them are mothers? Have you seen them with their children or talked to them about how they deal with children? Let's list them.

(If you don't get enough response at this point, focus on media moms. It may be easier for some women to relate to this intervention using media moms because it's less personal and threatening if they criticize how such a mom handled a situation and suggest a way to handle it better.)

What TV shows do you like to watch? Have you seen any movies lately? Read any books with women as leading characters? How many of the women in those shows, movies, or books are mothers? Let's list them.

(The list of media moms can be a starting point, but TV shows come and go. It's very easy for the list to become outdated when shows go off the air. You may need to update the list each year as shows or your clients' viewing preferences change.)

INTERVENTION
(choose one or more of the interventions listed below)

1. Share and discuss the Media Mom Examples handout. Have your client or group add to this list.

2. Use the Media Moms worksheet to explore some of the different mothers your client(s) have observed, what they liked about them, and what they disliked.

3. Choose one particular mother, either from the examples provided or one your client knows, to explore further using the Media Moms Discussion Questions.

OPTIONS
- Rent a movie or tape a particular TV show and watch it with your mother-to-be, using this as a format to discuss the positive and negative pieces of mothering observed.
- In a group format, use video clips (tape them from TV or rent a movie) to generate discussion about mothering roles, differences, positives, and negatives. You may also have each participant bring in a scenario and media example to share with the class for discussion and critique.

Media Mom Examples

TELEVISION SHOWS
Alice
All My Children
Any Day Now
Bewitched
Boy Meets World
Brady Bunch
Cagney and Lacey
Cosby Show
Dawson's Creek
Days of Our Lives
Dharma and Greg
ER
Geena Davis Show
General Hospital
Gilmore Girls
Golden Girls
Happy Days
Home Improvement
Hughleys
I Love Lucy
Jeffersons
Judging Amy
Julia Show
Leave it to Beaver
Little House on the Prairie
Lizzie McGuire
Mad About You
Malcom in the Middle
Married...With Children
Murphy Brown
Partridge Family
Roseanne Show
Roswell
Seventh Heaven
State of Grace
Strong Medicine
The Division
Third Watch

Touched by an Angel
Wonder Years

CARTOONS
Arthur
Flintstones
Jetsons
Little Bear
Rugrats
Simpsons
Thornberrys

MOVIES
A Home of Our Own
Beetlejuice
Denise the Menace
Erin Brokovich
Freaky Friday
Fried Green Tomatoes
Good Mother
Home Alone
Hook
Kramer vs. Kramer
Little Women
Lorenzo's Oil
Mary Poppins
Meet the Parents
Mr. Mom
National Velvet
Old Yeller
One True Thing
Parent Trap
Postcards from the Edge
Something to Talk About
Sophie's Choice
Sound of Music
Steel Magnolias
The Client
The Stepmother
When a Man Loves a Woman
Yours, Mine, and Ours

Media Moms

Next to the TV shows or movies you have listed, write down what you like and/or dislike about these women as mothers.

MOTHERS YOU KNOW

Like   Dislike

TV SHOW MOTHERS

Like   Dislike

MOVIE MOTHERS

Like   Dislike

MOTHERS IN BOOKS

Like   Dislike

Media Moms Discussion Questions

Choose one of the mothers from your list and write down your responses to the following questions.

• What did you like about this mom?

• What didn't you like about this mom?

• If you were the mother in that particular situation (situation she might have described or that you watched together), how might you have handled things differently?

• What kind of things do you think are important in a mother?

• What kind of things do you think mothers should never do? Are there any exceptions you can think of?

• Many times our past, what we have seen or experienced, can have an impact on what we choose to do in the present. How do you see your experiences, or what you have observed, affecting how you mother your child?

INTERVENTION 2

Parenting Observation

TASK
To compare different mothers, what they do, how they do it, what is good, and what changes might be needed.

REFERENCE
Chapter 3

ABOUT THIS INTERVENTION
Each mother is equipped with her own unique strengths and faced with her own set of challenges. Every woman is different, just as every mother is different. Watching mothers with their children in various situations helps us to look at different ways of mothering from different perspectives. We gain new ideas and insights when we watch mothers interacting with their children in daycares, playgrounds, churches, grocery stores, or restaurants. In this intervention, the focus will be on observing mothers from these different perspectives.

INTRODUCING THIS INTERVENTION
(Let the mother-to-be or group know about this intervention the session before you do it so plans can be made for the outing.)

We've talked about ways mothers can plan for how to treat their babies. Now let's look at moms and caregivers in public situations to learn of the challenges you may face and consider ways to deal successfully with those challenges. There are lots of possibilities—neighborhood parks or playgrounds, coffee houses, libraries, swimming pools, stores, malls, daycare centers, doctors' waiting rooms, churches, and restaurants. Do you have a favorite place to watch mothers and babies? Let's arrange where we'll go next time to observe how mothers deal with their babies.

(When you get to your observation site, tell the mother-to-be to write notes about what both the mother and baby do.)

All mothers and babies are different. A mother who can put her baby down for a nap at home faces a different challenge when she's shopping on the way home from work and daycare and her baby is tired, fussy, wet, and hungry. If you look at mothers in different situations, you can compare their ways of handling their babies, get tips for being a good mother to your baby, and decide what you don't want to do to your baby. Let's watch, take notes, and later discuss what we see.

(If this is helpful, you could have mothers-to-be make observations on their own between future sessions and discuss their notes.)

INTERVENTION

1. Either in a group or on an individual basis, make a plan to go to a park or playground to observe mothers and children (these areas tend to have older children and mothers. You may also want to find some places in your community to observe younger babies and mothers. In Seattle this often means coffee houses!) Have mothers-to-be record their observations on a pad of paper.

   You can vary this intervention by having the group all watch the same mother and child and then compare their observations and thoughts, or have each mother-to-be observe different mothers and children.

2. Following the observation, you may use the Observing Mothers and Children worksheet to help process what was observed and to facilitate discussion of what was observed.

Observing Mothers and Children

Think about what you observed between one mother and child and write down your responses to the questions below.

• What did the mother or caregiver do well in caring for this child?

• What did the mother or caregiver seem to have difficulty with?

• How did the child respond to the mother or caregiver?

• How would you have handled parenting this child in this situation?

• What would you have done the same as the mother or caregiver you are watching? Why?

• What would you have done differently? Why?

• How often did the mother or caregiver make eye contact with the baby?

• Do you think she was really aware of what the baby needed or wanted?

• If the baby was upset at all, how did the mother or caregiver soothe the baby or child? Do you think she did a good job? How did the baby respond?

• What kinds of things did the mother or caregiver do to play with the baby? Do you think this was a good idea? How did the baby respond?

• Did the mother or caregiver ever get frustrated? How did she handle it? What might have been a better way of handling the situation?

• Other observations you made:

INTERVENTION 3

Motherhood Myths

TASK
To explore different beliefs about motherhood.

REFERENCE
Chapters 1, 3

ABOUT THIS INTERVENTION
There are many beliefs about motherhood that have been created over hundreds of years. Some of these were based on superstition, others were created to make mothers behave in a certain way, some were created as a way to protect babies from things that had happened to others in the past, and still others have just become family honored ideas that have been passed down over generations. While some beliefs are based on fact, others are just myths. Becoming a mother means considering different beliefs and myths seriously and evaluating their truthfulness and accuracy.

INTRODUCING THIS INTERVENTION
Most of us have picked up ideas about what a good mother should be or do. It may be that we were raised with those ideas in our families, we picked them up from people around us, or that others imposed the ideas on us. Some of these beliefs about mothers are superstitions—"Stand on your head after intercourse if you want a boy baby." Some were created to make mothers behave in certain ways—"If you work outside the home, your baby will suffer." Some were created to protect babies from things that happened to others in the past—"Lock the door to the laundry chute so your toddler won't fall into the basement."

When you become a mother, it helps to know which beliefs are true and apply to you and which are myths and don't have to be followed. If you have to work outside the home after your baby is born, it helps to know your baby won't be permanently damaged if the baby is left with a responsible, caring adult. Here is a questionnaire with things some people believe about motherhood. Decide whether you think each statement is true or false.

INTERVENTION
1. Discuss with the mother-to-be or the group what beliefs they might have heard from their parents or others about being a mother or a parent.

2. Have each mother complete the Motherhood Myths worksheet.

3. Once the questionnaire is completed, hand out the answer sheet with answers and explanations.

4. Discuss each myth, encouraging ideas and conversation around each item using the following questions
   • Have you ever heard this idea before?
   • Where or who did you hear it from?
   • What do you think about it?
   • What do you think about the explanation provided for each item? (Go over each individually)

5. This questionnaire can always be divided between two meetings or revisited throughout the course of the pregnancy. Also, if the mother-to-be has difficulty reading or is resistant to completing a form, questions can be read and discussed.

Motherhood Myths

Please answer true or false for each item.

1. _____ Mothers always know why their babies cry.

2. _____ Mothers sometimes feel frustrated with their infants.

3. _____ Mothers always need to handle all baby care themselves.

4. _____ Babies can do much more than eat, sleep, and cry the first three months of life.

5. _____ Breastfeeding is the only type of feeding that provides the baby with both the necessary nutrition and interaction needed for healthy development.

6. _____ Mothers should be with their infants 24 hours a day the first three months.

7. _____ Mothers have to be perfect or their children will grow up to hate them.

8. _____ Mothers get three coffee breaks a day.

9. _____ Mothers have to pick up their crying babies immediately, even if those mothers are in the middle of going to the bathroom.

10. _____ Even at birth, babies can be very different; they each have a personality of their own.

11. _____ All mothers automatically "love" their babies the first time they see them.

12. _____ Mothers never feel sorry for themselves.

13. _____ Babies can cry for many reasons, not just when they are hungry or wet.

14. _____ All babies have the ability to recognize their mother's face immediately.

15. _____ All babies cooperate with their mothers, if the mother is doing everything right.

16. _____ Mothers sometimes wonder if having a baby was a good idea.

17. _____ Many mothers fantasize about what it used to be like without children.

18. _____ No matter how much a mother loves her baby, it can still feel like caring for them is hard work.

19. _____ Feeling depressed after having a new baby can be part of the normal adjustment to motherhood.

20. _____ If a mother and baby are separated the first few hours after the baby's delivery, the bond between that mother and child will be broken forever.

Motherhood Myths Answer Sheet

1.__F__   Mothers always know why their babies cry.

False. Crying occurs for a variety of reasons, including hunger, discomfort, colic, sleepiness, fear, a need to be physically close to mom, etc. While many times a mother can easily figure out what the crying means and how to soothe her crying infant, there are times when no one can figure out what is behind the tears of an infant.

2.__T__   Mothers sometimes feel frustrated with their infants.

True. All mothers get irritated or frustrated with their child's behavior at times, even the behavior of an infant. They also become overwhelmed and frustrated with being a mother sometimes. Mothers need to learn healthy ways to deal with these feelings so they can express these tough feelings without taking them out on the child. Mothers who take good care of themselves and learn to decrease the stress generally seem to be more successful at dealing with tough feelings. These mothers also become good role models for their babies and children on how to deal with tough feelings.

3.__F__   Mothers always need to handle all baby care themselves.

False. In many countries, care for a new baby is shared with certain family members. It is taken for granted that a new mother needs help adjusting to her new role. Besides the adjustment, mothers sometimes need a little mothering themselves. It is important to plan on needing, and to ASK for, help from others.

4.__T__   Babies can do much more than eat, sleep, and cry the first three months of life.

True. Babies are very active in the first three months of life. They begin to listen for and track familiar voices, they figure out who their mom is and who their dad is, they track objects, they begin to smile, and they develop patterns of behavior and interaction with others.

5.__F__   Breast feeding is the only type of feeding that provides the baby with both the necessary nutrition and interaction needed for healthy development.

False. Breastfeeding is the preferred way of feeding for many reasons, including closeness to the mother and the health benefits of the mother's milk for the baby. It is not, however, the only choice. Feeding a baby with a bottle filled with pumped breast milk or formula can be nutritionally healthy for the baby and can also still lead to balanced, secure relationships between mother and child. Mothers should not feel guilty for choosing bottle-feeding over breast-feeding. They should, however, give it a lot of thought and discuss it with their health care professionals.

6. _F_   Mothers should be with their infants 24 hours a day the first three months.

False. Being with anyone 24 hours a day for a long period of time can be a trying experience. Mothers need a break, too! It is perfectly okay to leave your baby with a trusted adult while you take a walk or go to the store.

7. _F_   Mothers have to be perfect or their children will grow up to hate them.

False. No mother could ever be perfect and many, many children grow up to admire and love their parents despite the faults they may have. All mothers make mistakes. The most important thing is to recognize your mistakes, correct the problem, and learn what not to do as well as what might work better in the future.

8. _F_   Mothers get three coffee breaks a day.

False. While mothers should take frequent rest breaks while adjusting to a new infant, it often seems like there is never enough tine. It is important to fit in little naps and quiet times whenever possible, like when baby is sleeping. Housework can always wait!

9. _F_   Mothers have to pick up their crying babies immediately, even if those mothers are in the middle of going to the bathroom.

False. A good rule of thumb is to always respond to your baby within 15 seconds of his signaling you with his cry. This can be picking him up or it could be a verbal response. Sometimes you do have to let a baby cry, however. If you are in the middle of doing something, such as using the bathroom or showering, as long as your baby is in a safe place, like his crib, it would be okay to let them cry occasionally. As your child gets older, he may need to cry a little before he can put himself to sleep. Over time, mothers begin to know which cries they need to respond to quickly and which can wait a little.

10. _T_   Even at birth, babies can be very different; they each have a personality of their own.

True. Each child is born with a unique set of qualities and personality features. No two are the same, even within the same family.

11. _F_   All mothers automatically "love" their babies the first time they see them.

False. Any relationship is a process and each mother and baby is different. Some mothers report falling in love with their babies during pregnancy, some at birth, and others say it took several weeks or months. All of these experiences are normal.

12. _F_ Mothers never feel sorry for themselves.

False. All mothers feel sorry for themselves at times, no matter how much they wanted to be a mother or how much they love their babies. Mothering is a hard job. It is important to talk about those feelings with someone you trust. If you feel these feelings are interfering with the way you take care of yourself and your baby, talk to someone who can provide you the proper help, such as your health care professional.

13. _T_ Babies can cry for many reasons, not just when they are hungry or wet.

True. Babies cry for a number of reasons, such as just needing to be near you, becoming frightened, hunger, discomfort, when waking up, when in pain, when their diapers are wet, when they are tired, or for many other reasons. As you and your child get to know each other, you will be able to figure out that cries can sound different and mean different things.

14. _F_ All babies have the ability to recognize their mother's face immediately.

False. Babies begin to recognize their mothers at birth as their different senses develop and mature. Babies can often know their mothers' smells, especially the smell of her breast milk, shortly after birth. They may also be able to know her voice shortly after birth. As their vision becomes clearer, they soon learn their mothers' face on sight. So, many babies can recognize their mothers shortly after birth through their senses of smell or hearing, but until their vision matures they cannot usually know their mothers' faces.

15. _F_ All babies cooperate with their mothers, if the mother is doing everything right.

False. First, no mother can always do everything right, no matter how hard she tries. Second, no child ever cooperates all the time no matter how old they are. Mothers and babies are always learning from each other. They have good days and difficult days. All mothers experience bumps in the road when dealing with their babies.

16. _T_ Mothers sometimes wonder if having a baby was a good idea.

True. Many mothers report questioning their decisions and their new job as a mother. Thinking about the changes you have gone through in going from woman without child to woman with child is normal and natural. If these feelings become overwhelming or if they begin to interfere with taking care of yourself or your baby, talk to someone about them.

17. _T_ Many mothers fantasize about what it used to be like without children.

True. Any change involves fantasizing about what things used to be like before the change. Fantasies are a good way to work out feelings and thoughts in a safe way. Many mothers fantasize about the days when they did not have children.

18. __T__   No matter how much a mother loves her baby, it can still feel like caring for them is hard work.

True. Mothering is hard work no matter how much you love your child. It is not only okay to acknowledge this hard work but it is important to give yourself credit for doing the hard work.

19. __T__   Feeling depressed after having a new baby can be part of the normal adjustment to motherhood.

True. Depression after having a baby is very common. Many, many mothers feel depressed, sad, hopeless, or "blue." While it may be normal, it is still important to talk to someone about these feelings. While some depression right after childbirth is okay, depression that lasts more than a couple of weeks is often more serious. It is called postpartum depression and can be helped through therapy, group participation, or, sometimes, medication. No one has to suffer alone with feelings of depression.

20. __F__   If a mother and baby are separated the first few hours after the baby's delivery, the bond between that mother and child will be broken forever.

False. While having mother and baby together the first few hours after birth can be a wonderful experience for both the mother and the baby, it does not guarantee a strong and secure bond between that mother and baby. Mothers and babies may need specific medical treatments right after delivery, mothers may have had to have sleep medication during the pregnancy and may not be awake right after delivery, and some mothers, such as adoptive mothers, do not have that experience of being with their baby right after birth. Still, many of these mothers develop strong, secure, positive bonds with their babies. Bonding between mother and child is a process. This relationship will grow and strengthen over time; there are no magic moments.

INTERVENTION 4

The Many Hats of Motherhood

TASK
To explore the different roles a woman has to take on when she becomes a mother.

OPTIONAL MATERIALS
Art supplies for optional art interventions

REFERENCE
Chapters 2, 3

ABOUT THIS INTERVENTION
Becoming a mother means having to wear many different hats when caring for and raising a child. In addition, mothers must also take care of themselves and nurture the woman within them. Finding balance between these roles is important and leads to a more relaxed relationship between mother and child. It is also important to acknowledge all of the ways in which a woman mothers her child.

INTRODUCING THIS INTERVENTION
A mother plays many roles and wears many hats that women who aren't mothers don't play or wear. For instance, if you nurse your baby, you're its main source of food. Mothers can also share roles with other caregivers—changing the baby, protecting the baby from danger, cuddling the baby. In addition to all these roles, you have to take care of yourself. If you become too tired, you can't properly care for your baby or yourself.

This means you have to find a balance between your current roles, your need to care for yourself, and the baby's need for care. When you can find a workable balance, you'll be more relaxed with your many roles. This will lead to a better, more relaxed relationship with your baby. What are some of the roles you can think of that you'll have to play when you start caring for your baby?

INTERVENTION

1. Hand out the Many Hats of Motherhood worksheet.

2. Discuss the many roles a woman takes on when she becomes a mother. (Use the information provided on the Many Hats of Motherhood Master Sheet and the following questions to help with the discussion).

   - What roles do you have now? Examples: wife, daughter, friend, lover, homemaker, employee, babysitter, grandchild, sister, etc.

   - How might these roles change when you become a mother?

   - How might others' expectations of you change when you become a mother?

   - Taking on new roles means changing or letting go of other roles. How might others feel about these changes? For example, as a wife, your role with your spouse will now include a baby. Sleep will change, your energy levels will change, and you will have a responsibility to take on mothering roles. How will you feel about the changes with your role as a wife? How will your husband or partner feel?

3. Revise the roles listed by adding roles a woman might need to take on and by noting roles that need to be altered.

4. An optional art intervention would include actually making hats out of paper plates (or another material). These hats can be decorated with things representing the many hats a woman wears once she becomes a mother.

The Many Hats of Motherhood

MOTHER AS PROTECTOR

- Safe from others
- Safe from household products
- Safe from health risks
- Safe from travel risks

MOTHER AS PROVIDER

- Gives nourishment
- Provides warm, safe place to sleep
- Makes home feel good
- Provides access to medical care
- Provides fresh air

MOTHER AS NURTURER

- Snuggles and cuddles
- Hugs and kisses
- Kisser of "boo-boos" and "owies"
- Nurturing self

MOTHER AS EDUCATOR

- Makes and teaches safety rules
- Teaches and models qualities of a good person
- Interacts to teach communication
- Models patience and understanding

MOTHER AS WOMAN

- Responsible to care for self
- Balances self needs with baby needs
- Nurtures self
- Doesn't judge self too harshly
- Maintains a sense of humor
- Conserves and prioritizes time and energy

MOTHER AS PILLAR OF STRENGTH

- Buffers intense emotions
- Soothes tears
- Provides security
- Helps to calm out-of-control feelings and crying

The Many Hats of Motherhood Master Sheet

MOTHER AS PROTECTOR

• Safe from others

• Safe from household products

• Safe from health risks

• Safe from travel risks

Mothers are responsible for keeping their children safe from dangers of any kind.

MOTHER AS PROVIDER

• Gives nourishment

• Provides warm, safe place to sleep

• Makes home feel good

• Provides access to medical care

• Provides fresh air

Mothers have the greatest responsibility in making sure their infants are provided for.

MOTHER AS NURTURER

• Snuggle and cuddle

• Hugs and kisses

• Kisser of "boo-boos" and "owies"

• Nurturing self

Nurturing is a way of sharing love, care, and worth from one person to another or to yourself. It helps to support good self-esteem and good relationships.

MOTHER AS EDUCATOR

• Makes and teaches safety rules

• Teaches and models qualities of a good person

• Interacts to teach communication

• Models patience and understanding

Mothers teach children through example, actions, words, and coaching. This process goes all through childhood.

MOTHER AS WOMAN

• Responsible to care for self

• Balances self needs with baby needs

• Nurtures self

• Doesn't judge self too harshly

• Maintains a sense of humor

• Conserves and prioritizes time and energy

Motherhood can be a wonderful part of being a woman. It should be celebrated. Mothers should never forget the powerful, sensual woman inside.

MOTHER AS PILLAR OF STRENGTH

• Buffers intense emotions

• Soothes tears

• Provides security

• Helps to calm out-of-control feelings and crying

Babies are not born with the ability to deal with intense emotions, positive or negative. This is a learned skill that comes from observation, practice, and growing up. Until children develop this ability mothers become the buffers or the holders for the intense feelings for their babies. The more mothers help sooth and calm their babies, the easier children learn to do it for themselves.

INTERVENTION 5

Balancing Needs—Mother's and Baby's

TASK
To explore ways of balancing needs through conserving energy, making time for both mother and baby.

REFERENCE
Chapters 2, 4

ABOUT THIS INTERVENTION
Every woman needs time to care for and nurture herself as well as her baby. Feeling cared for helps reduce stress and increase feelings of well-being over life's daily demands. A woman who is healthy and fit feels more confident and able to care for and provide for others. The difficulty is often balancing how to do the things we need to do for others with the things we need to do for ourselves. Different activitiess compete for our time. And, there never seems to be enough time in a day to do the things we think we should do. In this intervention, how to balance the demands of motherhood, the demands of daily life, and personal demands will be explored.

INTRODUCING THIS INTERVENTION
Your baby will add more activities to your daily schedule. If you don't plan now, you could be terribly overwhelmed by the new tasks. Let's look at your current schedule to see how you can change what you do to create extra time for yourself, not time to do more things for other people. When you're more refreshed yourself, you'll gain the energy to do more for others.

Many women are tired at the end of the day. Yet, that's when they have to cook their biggest meal for the family. Maybe they could prepare and freeze meals ahead of time to make the daily dinner preparation go faster. Do you have to make every bed every day? If you wash dishes by hand, can you let them dry in the rack instead of hand drying them? What other things can you think of to skip or combine and give you time for relaxing activities for yourself?

INTERVENTION
1. Using the following questions, discuss different ways one might conserve energy.
   - What could you do to save time?
   - How would you feel about leaving things, such as housework, undone for a few days?
   - What things would be rewarding for you, if you had time each day to do them? Examples might include reading a magazine, calling a friend, having a cup of tea, doing nothing, or listening to music.
2. Make a list of things you feel you need to do every day. Decide which are the most important, which you could leave out, and which might be altered to save you time. Use the worksheet to explore these tasks and set priorities.

3. Discuss what you might do with the 15-30 minutes you could save each day, such as take a bubble bath or read a book. Focus these interventions on what you could do for yourself, not anyone else.

4. Make a contract to try one or two days of conserving energy over the next week.

5. Report back the following week on how the days of conserving and balancing went. Troubleshoot as necessary.

Conserving Energy & Balancing Needs

DAILY THINGS TO DO	PRIORITY	CAN LEAVE OUT	CAN WAIT	CHANGES TO SAVE TIME

Things I could do for myself in 15 minutes:

Things I could do for myself in 20 minutes:

Contract

I promise to make changes in my daily activities on _____. I will keep a list of the time I save and I agree to use that time for myself. I plan to do _____ with my time.

Signed _____

INTERVENTION 6

Mother Interview

TASK
Learning from others' mothering experiences.

REFERENCE
Chapter 3

ABOUT THIS INTERVENTION
As with any other behavior or job, we can learn about mothering by thinking about others' experiences, successes, and mistakes as mothers. Opening up discussion with other mothers can facilitate a valuable learning experience as well as help to develop some supportive connections. It is important to think about mothering from many dimensions, including the things that are easy, those that are difficult, the things mothers liked best, and their biggest mistakes. All of these things can contribute to helping the mother-to-be begin to develop a more realistic picture of motherhood.

When people are hired for new jobs, the supervisor will often team them with a skilled worker who can offer advice and guidance. In the same way, women can learn more about the job of mothering when they talk to other skilled mothers. A lot can be learned from other women's experiences—such as what babies typically do at different ages. They can learn from their successes—how they helped baby learn to talk. But they can also learn from their mistakes, allowing them to avoid the same mistakes with their babies.

INTRODUCING THIS INTERVENTION
The more mothers you talk to, the more you can learn, and the more options you'll have when you and your baby face a "first." You'll learn that some things are easy with some babies and hard with others. You'll find what mothers find rewarding about motherhood. You'll learn about the problems you'll have to face. You'll hear about the joys and sorrows of motherhood. When things happen with your baby, you'll be able to think back on these conversations and know others have had similar experiences. You'll know you're not alone. These talks will help you form a more realistic picture of motherhood.

What mothers do you know and admire? List some of them. Which one could you talk to before our next session? Pick one or two. Here's an interview worksheet. Look it over. Are there any other questions you'd like to ask the mothers?

INTERVENTION
1. Have the mother(s)-to-be identify women they will interview so it can be agreed upon before the session is over. Deciding whom to interview is often the most difficult piece of the intervention. In a group session, you may want to enlist seasoned mothers within your staff or volunteers to be available to be interviewed. This intervention may also be given in the style of "home work," meaning it can be done over the week for the next session. For the individual client, giving her a week to interview someone will probably be necessary.

2. Have mothers review the questions in the Mother Interview Worksheet. Discuss any additional questions anyone wants included.

3. Once mother(s)-to-be have completed the interviews, review and discuss the responses using the following questions.

    -   Do you think this mother's experiences are common?
    -   How do you think it might be different or the same for you?
    -   Do you feel the mother you interviewed was a good mother? Why or why not?

4. A variation with clients who do not reliably complete homework assignments would be to use interview questions to think about "what do you think it will be like?"

Mother Interview Worksheet

Use the following questions to interview a mother you know. Write down her answers in the space below each question.

How long have you been a mother?

What is the best thing about being a mother?

What is the most difficult thing about being a mother?

What did you do with your child that was the same as your mother did with you?

What did you decide not to do with your child even though your mother or father did it with you?

Who gives you advice?

If the mother has more than one child, ask what kinds of changes happened when she had second (or third, etc.) baby?

If you had it to do all over again, what would you have done differently?

Other questions you asked:

INTERVENTION 7

Celebrating the Transition

TASK
Acknowledging and celebrating the transition from woman-without-child to woman-with-child.

OPTIONAL MATERIALS
Miscellaneous items based on type of celebration planned

REFERENCE
Chapter 2

ABOUT THIS INTERVENTION
Becoming a mother is a HUGE deal. It changes a woman's life forever. It is significant and important, and women need to celebrate this major turning point in their lives. We already have some rituals or celebrations, such as baby showers. However, these are often more focused on the baby than on the mother. It is important to honor women as they transition to "mother-women."

INTRODUCING THIS INTERVENTION
Lots of us as children looked forward to a birthday party to celebrate becoming one year older. Adults may have celebrated weddings, anniversaries, and other special events. Many people celebrate getting a new job or a new car. Some have a house-warming party when they get a new apartment or house. Having a new baby is bigger than any of these events. It will change your life forever.

How can you celebrate it? Baby showers focus on gifts for the baby. But, how about you? How can you celebrate your change from woman to mother? What will help you and mark this change in your life in a happy way?

INTERVENTION
1. Either individually or with a group, discuss the different ways important events are celebrated within different families, cultures, and communities. Make a list of these ideas.

2. Using the questions below discuss their feelings about the transition to motherhood.
   - How does it feel to know you are moving into a new phase in your life?
   - Do you think others know what a significant event it is for you?
   - How does celebrating make you feel?
   - What other important events in your life could (or do) you celebrate?

3. Discuss what kind of things could help celebrate the transition into motherhood. Use the worksheet to generate discussion about the type of celebration they would like.

4. Plan a celebration.

5. Celebrate!

Celebrations of Motherhood Worksheet

How do you want this celebration to be? (circle those you want)

Private	Open to others
With food	Without food
Inside	Outside
At home	Out in public
Simple	Elaborate
Daytime	Nighttime

List the people you want to invite.

What type of celebration might you like to have? (circle one or parts of many)

A graduation style celebration where certificates are handed out.

A banquet style celebration where favorite foods or comfort foods are shared.

An elegant style celebration where sparkling cider and candles decorate a fancy table and each person toasts the mother-to-be.

A symbolic celebration where each person attending brings a gift for you (not the baby) which will be helpful to you as a mother, such as a comic strip involving mothers to help you remember to use your sense of humor or a sprig of lavender to symbolize tranquility.

A strength giving celebration where each attendee brings something to give you extra strength and support throughout delivery, as you transition into motherhood. For example, each person could bring a bead or button that can be strung together as a bracelet for you to wear during delivery.

The gift of celebration for the mother-to-be, who is shy or resistant to celebrating her transition might be a bouquet of flowers with a congratulations card, an invitation to lunch at her favorite restaurant, or just a card praising her accomplishments.

What makes you happy?

What and who would make this celebration special for you?

INTERVENTION 8

Taking the Good

TASK
Making a conscious decision to take the good from your family of origin (or past) and leave the rest behind.

REFERENCE
Chapter 3

ABOUT THIS INTERVENTION
As with many of life's more difficult decisions, the things we need to think about in order to make those decisions are often painful. Even if a difficult memory or past trauma cannot be physically removed, symbolic ways to move on can be created. The first step is bringing the past into the present by talking about what happened or having the mother-to-be just think about the past. The mother-to-be does not have to completely share her past for this intervention to be successful. Using symbolic techniques, troubling issues and memories can often be released so they have less power over the mother-to-be's future relationship with her child.

INTRODUCING THIS INTERVENTION
When we think back on our years of growing up, we may have a mix of happy memories and hurtful memories. If we want our children to have some of those same happy memories, we need to think about what happened to cause that happiness and see if we can create similar experiences for them. If we don't want our children to have the same hurtful memories, we have to do a couple things: we have to think about the causes of those problems and ways we can keep that from happening to our children; we also have to free ourselves from the power of those hurts so they won't damage our relationships with our children.

INTERVENTION
1. Ask the mother(s)-to-be to think about and write down several things she liked or valued about her life growing up. Discuss which three she would most like to carry on into her relationship with her child.

2. Ask her to think about and write down several things she did not like or that were hurtful to her growing up. (If there is resistance to writing them down, encourage them to write one word. Only they will know what it means. Or they can hide their papers or just hold the thoughts in their minds.) Discuss which ones she wants to let go of or get rid of and not carry into her relation ship with her child, using a maximum of three.

   • How did it feel to get rid of some of those old issues from your past?

   • How can you use the desired pieces of your past to help guide your mothering?

   • What was hard about this exercise?

   • What was easy about it?

   Remind them that repeating this exercise with the same issues or with new issues can contribute to the mother's feelings of power and control over her life.

3. There are several ways the next step can be performed, depending on the woman or group. It is the symbolic action that is important. Use one of the following or come up with one of your own.

   a. Have each of the six things, events, or memories written on individual slips of paper. Have each mother take one of the negative things and tear it up into little pieces, throwing into a trash can or some other container. Do this with each unwanted thing as well. The unwanted things can be burned as the mother makes a wish or a statement that these things are in the past and no longer have power over her. The wanted things can be saved in a special box or pouch, or they can be mixed with soil into which a new plant is planted to help the desired things grow and carry on. The desired things can also be tied to a helium balloon and set free to symbolize carrying them into the future.

   b. Six sticks could be selected, each to represent one of the experiences or events. The mother-to-be could then break the sticks that represent the unwanted items. Then she could construct a symbolic triangle with the desired sticks to then hang in her home or in the baby's room; or she may want to create a special place in her garden or yard to hold the desired traits or events.

   c. This intervention could also be done with clay or play-dough where the desired three balls of clay are used together to construct a symbol the mother can keep (the best type medium is a clay that will dry solid and will not rot or decompose). The unwanted traits or events could be pounded with a hammer or with the hand.

Unit 1

Points to Remember

Entering motherhood is a major transition for women. It involves a great deal of preparation, changing (temporarily and permanently), evaluating, research, surrender, and forging forward. The interventions in this unit help to facilitate the work the pregnant woman engages in. Let us review these interventions:

- *Other Mothers* focuses on what other mothers do—what they do well and what they could do better. This intervention helps women to research what other women do and evaluate what they discover.

- *The Parenting Observation* intervention allows women to take the time to observe and make sense of how other women act in the role of a mother. Oftentimes mothering is taken for granted—it just happens, in this intervention women work to make sense of what they see.

- *Motherhood Myths* encourages a new understanding of the myths that often become easily accepted in our society. This intervention supports the idea that women need to challenge myths and old wives' tales, deciding for themselves what makes sense.

- *The Many Hats of Motherhood* is an intervention designed to examine the many, many hats worn by mothers today, and the many, many roles they take on.

- *Balancing Needs—Mother's and Baby's* allows women to begin thinking about how they will take care of themselves as well as their new baby. The addition of a new baby into a woman's life is always a major impact. However, the intensity of this impact can be lessened if she is able to continue to care for herself and find ways to meet her own needs as well as those of her baby.

- *The Mother Interview* provides a personal, one-to-one way of exploring what being a mother is all about for some women.

- *Celebrating the Transition* is an intervention designed to help women acknowledge the change occurring in their lives. Becoming a mother to a new baby is a HUGE deal and as women, we should honor each other as well as ourselves when this transition is made.

- *Taking the Good* is an intervention that reminds us we all have certain things from our past we want to take with us into the future just as we all have certain things we want to leave behind. Some cycles needs to be broken, while some cycles need to be nurtured and cherished. We can only make decisions about these issues when we have identified them and given them some serious thought.

"Having a baby is definitely a labor of love."

JOAN RIVERS

Unit 2

Connecting With My Baby

KEY CONCEPT

The first connections of a mother with her child generally begin during the pregnancy when the mother-to-be begins to acknowledge and connect with her fetus. This act of connecting is a normal and helpful part of pregnancy. It is thought to pave the way for the future relationship between mother and baby. When an individual is stressed, overwhelmed, depressed, or simply uncomfortable with the idea of being pregnant, certain interventions aimed at easing that act of connecting can be a supportive way of helping the mother-to-be begin with her fetus and adjust to the idea of the child she will soon give birth to.

OUTCOME GOAL

The mother-to-be will acknowledge and discuss her growing fetus as a dependent individual soon to be born as her baby.

INTERVENTIONS

1. Baby Kicks and Wiggles

2. Baby Predictions

3. Listening to the Heartbeat

4. From Me to You

5. Imagining My Baby

6. Birth Plan

7. Baby Care Plan

8. Dear Baby

INTERVENTION 1

Baby Kicks and Wiggles

TASK
To identify fetal movement, patterns of fetal movement, things that affect fetal movement, and the interactive possibilities between mother-to-be and her unborn child that can be understood through fetal movement.

REFERENCE
Chapters 3, 4

OPTIONAL MATERIALS
Clock or timer

ABOUT THIS INTERVENTION
Fetal movements are one way for the mother-to-be to learn about her baby. Babies all have periods of waking, high activity, and sleep both before and after they are born. Many times the periods or rhythms established during pregnancy continue after birth. Exploring fetal movement may be a fun way for the mother to learn more about her child. It may also be helpful for her to begin thinking about how the baby's rhythms may or may not match up to her own rhythms and patterns. Exploring fetal movement may also help the mother to begin a pattern of communication with her baby in a fun and interactive manner through playfully pushing on different places on her belly and seeing baby's response. Additionally, it may help her to begin to get a sense of the fetus as her soon-to-be child through playfully counting and tracking movements and by trying to identify the different body parts on the fetus.

Some general points to remember regarding fetal movement:

- Movement can begin as early as 20 weeks into the pregnancy. When a woman first feels her fetus move is very individual, however. It is dependent on the actual fetal activity level as well as the mother's level of activity. In general, the busier and more active she is, the more difficult it might be to feel those early movements.

- The most active time of fetal activity is between 27 and 32 weeks of the pregnancy.

- Babies are usually more active after meals.

- Not all movement is kicking and turning of the fetus. For example, sometimes little twinges can be felt that may be the fetus hiccupping. Encourage discussion about what different sensations to the mother-to-be might indicate.

- Fetal activity becomes more organized as the baby enters the third trimester.

- Lying down in a quiet, undisturbed location may help with relaxation and create a heightened sensitivity to the fetal movement.

- When counting and recording fetal movement, it may help if the mother:
  - Lies down on her left side (this provides more oxygen to your baby).
  - Places her hands over the larger part of her abdomen where she may have felt the baby move.

- Counts and records at the same time every day.
- Uses a clock or a timer to track the length of time the fetus is active and quiet.
- Counts the actual number of kicks or other movements she senses.
- Keeps a journal each day or uses other ways of recording to maintain an accurate picture of her baby's activity over time. This will help her to later recall her experience with baby movement.

- If she becomes worried that her baby is not moving or if the amount of moving has decreased, encourage her to notify her doctor or health care professional.

Note: The Mayo Clinic suggests that if a mother wants to check on her baby's activity, she may want to use the following procedure: Have mother-to-be find a quiet place in her home and lie down on her left side for about 30-60 minutes. During this time, ask her to note on a sheet of paper or in her mind the amount and type of movement she feels. She should feel no fewer than 10 movements in two hours. Encourage her to discuss this issue with her health care professional who may want to use different guidelines. If the mother-to-be is at all concerned, she should call her health care professional immediately.

The following are examples of some general discussion questions and discussion points that may be addressed in your visits with the mothers.

- At what point in pregnancy did you first feel your baby move?
- (If the baby has not moved yet) When do you think the baby will begin to move?
- What do you think it will feel like?
- (If they have other children) Does this baby move like your other children did?
- Have you ever let anyone else feel the baby move in you? How did they respond?
- Do you like it when your baby moves? Is it ever difficult having your baby move around?
- Fetal movements are one way of learning about your baby. Babies all have periods of waking, high activity, and sleep both before and after they are born.
- Babies are usually more active after meals.
- Lying down in a quiet undisturbed location will help you to relax and sense your baby's movement more.

INTRODUCING THIS INTERVENTION
Do you wonder how your baby will behave when it is born? You can learn a lot by tracking your baby's activity periods and movements now. Even now, your baby has periods of sleeping, waking up, being highly active, and falling asleep again. Those same patterns of waking and sleeping may continue after birth. If you can predict them now, you'll be better able to plan your rest periods after your baby is born.

You can start communicating with your baby now. If you touch your belly, does the baby respond by pushing or kicking back? When is your baby most active? when you're trying to rest? after a meal? when you're exercising?

We have a worksheet you can use to track your baby's movements. When you lie down to rest during the day, lie on your left side. This gives the baby more oxygen. Use a timer if you want and the Baby Kicks & Wiggles chart to record your baby's activity.

INTERVENTION

1. Introduce the Baby Kicks and Wiggles Chart.

2. Review the chart areas, type of movement and how it felt, position of the baby, body parts of baby, what baby's feelings might be, how the mother was feeling, and what the mother had been doing before the movement started.

3. This chart can be used in a variety of ways:

   - Explore the movement felt just during that session.

   - Give as homework where the mother could explore fetal movement one or more times over a day or several days.

4. For mothers who want to track baby's movement over a longer period of time to explore patterns and rhythms, the My Activities and Baby's Responses worksheet found in intervention 3 of Unit 7 (page 454) can be used as a framework for tracking. This can be a fun intervention to do before the baby is born tracking fetal movement and after the baby is born tracking baby's sleep and wake cycles.

5. Once a recording has been done, use the Fetal Movement Review to discuss and process the experience.

OPTIONS

Have mother share the movement of her baby with her spouse, others, or you.

NOTE

Make as many copies of the Baby Kicks & Wiggles chart as needed for the way you choose to do the intervention:

- One copy if used during this session.

- Multiple copies if the mother is to track all movement periods in one day.

- Multiple copies if the mother is to track the baby's movements during her rest period each day.

Baby Kicks and Wiggles

TIME STARTED	TIME ENDED	WHAT DID THE MOVEMENT FEEL LIKE?	POSITION OF BABY	I THINK I COULD FEEL MY BABY'S...	BABY'S FEELINGS	HOW WERE YOU FEELING?	WHAT WERE YOU DOING JUST BEFORE THE BABY STARTED MOVING?
		___Vigorous	___Head up	___Head	___Curious	___Bothered	___Resting
		___Slow	___Head down	___Bottom	___Upset	___Upset	___Sleeping
		___Rapid	___Facing front	___Knee	___Disturbed	___Happy	___Talking
		___Sharp	___Facing back	___Foot	___Scared	___Content	___Bathing
		___Rhythmical	___On right side	___Hip	___Content	___Sad	___Walking
		___Painful	___On left side	___Back	___Happy	___Frightened	___Exercising
		___Tickling	___Head front	___Hand	___Startled	___Surprised	___Eating
		___Spasms	___Bottom front	___Elbow	___Angry	___Excited	___Watching TV
		___Like a breeze	___Sideways	___Shoulder	___Puzzled	___Angry	___Driving
		___Other:	___Other:	___Other:	___Other:	___Other:	___Other:

Fetal Movement Review

START AND END TIMES
- Does the baby usually move around a lot during this time period?
- Is this episode of movement normal for you?
- Did the baby surprise you when he started moving at this time?

MOVEMENT
- Is this the typical way your baby moves?
- How often has your baby moved like this before?
- (If vigorous or rapid) Does your baby ever move more slowly or lightly like a tickle or a breeze?
- (If tickling or like a feather) Does your baby ever move more rapidly or vigorously?
- (If painful) Are there times when your baby moves when it does not hurt? Are there times when the baby's movement kind of feels good?

POSITION OF BABY
- Is your baby in this position very often?
- What other positions have you felt him in?
- Does your baby like to change positions a lot?
- What position of the baby is most comfortable for you?

BABY BODY PARTS
- Describe what you could feel.
- How did you know it was a _____?
- Does your baby place his _____ in that spot a lot?

BABY FEELINGS
- What told you the baby was feeling _____?
- What do you think caused your baby to feel that way?
- Have you recognized other feelings in your baby?
- What tells you how your baby might be feeling?

MOTHER FEELINGS
- You said you felt _____ when your baby was moving. Is this the way you normally feel when he moves like this?
- What about the baby's movements made you feel this way?
- Did you feel this way before the baby started moving or after?
- Does the baby respond a certain way whenever you feel _____?
- Are there differences in the way the baby moves when you have different feelings?

ACTIVITIES
- Does your baby normally respond like this when you _____?
- Are there other activities that seem to make the baby move more? Less?
- Can you do things to interact with your baby? For instance, can you push against your belly and then see what the baby does?

INTERVENTION 2

Baby Predictions

TASK
To begin to think or fantasize about the possibilities of what the baby may look like and what the baby may be like.

REFERENCE
Chapter 4

OPTIONAL MATERIALS
Assorted art supplies

ABOUT THIS INTERVENTION
Mothers have always thought about what their babies might be like. They imagine the physical qualities, such as hair, eyes, shape of nose, or dimple in chin. They think about what the baby might be like once it is first born, such as crying, hungry, or quiet. Thinking about the baby helps to connect to the idea that there really will be a baby, and thinking about the birth helps to connect the idea that childbirth is inevitable.

INTRODUCING THIS INTERVENTION
Do you know whether your baby will be a boy or a girl? Have you imagined what your baby will look like? How big he will be? Will she have hair or be bald? What color hair and eyes will he have? Will she resemble you, the father, or another relative? How do you think the baby will behave right after birth? Will he cry or sleep? Will she be hungry? Here's a worksheet to help you record your guesses. I'll give it back to you after the baby's birth so you can see how accurate your guesses were.

If you do the optional art project: Now why don't you do a portrait of your baby. You can put it in the nursery to remind everyone of the baby who is coming.

INTERVENTION
1. Ask the mother-to-be to think about what her baby might be like. Who might the baby resemble?

2. Work with the mother-to-be to complete the Baby Predictions handout. Doing it with her can give the person working with the mother an opportunity to assess the quality of the predictions. For example, does she think this baby will be 14 pounds at birth and difficult to deliver.

3. Once completed, seal the predictions in an envelope.

4. The mother-to-be should decide to either keep the envelope so she may open it when she chooses or leave it with you to save until the baby has been born. If she leaves it with you, it can be given to her in a follow-up visit where the two of you can discuss how close the predictions were or mail it to her in a Congratulations on Your New Baby card.

VARIATIONS
- Art activities, such as painting or drawing their idea of their baby, can both provide an alternative for those who find it difficult to use words to describe their babies and can also make a fun group intervention.

- Within a group, participants can discuss their predictions or make predictions for one another's babies. The group leader may combine the information to make group predictions (the groups may predict that there will be four girls and two boys born, one with red hair, three with black, and two blondes, etc.) This can be then used at a postpartum group to bring the mothers back together and discuss the accuracy of their predictions, as well as to reunite group members.

My Baby Predictions

DATE AND TIME OF BIRTH

My child will be born on a _____(day of week), on the ___(date) of _____(month), in the year _____, at _____(time) a.m./p.m.

GENDER

My child will be a: Boy   Girl

WEIGHT AND HEIGHT

Weight:_____   Length:_____

HAIR COLOR

Black   Red   Blonde   Brown   White   Other_____

AMOUNT OF HAIR

A lot   Average   Not much   Bald

TYPE OF HAIR

Long   Medium   Short   Straight   Curly   Fine   Coarse   Silky

EYE COLOR

Blue   Brown   Hazel   Black   Green   Other_____

HEAD SHAPE

Round   Oval   Square   Flat   Other_____

SKIN TONE

Dark   Medium   Light   Fair

BEHAVIOR

When my baby is first born, he/she will be:

Active   Calm   Sleepy   Crying a lot   Hungry   Other_____

RESEMBLANCE

My baby will look most like_____.

UNIQUENESS

I think my baby will have some special characteristics like:

NAMES

The names I like for my baby are:

INTERVENTION 3

Listening to the Heartbeat

TASK
To connect with the fetus through listening to fetal heart tones.

REFERENCE
Chapters 3, 4

OPTIONAL MATERIALS
Stethoscope designed to listen to fetal heart tones, clock with second hand

ABOUT THIS INTERVENTION
The fetal heartbeat is often one of the earliest confirmations that a child is growing inside the mother. Generally, the sound of the heartbeat can be detected by 12 to 14 weeks of gestation; however, this is very individual, depending on the mother, fetus, and the instrument used to hear the heartbeat.

If the mother-to-be has been seeing her health practitioner, ask if anyone has listened for fetal heart tones. Ask if she has heard them herself. Explain to her that finding them can sometimes be difficult depending on which way the baby is lying. If she has not heard them yet with her health care practitioner, encourage her to ask at the next prenatal visit.

Let the mother know that the bell of the stethoscope will need to be placed on her abdomen. It will often need to be moved around to locate the heartbeat and may need to be adjusted after the heartbeat is located if the baby is moving a lot. If the mother-to-be is at any time concerned about the heartbeat, have her call her health care practitioner.

INTRODUCING THIS INTERVENTION
By the time your pregnancy is three or four months along, the baby's heartbeat can usually be detected by placing a stethoscope on your abdomen. Has you doctor done this yet? Have you been allowed to listen to the heartbeat? It's sometimes hard to hear the heartbeat, depending on which way the baby is lying. If the baby moves, you may lose the sound of the heartbeat temporarily.

Would you like to try to locate the heartbeat? The baby's heart beats almost twice as fast as yours, so it's easy to tell your heartbeat from the baby's. To do this, we'd have to place the bell of the stethoscope against your abdomen and move it until we find the baby's heart. We can record the results on this chart. If you like, we can do this at other sessions, too.

INTERVENTION
1. Have the mother-to-be get into a comfortable position.
2. If this is new for her, explain that the baby's heartbeat can be located with the stethoscope. Explain it will be rapid, which is one way of differentiating the mother's heartbeat from that of the fetus. The mother's heartbeat will generally run around 80 beats a minute, the heartbeat rate of the fetus will generally run around 110-160 beats a minute. The fetal heart rate can also vary several beats from one minute to the next.

3. Record the fetal heart rate using the Fetal Heartbeat Rate handout. The mother may want to track the fetal heart rates over a period of time, week by week, or after various activities. She may want to look for patterns in the baby's heart rate.

Fetal Heartbeat Rates

DATE	TIME	MOTHER'S ACTIVITY	HEARTBEAT RATE

How does it feel to hear your baby's beating heart?

Are there any patterns to the rhythms you heard?

INTERVENTION 4

From Me to You

TASK
To connect with the fetus through the preparation of a gift designed from the mother-to-be's experience and interests.

OPTIONAL MATERIALS
Cassette tape, recorder, words to songs, children's stories

REFERENCE
Chapters 3, 4

ABOUT THIS INTERVENTION
Explore with the mother-to-be her own childhood and what things she may remember enjoying. Focus on songs, lullabies, stories, books, and music. For some mothers-to-be, this may be difficult, as they may not have many fond memories of their early childhood. If this occurs, then it may be helpful to explore what she has watched others do or what she may have learned in a class, book, or through a conversation.

Two main points need to be discussed. First, any memories the mother has of things that helped her to feel nurtured as a child herself can help her to create a similar atmosphere for her infant. If the mother feels good, warm, and nurtured by something such as a song, those feelings are often sensed by the fetus and later the baby. Second, establishing nurturing activities for the fetus can carry over once the baby is born and provide a sense of continuity and familiarity, leading to a soothing, comforting environment. The sense of hearing in the fetus is fairly well established by 24 weeks into the pregnancy. The fetus will begin to hear and react to noises outside the womb at this point.

INTRODUCING THIS INTERVENTION
When you were a child, did you have favorite songs or stories? Was there a time of day set aside for singing or stories? Some families have a tradition of reading or telling nursery rhymes or stories to quiet children at bedtime. Others had family members sing lullabies. Maybe you've read books or seen shows that pictured adults caring for little ones and you've thought you'd like to do something similar for your baby.

You can start now. By the time you're 6 months pregnant, your baby can hear and will react to things you say or hear. When you feel warm and cared for, your baby will also feel have the same feelings. If you start reading or singing to your baby now, the baby will recognize those stories and songs after birth. This is a way to start soothing and comforting your baby now.

INTERVENTION
1. Assist the mother-to-be in remembering some songs, stories, nursery rhymes, music, books, or lullabies that she found comforting or relaxing as a child. Talk about what kind of memories these bring up for her or why she might have chosen those particular songs.

2. Assist her in taping herself singing a song, reciting a poem, or reading or telling a story. It can be a combination of activities and should last no more that 15-45 minutes.

3. Encourage her to sing, recite, or tell the song, poem, or story daily to her fetus. A second option would be for the mother to play the tape she makes so the fetus could hear it.

4. Discuss that the way in which she says the word is as important as the words she uses.

5. Encourage the mother-to-be to listen to the tape with her fetus, or talk to her fetus herself, three times each week. Stress that a fetus, like a baby, likes consistency.

VARIATIONS

Song Tape: Favorite songs, songs popular at the time of the pregnancy, nursery songs, songs she loves to sing or songs she writes. If she doesn't know the words, many books of children's songs and rhymes are available for purchase or from the library.

Story Tape: Favorite childhood story, favorite book, story made up by the mother, family story, story of how the mother chose the baby's name. Again, if she doesn't know the words to a story, she can make them up or get a book and read it into the tape. If she does not know any stories appropriate for babies the following books may be helpful

Mama, Do You Love Me?	*by Barbara Joosse*
Mama, If You Had a Wish...	*by Jeanne Modesitt*
Love You Forever	*by Robert Munsch*
A, You're Adorable	*by Buddy Kaye*

INTERVENTION 5

Imagining My Baby

TASK
To connect with the fetus through fantasy and imagery.

REFERENCE
Chapter 4

ABOUT THIS INTERVENTION
Fantasizing about what it is like to be a mother and imagining what the baby will look or be like is a normal part of being pregnant. We all have ideas of what we might be like or what we want to be like when we become mothers. Many of these ideas begin when we are children and playing dolls. We also create images in our minds of what our baby might one day look like. These things are important as they prepare us to be mothers and to be ready for our babies.

This intervention is helpful in assisting the mother to relax and feel calmer and refreshed. Through this intervention, she should also begin to develop images of herself as a mother and of her baby. It is important to discuss that images created in our minds are not necessarily like photographs; these images can be a collage of colors, a shadow, a flash of lights, or a dreamlike picture. There are no rules to what is imagined.

One of the most important areas to discuss when preparing for this intervention is the ground rules. This is not hypnotism; it is guided imagery and relaxation. Some people confuse the two. The mother-to-be may stop at any time; she should never feel vulnerable or overwhelmed by this intervention. At first, some people are concerned or embarrassed by the process of relaxation exercises. Options to dealing with this might include giving the mother a copy of the script and having her use it in private or have her tape it onto a cassette tape. The home visitor may also tape the imagery script and leave the tape for the mother. This can easily be done as a group intervention. Also, over time, the mother-to-be may want to modify the script to help her get deeper into more specific areas, whether to further relax her back muscles or to develop a more detailed image of her baby.

INTRODUCING THIS INTERVENTION
One of the ways you can help yourself and your baby is to relax. Very few people can automatically relax. Most of us need to tell ourselves or be told what to do to relax. Guided imagery is a relaxation technique that suggests relaxing activities to us. It is different from hypnosis because the person relaxing is always conscious and in control. If you feel uncomfortable with the exercise, you can stop it. If you find it helps you, you or I can make a tape to play between sessions. You can even change the tape to emphasize the things that relax you and your baby.

All of us imagine a bit differently. Some people see pictures that look almost like a movie. Others imagine colors or feelings without actual pictures. There is no right or wrong way to imagine.

The guided imagery we will try today focuses on relaxing your body and sending warmth and love to your baby.

INTERVENTION

1. Have the mother-to-be find a comfortable, safe, quiet place to sit or lie down during the exercise.

2. Encourage anything that aids in her comfort, such as dimming lights, turning off the radio or television, turning down the answering machine, or even turning off the ringer of the phone.

3. Make sure the mother-to-be has enough pillows to support her legs or head during the exercise.

4. Beginning in a soft, quiet, melodic voice begin to read the relaxation script (this should have been reviewed prior to the first time using it to prepare for pauses in text.)

5. Pace yourself; go slowly but steadily. In between the words, a series of three periods signals a brief pause.

Imagining My Baby Script

Get into a comfortable position. Take a deep breath. Take another deep breath, hold it for a few seconds...and exhale...relax and breathe normally. Feel the air enter, soothing your lungs with each breath. Feel stress and discomfort flowing out of you with each exhale. As you prepare to take your next breath, I want you to hold it as long as you can, expanding your chest as far as you can. Okay, now inhale...hold it...hold it...good. Now exhale, releasing any tension you may still be holding in your chest. Relax and begin to breathe normally, using the occasional deep breath to help you continue to feel relaxed and alert.

Begin to let your arms rest...and your legs. Move around until you find the best way for you to be...you will begin to feel your body getting heavy and sinking into the spot where you are right now. Become aware, as you get more settled and relaxed, how heavy your head is getting...how heavy your neck is getting...feel the weight of your shoulders as you sink into your warm, comfortable spot...take another deep breath, releasing more tension as you exhale...become aware of how heavy your chest is getting...take a breath, releasing any tension you are holding in your chest...feel your stomach relaxing and sinking into the spot you are lying in...feel how heavy your bottom has become...heavy and relaxed...breathe... begin to focus on your legs, starting with your thighs, your knees, your shins...and ankles...and feet...begin to feel how relaxed, heavy, and warm your entire body is becoming. Feel your womb relaxing and your genital area. As you breathe, release any tension you may be holding there. As your womb begins to relax, try to feel your baby beginning to relax. Picture your baby floating in the warm fluids of your womb, feeling warm, relaxed, and content. Focus on this for a moment. (Wait 30 seconds to a minute before continuing)

Now, take a slow deep breath and as this breath reaches your lungs, imagine it beginning to glow, looking like a soft, soothing, bright stream of light. As you breathe, imagine this stream of light getting brighter and brighter as it becomes filled with your goodness and positive energy you want to send to your baby. When you are ready, take another deep breath. As you exhale, send this warm, bright, soft light swirling out of your body. Notice this light as it gently floats above you. Be aware of the good feelings it holds. Notice how warm and comfortable and safe you feel as you imagine this light floating in the air. Now with another breath, send this swirl of light down towards your

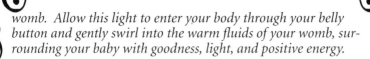

womb. Allow this light to enter your body through your belly button and gently swirl into the warm fluids of your womb, surrounding your baby with goodness, light, and positive energy.

Become aware of your baby. Notice your baby's head, the fine, soft hair, the tiny nose...notice your baby's eyes. Are they open or shut?...notice the eyelashes and eyebrows...see your baby's small mouth surrounded by tiny smooth lips. Become aware of your baby's ears. Notice all the ridges and twirls, notice the little round earlobes...continue to breathe and as you exhale, send your breath out and down into your womb, continuing to feed the light with your goodness and positive energy...Become aware of your baby's neck and shoulders. Follow the shoulders down to the elbows and onto the wrists and hands...become aware of each tiny finger...the fingernail and the ridge of each joint...notice your baby's hands moving in the light, being bathed in your positive energy. Become aware of how relaxed and warm and safe your baby is feeling. Your baby recognizes this goodness and warmth as coming from you. This is from mommy...take a moment to notice the light continuing to swirl around your baby. Follow this light to the chest, noticing the heart beating steadily with a quiet rhythm. Follow this light down, noticing the baby's stomach and the belly button where the cord connects you with your baby. Notice the shape of the baby's hips and the back. Notice your child's genital area and the tops of the legs. Follow the light as it swirls down the legs past the thighs, the knees, the shins, and to the ankles. Then slowly watch as the light bathes each little toe.

Watch your baby gently floating in this warm, good light...notice how your baby is feeling relaxed, safe, warm, loved. Feel as you and your baby connect through these feelings, both of you feeling content and calm, alert and aware, safe and warm. Let your baby know you will leave the light there to protect and comfort...begin to say goodbye. Encourage your baby to grow and develop in the positive energy and goodness you are leaving behind. Take a moment to notice your baby... and all that is within your womb. Now, slowly, take a deep breath and move your focus to your stomach, breathing in and out slowly...become aware of your chest... notice how it rises and falls with each breath (allow 3-6 breaths depending on the woman's comfort). Your body feels warm and comfortable and safe. You feel connected to your baby in a good and loving way, and you are feeling relaxed and alert. Slowly, when you are ready, begin to open your eyes, coming back into the spot where you are lying. Notice the room, the light...notice the furniture and gently allow yourself to come back into the here and now, still feeling safe and relaxed.

INTERVENTION 6

Birth Plan

TASK
To connect with the unborn child by preparing a plan for the birth of the baby that supports the mother and welcomes the baby.

REFERENCE
Chapters 3, 4

ABOUT THIS INTERVENTION
Creating a birth plan can be a powerful way of taking charge of certain aspects of the pregnancy and birth. Pregnancy can make a woman feel she has no control or power over her own body. Making choices is always supportive of personal control and power. Women who make birth plans take active roles in welcoming their baby and in their own transition into motherhood.

It is important that the home visitor be supportive of the woman's choices. However, it is equally important that the home visitor help the woman in exploring which choices are realistic. While a woman may want a home birthing experience, her doctor or health care professional may not support a home birth, or the pregnancy may be too high risk to attempt a home birth. Also, even with the best plans, circumstances may arise that make the revision of certain plans necessary. For instance, there may be a dozen women getting ready to deliver on the same day (it does happen!) or a hospital emergency. A woman's choices must be made from true options, not idealized wishes. Additionally, the choices a woman makes must take into account the baby's safety and well being, not only the woman's desire and vice versa. The plan must take into account the comfort, safety, and well-being of the mother-to-be, not just idealized visions of what the baby needs. Having the mother-to-be list her first and second choices is one way of balancing wishes and reality.

INTRODUCING THIS INTERVENTION
During your pregnancy, you may feel at times that you have little or no control over your body. But when it comes to your baby's birth, there are some things you can plan for and help control. If you make the plan now, you can later adjust it if needed. But the sooner you start thinking about the issues involved and learning about the options you have, the more control you will have over the decisions made.

The plan is fairly detailed. But when you're in labor, you won't feel like trying to remember the names and phone numbers of people to call. If you gather all of the information now when things are relatively calm, your labor won't have that additional stress. When you've completed your plan, you can discuss your wishes with your health care provider and the delivery facility. Depending on their feedback, you may have to revise some aspects of the plan. For instance, if there are high risk factors, you may not be able to have a home delivery.

Your final version of the plan should take into account your wishes, the options available to you, and the safety of both you and your baby. And remember this is a plan, and it may be revised when it's time to put it into practice. For instance, a dozen other women might go into labor right before you, and your preferred birthing room may not be available. But the better you've planned, the better your chances of having the kind of delivery you want.

INTERVENTION

1. Explore and discuss various birthing procedures and options. There are many books and materials available describing these experiences. (See, for example, *What to Expect When You are Expecting* by Arlene Eisenberg, Heidi E. Murkoff, and Sandee E. Hathaway; *The Birth Partner* by Penny Simkin; *Mayo Clinic Complete Book of Pregnancy and Baby's First Year,* edited by R.V. Johnson)

2. If the woman knows which hospital she is going to be using, it will be important to find out what options are available there. For example, do they have a home-like birthing room or a typical hospital delivery room?

3. Work with the mother-to-be to develop the birth plan using the Birth Plan and Directions for Completing the Birth Plan worksheets provided but tailoring them to the woman's needs.

4. Once the birth plan is done, encourage the mother-to-be to share it with her health care provider. It is often best to leave a copy of the birth plan with the provider and ask that they review it and give feedback at a later date. This is helpful as it gives the provider time to assess the safety of the plan, as well as how realistic it may be. They may also have some ideas the mother-to-be had not thought of.

5. Once a final birth plan has been made, copies should be made for the mother-to-be, the health care provider, the hospital or facility where the delivery will take place, and one for the baby's book.

Birth Plan*

I have prepared this birth plan as a way of welcoming my baby into this world and for myself, as I see my baby for the first time. I understand that this is only a plan and that circumstances may come up that make it difficult or impossible to support my choices. I have tried to include second choices in the event my first choices cannot be honored. Above all, I want my baby to be born safely and as comfortably as possible, and I want to remain as safe and ready as I can be in order to welcome my baby.

1. ABOUT ME

Name:

Address:

Phone:

Date of Birth:

My main language is _____. I can read/write/speak in this language.
I can also read/write/speak in

_____.

I do/do not need an interpreter.

Health Problems/Concerns (List any health care conditions, such as diabetes, asthma, etc.)

Medications/drugs (Current prescriptions, over-the-counter, recreational)

Allergies (List any food, medication, or other allergies)

---

* *Based on work by Moore, M. & Hopper, U. (1995); Peacock-Albers, M. (1996); and Simkin, P., Whalley, J., & Keppler, A. (1991).*

I have the following special needs (List any special needs, such as special food restrictions, handicapped access):

My concerns or fears about delivery are:

2. OTHERS INVOLVED
(List names and phone numbers of important others, including father of the baby, spouse, partner, boyfriend, girlfriend, etc.)

Name   Phone

3. PRE-DELIVERY

My baby will be delivered by_____ . He/she is a doctor/midwife/nurse practitioner.
 The phone number is _____.

_____ will be the backup person who will deliver my baby if the need arises. He/she is a doctor/midwife/nurse practitioner. The phone number is _____.

My child's birth will take place at
_____.

The address is:
_____

_____

and the phone number is _____.

I have prepared for my delivery by:

• Touring the delivery unit

• Taking childbirth preparation classes (dates_____)

• Discussing my plan with my health care provider

• Selecting a birth coach, name_____
  phone_____

• Selecting a backup coach,
  name_____phone _____

• I have packed a bag with the following items:

  _____

• I will get to the hospital by car/bus/taxi/other_____. The phone
  numbers are _____. I have asked
  _____to take me. The phone numbers to reach him/
  her are: _____. If he/she is
  not available, I will call _____to
  take me. The phone numbers to reach him/her are:
  _____. I know that I can call 911 if I
  need immediate assistance.

• I have asked others to be with me and support me at the time of delivery.
  They are:

  _____

• My other children will be taken care of by

  _____
  phone_____. My other children's names and ages are:

  _____

• I want the following people called when I am in labor:
  _____ will call them for me.

Names   Numbers

• I want the following people called when I have delivered:

_____ will call them for me.

    Names   Numbers

These are the things I still need explained to me:
- Episiotomies
- Epidural
- Cesarean
- Pitocin
- Delivery of Afterbirth
- Possible Medications
- Breast vs. Bottle Feeding

4. LABOR & DELIVERY TIME

The most important things to me are:

Regarding Labor
    Environment:

    Labor positions:

    Relaxation techniques:

    Medication/anesthesia decisions:

Regarding Delivery

Delivery positions (on back, on side, squatting, etc):

Feelings on an episiotomy:

I would like _____ to cut the cord.

Special considerations (desire a mirror to watch delivery, etc)

How I want to receive my baby for the first time (putting the baby immediately on my tummy, waiting until after the baby has been washed and dressed until I receive her, etc):

If a Caesarean birth is necessary (support person, medications, viewing birth):

Special Customs

The religious, cultural, and family customs I will be following include:

5. THE BABY

The doctor or health care provider I have chosen for my baby is_____
_____. The phone number is_____.

I would like to feed my baby in the following way:

I want the following type of contact with my baby in the hospital:

I want my baby to be dressed in:

If we need to...

If my baby has immediate medical needs (such as being born early), I understand he or she may need to be in a special care nursery. If that happens, I want my baby to have the following care and interaction guidelines (include type of contact, visitors, feeding practices, connection with support group, connection with social worker, chaplain, or other person):

6. ADDITIONAL CONCERNS OR COMMENTS

The only additional concerns I have are:

Comments:

I have prepared this birth plan to help make my transition into motherhood and my baby's birth be the best experience I think it can be. I know that the health and safety of my baby and me must come first and may mean that some of my plans may be changed.

Signature_____

Date_____

Directions for Completing Birth Plan

1. ABOUT ME

- Fill in all the blanks. Be sure to list phone numbers, as they are often difficult to track down when you are focused on your labor.

- List current and past health problems or concerns, such as diabetes, asthma, gonorrhea, herpes, etc. Sometimes different health issues can be affected by labor and some conditions may be harmful to the baby if they are not controlled for at the time of delivery.

- List any medications and drugs you are currently using, including prescriptions and over-the-counter medications.

- List any allergies, including food, medication, or things like animal fur, pollen, etc.

- Describe any special needs, such as certain dietary restrictions (vegetarian or religious food restrictions) or adaptive equipment that might be needed due to a disability, whether temporary or chronic.

- Discuss any concerns or fears that are present. Is there a concern over the amount of pain that might be experienced? Is there a fear that a cesarean section might be needed?

2. OTHERS INVOLVED

- List all the names and phone numbers of others who are involved with the baby and the delivery. This list might include the baby's father, spouse, partner, parents, siblings, best friend, etc. Be sure to include primary phone numbers, as well as work numbers, pagers, and cell phone numbers especially for those persons that are wanted at the delivery.

3. PRE-DELIVERY

- List both the primary health care provider and the backup person for the primary provider. Include phone numbers so they are easily accessible. Again, include any pager or answering service numbers for after hours.

- List the hospital or clinic where the baby will be born; include the address and phone numbers.

- Check off the items on the preparation list as they have been completed or as they apply. Fill in any open blanks completely.

- Check any of the areas where education or instruction is still needed. Explore and add other areas in which information is still needed.

4. LABOR AND DELIVERY TIME

- *Labor*—Describe any practices or techniques that will be helpful and supportive during the labor process. Use as much detail as possible. Attach any scripts or information sheets to the birth plan that might be needed to use these practices. If a cassette tape or other object is needed, it can be placed in a zip-loc bag and stapled to the birth plan that will accompany the mother to the hospital at the time of delivery. Environmental considerations might include subdued lighting, soft music, or a fan to remain cool. Labor positions may include on back, on hands and knees, squatting, sitting, walking, etc. Multiple positions are generally needed during labor to increase comfort and help labor progress. This needs to be considered. Relaxation techniques might include music, a specific relaxation tape, making sure the TV is off, having a special pillow or blanket from home, taking warm baths, cool washcloths to the forehead, or a bouquet of lavender near the bed. Medication choices generally include whether specific medications are used to help labor progress or to help decrease discomfort. Any of these choices can be changed depending on the circumstances at the time of labor and delivery.

- *Delivery*—Describe any practices or techniques that may be helpful and supportive during delivery. Include as much detail as possible. Some delivery choices may need to be first discussed with the hospital and/or the health care professional delivering the baby to assure they are available and/or allowed. Include backup plans and options if first choice options are not available (for instance, the plan may be to use one of the two home-like birthing rooms. However they may already be occupied by women who are already in labor). Delivery positions can include squatting, sitting, lying on side, etc.; these options need to be flexible depending on the circumstances at the time of delivery. Different birth settings and practitioners have different options regarding episiotomies, anesthesia, and medication. Explore these options with the health care provider before making decisions. Include second options when possible

- *Special Customs*— Include any religious customs that will be followed for this delivery and birth. Include directions that may help medical staff be supportive of these customs.

5. THE BABY
- List the doctor or health care provider that has been chosen for the baby. Include the phone number and address. Describe how that provider has agreed to be contacted once the baby is born. For instance, the parents call, the hospital calls, etc.

- Describe what preparations have been made for the baby's arrival. Type of feeding, the outfit or type of dress, and the type of diaper usage planned should all be described.

- If we need to...:If the baby is born premature or with some immediate health condition, it will be important to have a plan for the desired type of involvement with those procedures. These will have to be thought about in the context of the hospital's guidelines that maintain the health and safety of both the mother and baby. Issues that might be included or discussed would be feeding, diapering, people involved, contacts to be made, etc.

6. ADDITIONAL CONCERNS OR COMMENTS
- List any concerns or additional areas that need to be considered for this particular birth plan.

7. SIGNATURE
- Signing this document helps to make these plans important and reinforce that they be taken seriously. It is important to remember that flexibility is sometimes needed and that even with the best of efforts and well made plans, things may not go the way we want all of the time.

INTERVENTION 7

Baby Care Plan

TASK
To connect with the unborn child by preparing a plan for the care of that baby once it is born.

REFERENCE
Chapters 3, 4

ABOUT THIS INTERVENTION
Having a plan of care for the baby at the time of birth and after the birth is an important way to prepare both psychologically and emotionally. A mother who is informed of her options and has spent time thinking about her choices feels more in control of the intervention and is better prepared to welcome her baby.

It is important that the home visitor be supportive of the woman's choices; however, it is equally important that the home visitor help the woman in exploring which choices are realistic. It should always be a woman's choice as to the type of feeding she prefers, regardless of what those around her are telling her. She needs to make that choice. On issues like circumcision, the doctor performing the procedure may have a specific way he or she likes to do things that would be in the best interest of the baby. Regarding the issues of the choices available immediately after birth, hospital procedures and practices and/or the health and safety of the baby may interfere with the mother's choices.

INTRODUCING THIS INTERVENTION
Just as it was important to plan for the baby's birth, it is also important to plan for the care of your newborn. How soon do you want to hold your baby? How do you want to feed your baby? What kind of diapers do you want to use? If your baby is a boy, will you want him circumcised? There are many options for baby care to consider.

The worksheet, "My Baby's Care Plan," will help you think about some of the options. You may want to read about some of these issues. You may want to ask your health care provider and the baby's health care provider about options. Based on the information from all these sources, you can make decisions with providers that will honor many of your wishes and promote the health and safety of your baby.

INTERVENTION
1. Explore and discuss the various baby care procedures and options.

2. Learn what rules or procedures are followed regarding delivery, hospital stays, and circumcision, so informed decisions may be made.

3. Work with the mother-to-be to develop the baby care plan using the My Baby's Care Plan and Direction for Completing My Baby's Care Plan worksheets provided but tailoring it to the woman's needs.

4. Once the baby care plan is done, encourage the mother-to-be to share it with the health care provider she has chosen for her infant. It is often best to leave the baby care plan with the provider and ask that they review it and give feedback at a later date. This is helpful as it gives the provider time to assess

the safety of the plan, as well as how realistic it may be. The provider may also have some ideas the mother-to-be had not thought of.

5. Once a final baby care plan has been made, copies should be made for the mother-to-be, the health care provider, the hospital or facility where the delivery will take place, and one for the baby's book.

My Baby's Care Plan*

1. The names I have chosen for my baby are:

    If a boy:_____

    If a girl:_____

    I chose these names because:

2. My baby's doctor or health care provider is_____,

    the address is _____,

    and the phone number is _____.

3. Feeding (circle choices):
    - I plan to: breastfeed   bottle feed   a mixture of both

    - I plan to use: breast milk   formula   both

    - I plan to feed my baby: on demand   on a schedule   unsure

    - I would like: some assistance with feeding at first

                          some time alone to explore alone feeding with my baby

    - I would like a feeding consultant to visit me in the hospital: Yes   No

4. The first few minutes after birth:

    I understand that right after birth the medical staff will need to do several things for my baby, including checking the baby's breathing, heart rate, and reflexes; giving an injection of Vitamin K; and taking care of my baby's eyes. I also know they will clean my baby up.

    ___I would like to hold my baby as soon as possible after birth.

    ___I want to wait until all the procedures are done before I hold my baby.

    ___I want to wait until all the procedures are done and the baby has been cleaned up before I hold my baby.

* Based on Childbirth Education Plan by Peacock-Albers, M. (1996). Unpublished

5. The most important things to me after my baby is born are:

___Having my baby right next to me all the time.

___Having my baby in the nursery some of the time so I can rest.

___Having my spouse/boyfriend/partner there to support me.

___Having my friends and family visit.

___Giving my baby all of the feedings.

___Other: _____

6. I have the following concerns that I would like explained to me:

___my health	___when my baby should see the doctor
___my recovery	___breastfeeding
___breast feeding breast care	___bottle feeding
___breast care & drying up my milk	___family support
___my baby's health	___help with the baby
___care of the baby's skin	___exercise after delivery
___care of the baby's hair	___sexual intercourse after delivery
___diapering	___who should be allowed to see the
___baby's sleep	baby
___getting my own sleep	___circumcision
___what I should be eating	

7. My decisions on circumcision, if I have a boy:

___No circumcision	___Do the procedure in the hospital
___I do want my baby to be circumcised	___Do the procedure out of the hospital
___I want to be there to comfort my baby for the circumcision	___I need more information on caring for the circumsion.
___Give my baby anesthesia	___I need more information on
___ No anesthesia	circumcisions in general

8. I have decided to use:

cloth diapers   disposable diapers

9. Any additional plans or concerns:

Directions for Completing Baby Care Plan

1. Fill in name choices and how you came to choose them.

2. Fill in the name of your baby's doctor or other health care provider, the address, and the phone number.

3. Circle choices regarding the feeding of your baby.

4. Indicate how you want that initial time after the baby's birth to be handled.

5. Indicate what things are most important to you while in the hospital.

6. Indicate your concerns, questions you want answered, and any other information you might need.

7. If you have a boy, you will need to decide about a circumcision. Indicate your choices about whether you want your son to be circumcised and, if so, how you want that procedure handled.

8. Type of diapering you plan.

9. Any additional concerns or issues.

INTERVENTION 8

Dear Baby

TASK
To connect with the unborn child by writing of a letter or group of letters for the baby.

REFERENCE
Chapter 4

OPTIONAL MATERIALS
Colored pens/pencils

ABOUT THIS INTERVENTION
The relationship between a mother and child grows and develops through a variety of ways. Imagining, reflecting, talking, and sharing information and feelings with others all contribute to the developing mother-child relationship. Writing is also a very effective and simple way of communicating with the baby and of processing information and feelings. Beginning to write a diary or a series of letters to the baby is a way of tracking the changes going on for the pregnant woman and of helping her to think about the things that will be affecting her child's life. She may decide to save them for her baby or to get rid of them at some point. The goal is to write down what is happening and how she is feeling. Therefore, if one day she is feeling upset because she has been vomiting all day and cannot seem to sleep, she should be able to vent those feelings in a letter. The next day she may be feeling fine and may be embracing the entire idea of being pregnant. The letter she writes that day should reflect those feelings. Before the baby is born, she may sort through the letters and see what she wants to keep, to toss, to save for herself, or to save for her baby. It is the writing that is important.

INTRODUCING THIS INTERVENTION
There are lots of ways you can develop a relationship with your child. You can talk to your baby, pat it when it moves, sing lullabies to it, and talk to family and friends about your baby. Another powerful thing you can do is write to or about your baby. Some mothers keep a journal for recording their feelings and activities and the baby's behavior. Others write letters to their baby.

If you choose to write, anything is okay. If you're upset and vomiting one day, you can write that. If you're feeling great another day, tell the baby what was so wonderful. These letters or the journal can reflect the ups and downs of your life, how family members feel about the baby, and anything else that occurs to you.

Before the baby comes, sort through the letters. You may decide to toss some and to keep others. Some you may keep just for yourself; others you may save for your baby. When your baby is grown and expecting a baby with his or her partner, those letters may be very meaningful.

INTERVENTION
1. Give the mother-to-be the choice of a diary, journal, notebook, stationery, or the Dear Baby worksheets included here.

2. Encourage and assist her to write a letter or message to her baby. These writings or messages can be in words, pictures, drawings, images, photographs, a pressed flower, etc. There are no rules.

3. Some options for including in the letters or messages might include:

   - What I did today
   - What your dad did today
   - Who I want you to meet
   - Who is in the family
   - My favorite memory
   - My favorite season
   - My favorite place
   - My favorite....(anything)
   - What the weather is like

   - What traditions I follow
   - Things I want to do with you one day
   - Places I want to visit
   - What my best friend is like
   - What the doctor said today
   - What I am doing to prepare your arrival
   - Things I bought or made for you and why

4 The letters or messages can be as long or short as desired. They can be as emotional or factual as desired. They can be disposed of or saved as wanted.

5. See sample letter.

Dear Baby Sample Letter

October 7

Dear Baby,

I am sitting here in my favorite chair thinking about you. I think about what it will be like to be sitting here feeding you. You are supposed to be here in about two months. My midwife says you are due to arrive on December 18, but I think you will be a little late.

When you are born, I cannot wait to introduce you to your Uncle Oscar. He is almost more excited to see you than I am. He calls me every day and yesterday he brought you a football. I told him you were going to be too small to use it for a while, but he just laughed.

One day I hope I can show you this little park I remember going to when I was a little girl. It has swings, a merry-go-round, and a nice yellow slide. We can play there on sunny days.

Your Dad is very happy you are coming. He has been working hard to get everything ready. He painted your room yesterday. We picked white walls with red and blue trim. He is going to be putting up your crib this week.

I am thinking of you and wishing you were here right now. See you soon,

Love,

Mommy

Dear Baby,

Unit 2

Points To Remember

As soon as life begins within a woman's womb, a connection between that woman and the unborn child also begins. The quality of this connection will vary greatly among women. Some report feeling an intense sense of love and bonding, others report only an affectionate acknowledgment of the being inside of them, while still others work to deny their pregnancy and push any emotional responses away. The interventions in this unit were designed to support and enhance the connection between the pregnant woman and her unborn child. Let us review these interventions:

- *Baby Kicks and Wiggles* encourages pregnant women to acknowledge the movement of their unborn children, explore how it relates to their own activities, and take the time to think about their experiences and feelings.

- *Baby Predictions* provides a format for thinking about what the unborn child might be like. This activity encourages fantasizing and imagining.

- *Listening to the Heartbeat* is an intervention designed to help the pregnant woman connect with the sound of her unborn child's heart. Hearing this heartbeat helps the woman to make a connection using her sense of hearing and adds a new dimension to the acknowledgment of her baby.

- *From Me to You* allows the pregnant woman to begin to think about what special things she would like to share with her child.

- *Imagining My Baby* is a fantasy- and imagination-based activity encouraging the pregnant woman to think about and emotionally connect with her unborn child.

- *The Birth Plan* activity allows for the taking charge of the birthing process. It supports the pregnant woman in making choices that help her to connect.

- *The Baby Care Plan* helps the pregnant woman to think ahead to what her child will need and how she will meet those needs. Making these plans helps to support the connection by making the baby more real.

- *Dear Baby* is an activity that encourages the pregnant woman to connect with her unborn child by writing about her wishes, dreams, experiences, and feelings.

"A child can never be better than what his parents think of him."

MARCELENE COX

Unit 3

Attachment

KEY CONCEPT

A mother's attachment to her child is the result of many interactions between that mother and child beginning before birth and lasting over the lifetime of the relationship. These interactions can occur on many levels; they might include touches, words, smells, consistency, sounds, thoughts, images, and feelings.

OUTCOME GOALS

The mother-to-be will:

Identify different ways to help promote a positive attachment with her child.

Demonstrate two ways she has found helpful for herself and her child.

INTERVENTIONS

1. Dream Baby

2. Family Traditions and Celebrations

3. Attachment Moments

4. Carry and Cuddle: Using a Soft Baby Carrier

5. My Baby's First Picture!

6. My Own Relationships

7. Preparing to Be an Attachment Focused Parent: Feeding Time

8. Preparing to Be an Attachment Focused Parent: Diapering Time

INTERVENTION 1

Dream Baby

TASK
To help the mother begin to get a sense of her baby through connecting with her dreams.

OPTIONAL MATERIALS
Assorted art and drawing supplies

REFERENCE
Chapters 1, 2, 4

ABOUT THIS INTERVENTION
Dreams are powerful. They help clear minds and solve problems or worries. They allow a different way of thinking about things that may be difficult to think about. And they allow the development of ideas that may affect the future. Dreams are not always what they seem. Sometimes dreams are about what is really happening in daily life. Dreams can be of the real people, real places, and real activities. Other times dreams are made up of symbols. Dreams can be about animals, strangers, and impossible activities like being able to fly like a bird. Dreams are thought to carry meanings that can be discovered through the use of manuals and books that describe the content and meaning of dreams. However, not all books agree on the meaning of dream content. Because of this lack of agreement, the only real power in a dream is what it means to the dreamer.

When a woman is pregnant she will have many dreams of her unborn child and herself. She might dream about the things she will do in the future, or she might dream about conversations she will have. Some people dream about the sex of their baby or what that baby will look like. Dreams help women to prepare for their babies and for taking on the roles of a mother. This activity will focus on thinking about and recording dreams. These dreams will be explored for the meanings and content to the women who dreamed.

INTRODUCING THIS INTERVENTION
One way to get acquainted with your baby is to keep track of your dreams or daydreams about the baby. Do you wonder what your baby will look like? How it will behave? What it will do? Your dreams and daydreams may give you some clues. Of course, in dreams, we often see things through symbols, so the real meaning of a dream may not be the events we saw. This is part of the fun of dreams—thinking about the possibilities of what our dreams may mean. What is really important, however, is what they mean to us.

INTERVENTION
1. Have several Dream Baby Handouts (you can also use a notebook or journal to keep track of your dreams) and pens or pencils near the bed or in a spot where the woman can routinely sit for a few minutes each morning.

2. Have client agree to remain in bed for a few minutes upon awakening. Teach her to take several deep breaths and concentrate on what she dreamed about during her sleep. She can also focus on dreams that occur during nap times or even frequent thoughts that repeatedly occur.

3. Encourage the woman to write down words, sentences, descriptions, or a story of what occurred in her dream. If the dream cannot be translated into words, encourage the use of art materials to draw, sketch, or symbolize the dream.

4. For the client who is reluctant to share her dreams, who can't remember, or who denies dreaming, ask her to journal her daydreams or thoughts about the baby as an option.

5. An option might be to get a dream interpretation book, available at the library or bookstore, and discuss possible interpretations of dreams. It is said that the images we see in dreams are symbols for other things occurring in our life. For instance, dreaming about death does not mean there will be a death but rather there will be a major change occurring in some part of one's life. You might also look for things that remain the same in your dreams. For example, if every dream has an old owl with glasses in it, who might this owl represent or what might the presence of the owl mean—is there something missing in your life that you need to find or is there something you are going through that is making you wiser as you get closer to having your baby?

Dream Baby

INTERVENTION 2

Family Traditions and Celebrations

TASK
To help the mother-to-be begin to think about the traditions she has in her life now and to begin to get a sense of traditions and rituals she wants to establish with her baby.

REFERENCE
Chapters 2, 4

ABOUT THE INTERVENTION
Celebrations, traditions, rituals, and ceremonies are all ways that cultures, religions, and families connect and stay together. The tradition of Thanksgiving in the United States is a time-honored event that is designed to pull family and friends together. People travel cross-country just to be home for that one special get-together with all the family. Each family also develops other traditions that connect the members—these may not always be healthy or welcomed traditions. For example, while a birthday celebration in one family may involve grandparents, aunts, uncles, and cousins coming together for cake and ice cream, in another family a birthday may be marked by mass alcohol consumption and the inclusion of anyone who wants to come. Each client will need to evaluate which traditions she wants to continue with her family and which she wants to completely let go of or change.

One important event within each family is the manner in which a newborn baby is welcomed. For some families, this is a dreaded event: for others, it is a welcomed but uncelebrated event; and for still others, it is a cherished and celebrated event. Regardless of family traditions, however, it will be up to the client how she wishes to welcome her baby. Welcoming is a way of opening the family, opening hearts, and accepting a new member. It can be reflective of how the relationship with the baby will be treated. It can be a part of developing the mother-baby attachment.

INTRODUCING THE INTERVENTION
What are some of the events you celebrate with family members or friends? Is there a holiday you celebrate with others? What kinds of activities are at these celebrations—eating, singing, playing games, watching TV or parades, or whatever? Memorable events in our lives are often marked with celebrations. The birth of your baby will certainly be a memorable event.

How can you and those important to you and your baby celebrate this birth? What will be meaningful to all of you, as well as safe and welcoming to the baby? This birth gives you a chance to continue a family tradition or to start a new tradition.

INTERVENTION
1. Review the handout on creating a welcoming celebration. Discuss thoughts and feelings for the ideas listed. Have client(s) suggest other ways in which they might celebrate and honor the arrival of their child.

2. Have client choose one of the suggested celebrations or her own idea for a celebration.

3. Complete handout on designing the celebration.
4. Carry out the celebration when the baby is born.

Ideas for Welcoming Celebrations

LETTERS FROM FRIENDS AND FAMILY
Have three friends or family members write a letter to the baby. Save the letters in a special box (can be decorated specially for baby). Read the letters at a get-together after the baby is born. Then tuck the letters away for the baby when he or she comes to another significant point in life, i.e., marriage, graduation, birth of a baby, etc.

THREE GIFTS
Decorate a small box. Inside place three items you feel symbolize gifts you would like to give your child. For example, a rock for stability, a button from the father's shirt to represent father's love, a package of seeds for growth, a paintbrush for creativity, a crystal for healing, etc. For the first month after birth, keep this box under the baby's crib or bed. Afterwards, keep the box in a special place and add to it as your child grows.

GIVING TREE
Plant a tree or bush to grow with your child.

ANIMAL CONNECTION
Choose an animal that you feel represents a special quality you connect with your unborn child. Begin to collect items reflective of that animal. For example, you might choose a lion for courage and collect everything with lions on it—stuffed animals, posters, ceramic figures, books, t-shirts, etc.

CHARMED
Begin a charm bracelet. Add a charm for each significant event your child experiences as he or she grows. At birth, begin with a special charm that represents how you feel or what you think about your child.

BABY BRACELET
Have a get-together where each invited friend or family member brings a button or bead that represents a gift they would want to bestow upon your child. String these together with some elastic cord and make a ankle bracelet for the baby to wear for a special welcoming party after birth. (Of course, it needs to be loose enough not to hurt the baby's ankle.) It should never be placed on the baby's wrist due to choking concerns. The bracelet can also be designed to be worn by the mother or as a charm to be hung on the wall in the baby's room.

Creating a Welcoming Celebration

Choose one or two of the welcoming celebrations listed or design one of your own. It can be private or public, inside or outside, big or little.

TYPE OF CELEBRATION

INVITATION LIST

ACTIVITY PLANNED

MEANING OF ACTIVITY

WHAT I HOPE MY BABY WILL GET FROM THIS

INTERVENTION 3

Attachment Moments

TASK
To develop a repertoire of maternal behaviors supporting and promoting attachment.

REFERENCE
Chapter 4

ABOUT THIS INTERVENTION
All babies develop attachments to their caregivers. However, the quality of these attachments differs among children; certain patterns of attachment can lead to different outcomes. Children who are securely attached feel confident that their caregiver is dependable and will be there for them if they feel scared or get hurt. Babies with insecure attachments have learned that their caregivers are not always there for them or are not always helpful. Research has shown that children who develop secure attachments generally go on to become more successful in school and in their personal relationships with others. Children with insecure relationships, on the other hand, may go on to struggle more with school and with their relationships.

Attachment develops within the context of a relationship where there is a back-and-forth exchange between people, in this case mother and baby. While the mother is not yet face-to-face with her baby, there are several things she can do to begin to think about attachment and what goes into developing a secure attachment with her baby. The things that can be done fall into three general areas. These include:

•Self care—taking care of herself and respecting herself supports her as a parent and individual and begins a pattern of modeling appropriate self care and of self-confidence for her child. Feeling good about herself is part of the basic foundation for relating to others. For example, a mother who is getting rest while baby is also napping will tend to have more energy when they both wake up. A mother who is eating a healthy, balanced diet will not only set an example for her baby but will also feel better. This will be reflected in her interactions.

• Pregnancy— interactions and interchanges between the mother and her unborn child that help to promote attachment between mother and her child. For example, the mother can sway hips in a rocking motion as she does the dishes or talks on the phone or lightly massage her tummy and talk in a soothing voice to her unborn child as he or she kicks and somersaults within the womb.

• Postpartum— interactions and interchanges between the mother and her unborn child now occur within a new external environment. For example, the mother can talk to her baby during feedings or spend quiet moments each day rocking her baby.

INTRODUCING THIS INTERVENTION
When babies are born, they rely on their mothers and other caregivers for every-thing—food, clean diapers, clothing, shelter, comfort, hugs, conversation, medical care, and everything else needed for survival and happiness. A baby that knows you and others can always be depended on to be there to help has a better chance of

doing well in school and growing into a strong and loving person. Babies who find that caregivers are often absent or unreliable may later struggle in school and have more difficulty in relationships.

You can do several things to help your baby develop secure attachments to you as a caregiver. Right now, you can care for yourself. If you can respect yourself and your choices, you'll gain self-confidence and be better able to care for your baby. During your pregnancy, you can talk and sing to your baby, pat it, and send warm thoughts to it. After the baby is born, you can continue these activities to give the baby a sense of connection to you.

INTERVENTION

1. Review the Attachment Moments handout.

2. Discuss thoughts and feelings for each of the areas listed: self care, pregnancy, and postpartum.

3. Complete the handout.

4. Discuss different options available in each of the areas.

5. See Intervention Unit 5 for additional self-nurturing ideas and Intervention Unit 4 for ways to be kind to the body.

Attachment Moments

SELF CARE

I know that if I take care of and nurture myself, I will feel better and better about my baby and myself. I did the following things today to take care of myself:

PREGNANCY: MY BABY & ME

I know my baby can sense the way I feel and knows that I am already working at developing a warm and loving relationship between us. I have tried to communicate my feelings or ideas to my unborn baby today by:

POSTPARTUM: AFTER MY BABY ARRIVES

I understand that it is the little things I do each day that will help my baby and me develop a warm and loving relationship. I have thought of the following ways to help this relationship along after my baby arrives:

INTERVENTION 4

Carry and Cuddle: Using a Soft Baby Carrier

TASK
To help the mother understand that maintaining a physical closeness to her baby after birth is important as a way of meeting the baby's needs and of supporting attachment.

OPTIONAL MATERIALS
Soft baby carriers

REFERENCE
Chapter 4

ABOUT THIS INTERVENTION
Attachment theory suggests that being close to the baby helps promote a healthy, secure attachment. Soft baby carriers allow the mother to be close to her infant for longer periods of time with little restriction of activities. Research has shown that even women who wear their babies for short periods demonstrate better relationship patterns with their babies than mothers who never use the carriers. Using soft baby carriers may also improve the mother's abilities to be responsive and attentive to her baby. These are some of the behaviors that lead to secure attachments. Mothers can also develop a better awareness of their babies' needs. Also, babies cuddled in soft baby carriers may tend to cry less as they are already getting what they need: being close to mom.

For some women, especially those with histories of trauma to their bodies, having their baby so close to their front, upper body may be difficult. It will be important to respect any discomfort but also to explore it and see what the issues really are. Some infant carriers, such as the sling or a backpack style, can keep the baby close to mom but not be as intrusive.

The reason for introducing the concept of soft baby carriers during pregnancy is to help prepare the mother to use one, to work out any issues that may be present around wearing a carrier, and to establish the idea that soft baby carriers are both a helpful and natural way of meeting baby's needs.

INTRODUCING THIS INTERVENTION
One way to help your baby feel secure is to hold your baby. Yet, you can't stop what you're doing every time the baby fusses or you'd never get other things done. The solution for many moms is a soft baby carrier—one you can wear on your front. If you have a health issue that makes a front carrier painful or difficult, try a sling or backpack style of carrier.

These carriers allow you to do other activities while keeping your baby close. The closeness will make you more aware of when your baby is hungry or needs your attention. When you respond quickly to the baby's needs, the baby feels more secure and cries less. You and your baby can develop a close relationship, and your baby will grow into a stronger, more secure child and adult.

INTERVENTION

1. Have a selection of soft baby carriers that the mother-to-be can try on and test for comfort or take a trip to a baby store and support the mother-to-be as she tries on different styles. See Appendix C for information on soft baby carriers.

2. Once a style has been chosen, have the mother-to-be try it on repeatedly. Support the mother-to-be in learning how to secure it to her body and how to get the baby in and out in a safe and comfortable way. If the carrier is one that can be adjusted to different positions, discuss appropriate positions for appropriate baby age. These specifics need to be obtained from the manufacturer, as each carrier is a bit different. Always review the safety concerns of each individual carrier as well.

AFTER THE BABY IS BORN

Once the baby has been born, it will be important to follow up on the use of the soft baby carrier. After the mother and baby return home, the mother may need support, and possibly some further education, on how to use the carrier with her new baby. It will be important to discuss the benefits again and the ways in which the soft baby carrier can support the mother. The mother may record her use of the carrier as a way of tracking the effects on her and the baby, as well as providing some information for discussion during visits. She can use the Carry and Cuddle Time handout or make a form of her own.

If the mother is resistant or backs away from using a carrier, encourage her to experiment. If baby has been fussy, ask her to try just one or two days with a carrier to see if there is any effect. Show her how using the carrier may help to calm the baby when he or she is distressed.

Carry and Cuddle Time

Day _____

My baby is _____ (age) today.

PM
AM

7	8	9	10	11	12	1	2	3	4	5	6	7	8	9	10	11	12	1	2	3	4	5	6

In the first row are the hours in a day beginning with 7 a.m. and ending at 6 a.m.

In the second row please fill in the boxes for the times you are cuddling the baby in the carrier. Fill in half a box for half an hour, or smaller amounts as needed.

In the third row, please fill in how you think your baby was feeling while being cuddled in the carrier using the following letters:

C=Calm   H=Happy   A=Angry/Mad   S=Sleeping   R=Crying

Q=Quiet Alert   F=Frustrated   T=Content   F=Safe   D=Scared

U=Curious   O=Other (list other feelings you can identify in your baby):

How did you feel when cuddling your baby in the carrier?

Was this easy or difficult for you?

INTERVENTION 5

My Baby's First Picture!

TASK
To support the mother-to-be's connection with her unborn child through her focus on the ultrasound results and photos available to her.

REFERENCE
Chapters 1, 2, 4

ABOUT THIS INTERVENTION
Note: This activity is to be used if the woman's health care provider has already completed or has already recommended an ultrasound. This activity in no way advocates for an ultrasound for any purpose other than those medically warranted by the health care providers.

Ultrasounds can be very helpful when used to diagnose or determine factors related to the unborn child or the pregnancy. One of the bonuses of an ultrasound is the pictures the parents are given of their child in utero. With this picture, they can begin to learn what their baby is going to be like. They can learn about the sex of the baby, the shape of the baby's head, or how he or she moves or positions his or her body. If the pictures are taken at a special moment, they may see their baby already sucking his or her thumb.

For some parents the ultrasound experience may be uncomfortable. They may have only imagined a fully developed, real baby, not a fetal image. It is important to prepare parents for the images they may see. Often, sharing other ultrasound pictures at various stages in development can be helpful. Although ultrasounds tend to occur frequently during pregnancy, they may still bring a variety of feelings and thoughts to the mind of the mother and/or her partner. Discussing the experience is always important.

This activity is designed to help the mother focus on her unborn child and to begin to explore the possibilities.

INTRODUCING THIS INTERVENTION
Ultrasounds are used for medical diagnosis of things related to your baby or your pregnancy. The bonus is that they can give you pictures to learn things about your baby before birth. Let's look at your picture(s) and see what we can learn about your baby now.

INTERVENTION
1. Have the mother-to-be share any of her ultrasound pictures with you.
2. Discuss what each of you sees. Ask the mother to describe not only what she sees but also what she thinks it means or what it might indicate as to the future.
3. Use the My Baby handout to begin to take notice of and explore the pictures and the mother's thoughts.

My Baby's First Picture

Ultrasound Picture

Gestational Age:_____

Date: _____

This is how I would describe my baby at this moment in time:

This is how I feel about my baby at this moment in time:

INTERVENTION 6

My Own Relationships

TASK
To help the mother-to-be think about her own attachment history and her primary relationships.

REFERENCE
Chapters 1, 2

ABOUT THIS INTERVENTION
There are several events throughout a relationship between a child and the person who cares for that child that contribute to the ideas children develop about what people do and how people act when they take care of children. Some caregivers do things that can make a child feel special and loved no matter what mistakes he or she might make. Other caregivers do things that can make a child feel alone and scared. Some specific events that help to create the understandings children develop are times when the child was sick or hurt and needed taking care of. Many other experiences also contribute to the understandings developed. In this activity, the caregiving relationships and the events within these relationships will be explored.

INTRODUCING THIS INTERVENTION
We all have a variety of caregivers in our lives. When we were children, those caregivers may have included parents, older siblings, other relatives, foster parents, teachers, neighbors, baby-sitters, day care providers, and others.

Can you remember a time when you were sick? What did those caregivers do when you were ill? How did their actions make you feel?

Did you ever have a major accomplishment as a child—get a good grade, win a part in a play or concert, or make a sports team? How did caregivers react to your news? How did you feel?

Did you ever make a mistake—drop and break a dish, lose your homework, forget to do an assigned chore, or whatever? How did your caregivers react? How did that make you feel?

Our experiences as children affect how we regard other people. Are they fair and dependable, erratic and unpredictable, or hostile and negative? Did adults make us feel special or worthless? By thinking about our personal past relationships, we can decide what kinds of caregiver actions will create positive experiences for our children and what kinds of actions will be harmful to them. This knowledge can help us be better parents and caregivers.

INTERVENTION
1. Complete My Own Relationships worksheet.
2. Think about and discuss how the caregiving relationships you have experienced have contributed to what you think about relationships today.

My Own Relationships

Complete this exercise on the three most significant people in your childhood who were responsible at some time for your care.

PERSON IN YOUR LIFE			
Pick one word that describes your relationship with this person and describe why you chose that word.			
What did this person do when you got hurt or very frightened about something? How did that feel for you?			
What did this person do to show you how he or she felt about you? How did this feel for you?			

How do you think your relationship with your child will be the same as or different from any of these relationships?

INTERVENTION 7

Preparing to Be an Attachment Focused Parent:

Feeding Time

TASK
To prepare the mother-to-be to incorporate behaviors and interactions that are supportive of the mother-child relationship through everyday events.

REFERENCE
Chapter 4

ABOUT THIS INTERVENTION
When a baby is first born, feeding occurs many times each day. The focus of each feeding, initially, is satisfying hunger. As the baby begins to grow, he or she will be able to go for longer periods of time between feeding, although feeding times will still be numerous throughout the day (and night!) Whether breast or bottle feeding, feedings become more than just satisfying hunger; they also become times of interaction with mom! Feedings are wonderful times to cuddle, nurture, talk, and exchange warm, loving feelings. The baby begins to learn that "not only is this woman giving me food that warms my tummy and makes me feel good, but she is making me feel good in my heart with the way she talks to me and the way she holds me." Soon the baby begins to associate these wonderful feelings with "mother." It is these positive feelings that go into the development of a well-attached child and parent. The goal of this activity is to think of ways to feed that will be just as emotionally satisfying for the heart as they are nutritionally satisfying for the tummy.

INTRODUCING THIS INTERVENTION
Your newborn baby may need to be fed many times during the day and night. Over time, there will be longer breaks between feedings. However, your baby will want more than just food during feedings. This is a great time for you to interact—to cuddle your baby, talk and sing, and make the baby feel loved and welcomed. The more pleasant and loving an experience you make feedings—whether breast or bottlefeeding the baby—the happier and better adjusted your baby will be.

INTERVENTION
1. Review, complete, and discuss Developing the Mother-Child Relationship Through Feeding handout.

2. An optional intervention for either groups or individuals is to role-play feeding a baby using a doll or a baby volunteer.

Developing the Mother-Child Relationship Through Feeding

Things I want to say to my baby during feeding:

Songs I want to sing to my baby during feeding:

Number of times I want to smile at my baby during feeding:

I will also try to do the following:

Position my baby so we can look at each other during feeding.

Make eye contact with my baby when he or she looks at me.

Watch for signs that my baby uses to tell me when he or she needs a break from feeding just to be with me or that he or she is done eating.

Try to have no distractions in the room when feeding so we can make it a special time between us.

How I think I will feel as I feed my baby:

How I want my baby to feel during feeding time:

Preparing to be an Attachment Focused Parent:
Diapering Time

TASK
To prepare the mother-to-be to incorporate behaviors and interactions that are supportive of the mother-child relationship through everyday events.

REFERENCE
Chapter 4

ABOUT THIS INTERVENTION
Diaper changing occurs frequently each day of a child's early life. Each diaper change provides the parent and child an opportunity to interact. The parent can use these times to practice ways of interacting with the baby that enhance the relationship and bring them closer to each other. The baby can use these times to build trust and affection for his/her parent.

INTRODUCING THIS INTERVENTION
One of the most common activities you will have with your baby when he or she arrives is to change the diaper. This event can occur well over a dozen times a day at first, then lessening as the baby gets older. Diaper changes generally continue to occur through the second year of life and well into the third, and for some children even longer. While diapering is often thought of as a chore and teased about as a job you might save for someone else, it really is a wonderful opportunity to connect with your baby and provide many of the needed relationship components time after time.

Babies need the following things to help them develop positive, loving relationships with their caregivers: Dependability, Interaction, Adoration, Predictability, Excitability, Repetition, and Sensitivity. Each of these qualities helps babies learn to trust others and learn that the world is a great place to be in. Diapering time is a good time to practice some of these behaviors. In this activity, you will begin to think about how diapering can be a positive experience for both you and your baby.

INTERVENTION
1. Review Diapers handout and discuss other ideas about each of these items.

2. Complete Diaper Time worksheet.

Diapers

D ependability: Respond each time your baby cries or calls you.
Be prompt.
Be the one who responds the majority of the time.

I nteraction:Don't just change a diaper—talk with your baby.
Play games during the changing.
Take your time and enjoy the time with your baby.

A doration:Kiss your baby when you change the diapers.
Smile at your baby.
Change your baby with gentle hands.

P redictability:Change diapers with the same routine each time.
Sing the same song each time.
Tell your baby what you are doing when you are doing it.

E xcitability:Sing silly songs.
Play "I'm gonna get you."
Play "Peek-a-boo."

R epetition:Sing the same song over and over again.
Say the same things over and over again.
End with the same kisses after each diaper change.

S ensitivity:Use gentle hands.
Go slowly, try not to rush.
Use a gentle, soft, loving voice.

Diapering Time

RELATIONSHIP INGREDIENT	RELATIONSHIP ACTIONS
DEPENDABILITY	My baby needs me to be dependable. To show I am dependable, I will:
INTERACTION	The more positive interactions I have with my baby, the better it is for us. I will make our diapering interactions fun by:
ADORATION	My baby needs to know how much I adore him or her. I can show this by:
PREDICTABILITY	My baby needs to be able to predict what will happen when he or she has wet diapers. I will show this by:
EXCITABILITY	My baby will learn how to take care of his or her feelings through practicing with different feelings. I can teach my baby to have fun and get excited and then calm down by:
REPETITION	My baby learns through repetition. I can help teach my baby and support our relationship by:
SENSITIVITY	When I am sensitive to my baby's needs and behaviors, my baby learns that he or she is important and learns to be sensitive to others as well. I will show I am sensitive by:

Unit 3

Points To Remember

This unit on Attachment goes beyond the beginning connection and helps the pregnant woman begin to think about what kinds of interactions and activities will help facilitate a healthy, secure attachment between her and the baby after birth. Let us review these interventions:

- *Dream Baby* connects the pregnant woman with her child through her dreams.

- *Family Traditions and Celebrations* acknowledges that traditions and celebrations are a way of supporting relationships within a family, especially those between parent and child. One of the first traditions the woman can establish is how to welcome her baby into the world.

- *Attachment Moments* helps the pregnant woman begin to put her baby foremost in her mind in a way that also supports her self care. Women can use this activity to develop the understanding that they are connected with their child in many ways. What they do to take care of themselves can impact their baby, and what they do to care for and nurture their baby will impact them.

- *Carry and Cuddle: Using a Soft baby Carrier* helps to prepare the pregnant mother to connect with her baby through the use of a soft baby carrier. Wearing your baby has been supported as one way to enhance child-parent attachment.

- *My Baby's First Picture!* is a wonderful way to help celebrate that first picture of a baby taken by ultrasound. There are cautions for this activity, however. Never should an ultrasound be done for the express purpose of a picture—the decision for an ultrasound needs to come from the medical provider. Also, care needs to be taken that experiencing and viewing an ultrasound are positive experiences for the woman—some women become fearful or confused by the experience (see Chapter 7 on the Controversy of Ultrasounds).

- *My Own Relationships* helps the pregnant woman to take a look at relationships in her past and how they contributed to her own sense of being cared for and cared about.

- *Preparing to Be an Attachment Focused Parent: Feeding Time* is an activity that helps the pregnant woman begin to think about what types of things she might do to make feeding a special time between her and her child, enhancing the development of the attachment between them.

- *Preparing to Be an Attachment Focused Parent: Diapering Time* provides a similar experience as the activity just described only using diapering time as the focus.

"Our feelings are our most genuine paths to knowledge."

AUDRE LORDE

Unit 4

Relaxation and Well-Being

KEY CONCEPT

Stress and relaxation are common terms in today's busy world. We are constantly hearing about the stress we experience daily, ways to reduce stress, and the effects of stress. We hear that we need to relax, but we often do not know how. If we do relax, we only seem to be able to do so for no more than a day or two before we jump back into our busy lives.

When a woman is pregnant, these terms—stress and relaxation—take on an even more important meaning as they now pertain to her, her pregnant body, and her unborn child. Undue or excessive stress can affect how she sees the world, her health, her unborn child's health, and her relationships.

There are ways to reduce the stress on the woman, her body, and her unborn child—and that, of course, is relaxation. We know relaxation is important; we also know that relaxation can be difficult to attain. To make your pregnancy less difficult and more relaxing, it is important to make it comfortable, safe, and fun because when a woman feels comfortable and safe, and when she is having fun, she naturally becomes relaxed and naturally decreases the stress in her life.

OUTCOME GOALS

The mother-to-be will:

Identify sources of stress in her life.

Find ways to reduce identified stress.

Find ways to lessen the impact of this stress on her comfort level, feelings of safety, and her sense of fun and enjoyment.

Develop a healthy way of integrating stress management into her everyday life.

INTERVENTIONS

1. The Art of Pondering Poetry

2. Exercise: The Body's Release

3. Breathe...1...2...3...

4. Reach for the Stars!

5. Fantasizing for Calmness and Child

6. Gifts to Your Body

7. Vitamin L: Laughing It Out

8. Playing

INTERVENTION 1

The Art of Pondering Poetry

TASK

To help the mother begin to get a sense of her baby through use of quiet times and poetry.

REFERENCE

Chapters 1, 2

ABOUT THIS INTERVENTION

Focusing attention on something other than the normal everyday things often helps to shift the pregnant woman's mood and level of stress. When she is pregnant, a woman's mind bounces from thought to thought and concern to concern. She thinks about everyday things—like preparing dinner or paying the bills. She thinks about herself—when will she go into labor or can she really do this. And, of course, she thinks about her baby—what will she or he look like or act like. Thinking, dreaming, or fantasizing about the baby is a wonderful way to relax, let go of stress, and feel close to her unborn baby. In this intervention, poetry will be used as a way of shifting attention and developing good feelings around the baby.

INTRODUCING THIS INTERVENTION

One thing that can make your pregnancy more pleasant is learning to relax and shed stress. Often you can reduce stress if you can shift the focus of your attention away from everyday chores and activities. Thinking about your baby can be a wonderful way to relax. In this exercise, we'll use quiet time and poetry to shift your attention from routine chores and onto relaxing with your baby.

INTERVENTION

1. Review The Art of Pondering Poetry handout.

2. Follow the handout directions. (Case examples of Responding to Poetry Handouts can be found in Appendices G and H)

3. Complete and discuss one or both of the Responding to Poetry worksheets.

Your Child's Appeal

I am your Child
All the world waits for my coming.
All the earth watches with interest to see what I shall become.
Civilization hangs in the balance,
For what I am, the world of tomorrow will be.

I am your Child.
I have come into your world, about which I know nothing.
Why I came, I know not;
How I came, I know not.
I am curious; I am interested.

I am your Child.
You hold in your hand my destiny.
You determine, largely, whether I shall succeed or fail.
Give me, I ask you, those things that make for happiness.
Teach me, I ask you, that I may be a blessing to the world.

Written by: Mamie Gene Cole, adapted for this intervention

The Art of Pondering Poetry

STEP 1: QUIET YOUR HOUSE
- Turn off the TV, radio, stereo, and even the telephone.
- If you like, prepare yourself a cup of tea or something similar that helps you to feel relaxed a bit.
- Have the poem handout, worksheet, and something to write with available next to your seat.
- Find a comfortable spot where you can sit back and have some uninterrupted time just for you and your unborn baby.

STEP 2: ENJOY THE POEM
- Once you get comfortable, take out the poem and read it over once or twice.
- Think about it—think about what it means or what it is trying to say.
- Then read it again, this time very slowly as if you were taking a sip of water with each line, but instead you are sipping the words.
- Think about it again.
- Read it once again, this time pretending your unborn child is saying these words to you.
- Think about it again...and again...and again.

STEP 3: RESPOND TO THE POEM
- Once you have read the poem as many times as you want, take out the worksheet or your journal or whatever you might have ready.
- Begin by taking a deep breath, holding it for a moment, then letting out a complete exhale.
- Repeat this breathing exercise.
- Repeat again, as many times as you feel you want to now and as you proceed.
- Write or draw about the feelings you experienced as you read this poem.
- Write or draw about what it means to you.
- Write or draw what your baby might be trying to tell you if he or she did say these words to you.
- Write or draw what else you might envision your baby saying to you.

STEP 4: REMEMBER TO RELAX
- Remember the goal is to relax.
- If you feel uncomfortable at all, take some deep breaths and focus on relaxing your mind and your body.
- If it does not feel relaxing, try again later.
- Do not stress yourself over doing this "perfectly." The only perfect way is your way. You know what your mind and body need to feel good.
- Try this with other poems or writings you enjoy.
- Think about this as a way of feeling close to your baby.
- Try to have fun with this exercise. That's the point.

Responding to Poetry

Draw your initial feelings in response to the poetry exercise:

Responding to Poetry

What might your child say to you?

INTERVENTION 2

Exercise: The Body's Release

TASK:
To help the mother develop various ways of relaxing and decreasing the stress she encounters in her life.

REFERENCE
Chapters 1, 2

ABOUT THIS INTERVENTION
Modern science has been able to develop interventions, medications, and other therapies to treat stress overload, depression, and other difficulties that can affect individuals today. Surprisingly, one of the most effective interventions is the common sense intervention of exercise. Exercise combats depression and helps the body release stress and anxiety. It is free and available to everyone. The varieties are endless. This intervention will help the pregnant woman to think about how to integrate exercise into her life.

INTRODUCING THIS INTERVENTION
Science has come up with therapies and medicines to treat stress and depression. But one of the most effective and inexpensive treatments is regular exercise. Keep in mind that exercise doesn't have to be violent or extra-vigorous physical activity. It can be gentle walks to appreciate the flowers, shopping in the mall, doing gardening or household chores, and other activities. What we'll do today is list the activities you're already doing and come up with others that might be fun to add. Then you can check with your health care provider to see which exercises fit your needs and your stage of pregnancy.

INTERVENTION
1. Before starting any new exercise program or increasing your activity levels when pregnant, be sure to consult your health care provider.
2. Create a list of the things you do now that can be considered physical activity or exercise, using the What I Do and What I Want to Do worksheet.
3. Create a list of things you want to add to that list.
4. Using the Exercise Chart, keep track of the time you spend in physical activity or exercise. At the end of each day, chart your mood. Pay attention to the amount of activity/exercise and the nature of your mood on a daily basis and over time.
5. Discuss your experiences with someone.

What I Do and What I Want To Do

These are things I already do for physical activity and exercise:

1. _____

2. _____

3. _____

4. _____

5. _____

6. _____

7. _____

8. _____

9. _____

10. _____

11. _____

12. _____

13. _____

14. _____

15. _____

16. _____

17. _____

18. _____

19. _____

20. _____

These are things I would like to do for physical activity and exercise:

1. _____

2. _____

3. _____

4. _____

5. _____

6. _____

7. _____

8. _____

9. _____

10. _____

11. _____

12. _____

13. _____

14. _____

15. _____

16. _____

17. _____

18. _____

19. _____

20. _____

Exercise Chart

Minutes	M	T	W	T	F	S	S	M	T	W	T	F	S	S	M	T	W	T	F	S	S	M	T	W	T	F	S	S
120																												
115																												
110																												
105																												
100																												
95																												
90																												
85																												
80																												
75																												
70																												
65																												
60																												
55																												
50																												
45																												
40																												
35																												
30																												
25																												
20																												
15																												
10																												
5																												
Total																												
Good	□																											
Indifferent																												
Down/Depressed	○																											

Keep track of your exercise. Color in a square for each 5 minutes of exercise or activity you have. For example, one day you might have 20 minutes of walking around the mall shopping for baby items, 10 minutes vacuuming, and 30 minutes walking around the neighborhood with a friend. That would be a total of 60 minutes for that particular day. The goal is to develop a pattern of exercise and activity that keeps you active, feeling good, and that decreases the effects of stress on your body. Remember: CONSULT WITH YOUR HEALTH CARE PROVIDER BEFORE STARTING ANY NEW EXERCISE PROGRAM.

INTERVENTION 3

Breathe...1...2...3...

TASK

To help the mother-to-be to learn to use her own breathing patterns to decrease the impact of stress and enhance relaxation.

REFERENCE

Chapters 1, 2

ABOUT THIS INTERVENTION

Breathing is something we each do continuously everyday. It is an unconscious action. Unless there is some difficulty breathing or unless attention is purposely focused on our breathing, it is unlikely we think about it much. In this intervention, you will help the pregnant woman to use breathing to increase focus and relaxation.

INTRODUCING THIS INTERVENTION

Breathing is necessary for our survival, but we seldom think much about how we breathe. Our normal breaths give us enough oxygen to live. Deep breathing increases our oxygen flow and helps us relax. Today we'll focus on how to breathe deeply for relaxation. Then you can try this exercise during the week and see if it helps you relax.

INTERVENTION

1. Review and practice the intervention on the Breathing Exercises handout.

2. Complete the Breathe...1...2...3 worksheet over the next week.

3. Discuss the results with someone.

Breathe...1...2...3...

BREATHE
- Notice your breathing.
- How deep are the breaths that you take?
- Which parts of your body move as you breathe?
- Do you breathe through your nose or mouth?
- How long does it take you to breathe in and out?

NOW, TRY THIS
- Get into a comfortable position
- Breathe through your nose
- Pace your breath to the count of three, breathing deeply into your lungs and abdomen...1...2...3...
- Hold your breath for the count of three...1...2...3...
- Slowly exhale through your nose to the count of three, emptying your lungs and abdomen of as much air as possible...1...2...3...
- Rest for the count of three...1...2...3
- Repeat this process three times
- With each repetition, notice how your body feels
- Think about your emotions
- Think about your level of alertness
- Repeat the entire process as many times as you are comfortable
- Focus on the new sensations and feelings this slow, deep breathing creates for you

YOU HAVE JUST MASTERED A NEW SKILL!

Practice this breathing exercise daily for a week. Notice throughout the week the way your body feels. Many people describe feeling more energy, feeling calmer inside, not getting upset so easily, and slowing down to a comfortable pace in their lives. Use the Breathe...1...2...3 worksheet to track and describe your feelings.

Breathe..1...2...3...

DAY OF WEEK	NUMBER OF BREATHING PRACTICES	BREATHING REFLECTIONS (FEELINGS, THOUGHTS, AND EXPERIENCES)

INTERVENTION 4

Reach for the Stars!

TASK
To help the mother develop a way of reducing the impact of stress through stretching.

REFERENCE
Chapters 1, 2

ABOUT THIS INTERVENTION
Stretching is a way of reducing the tension held in muscles and thereby reducing the impact of stress on the body. It helps the body move better. It decreases the stress on the muscles when they are used for other things. It helps promote better circulation and it helps a person to feel good all over.

INTRODUCING THIS INTERVENTION
Simple stretches are another relaxing exercise you can try. Often our muscles tense or cramp if we've done something for a long time. When we stop and stretch the tense muscle, we relax it and the pain goes away. The stretching can help your blood circulate and make you feel better. Here's a simple stretch to try.

INTERVENTION
1. Follow the directions on Reach for the Stars handout.

Reach for the Stars!

Stand in a comfortable position

Reach your arms up over your head

Be aware of your balance.
If you get at all uncomfortable,
sit safely in a chair and
try this exercise.

Stretch your arms out toward the
sky, as if you were reaching for
the stars or the sun.

Hold that reach for as long
as you can—5-10 seconds is good.

Try this with your palms up,
palms down, your fingers laced,
or your hands loose and free.

You can easily do this stretch from
a chair or even standing on your
tip toes, if you have good balance.
Remember, pregnancy can change
your body's balance and take
you by surprise, so never push
to a point of discomfort.

Use this exercise several times
throughout the day to help you
decrease the effects of stress
and to also help you to
refresh yourself.
It can be very energizing!!!

INTERVENTION 5

Fantasizing for Calmness and Child

TASK
To help the mother begin to improve her sense of well-being and get a better sense of her baby through connecting with her fantasies.

REFERENCE
Chapters 1, 2

ABOUT THIS INTERVENTION
Fantasizing is one of the most helpful activities a woman can engage in during her pregnancy. Fantasy can help a woman to integrate what she once thought her life would hold for her with what her life is really offering to her. It helps prepare her to welcome and accept her child into the world and into her arms. Fantasizing can be a powerful force if practiced in a healthy, goal-centered manner. This intervention will be used to explore and practice using fantasy for both relaxation purposes and to connect mother with unborn child.

INTRODUCING THIS INTERVENTION
Many of us fantasize about what life will be like at some point in our future. Now that you've got a baby in your future, do you think about what life will be like for you and your baby? What are things you'll do for your baby? How will your baby react to your care? What will your baby do? When will your baby first call you "Mama"? How will that make you feel? What will you make or buy for your baby? How will your baby look in those new clothes? When you fantasize about all the practical things a mother needs to do and about how the baby will respond, you begin to prepare for your new life. This can ease your tension and stress. It will relax you and make your pregnancy more pleasant.

INTERVENTION
1. Follow the directions on Fantasizing for Calmness and Child handout.
2. Record your fantasy in your journal or the Fantasy worksheet.
3. Allow yourself to practice often.
4. Make it an enjoyable experience.

Fantasizing for Calmness and Child

Using the following directions will help to relax you and bring you to a place of feeling calm and centered. Through these techniques, you can choose an area to focus on and let your mind flow into fantasy. The letters in the word CALM can help you remember what the steps are so you can engage in this exercise anytime you want to.

C	A	L	M
CENTER	ALERT	LET IT GO	MEDITATE
Centering involves three simple steps: 1) Get comfortable 2) Breathe slowly and deeply, and 3) Feel connected to the earth as if there was an invisible string running from the center of your belly just behind your belly button to an anchor in the warm, brown, life-giving earth.	Staying alert is important, as you need to remain mindful of what you are focusing on and how your body feels. Staying alert simply involves saying to yourself "I am calm, I am relaxed, I am alert" several times at the beginning of your fantasy activity and as needed throughout it whenever you might begin to feel tense or sleepy.	Letting it go means just that: letting your mind empty itself of all the worries, thoughts, things to do, conflicts, concerns, and ideas you were carrying around with you. Pretend a warm wind gently blows through your head and washes out all the clutter it has been carrying around. Allow your mind to fill instead with warm, loving, gently drifting fog-like clouds. Remember to breathe and remain alert as you "let it go" and leave a space to create.	Meditate is a word that often reminds people of sitting cross-legged and chanting. It can mean this, but it can also mean thinking deeply about something. Once you are relaxed, centered, and calm, and your mind is emptied of all its clutter, it will be time to begin filling that warm and foggy space with your fantasies. Focus on the gently drifting fog. As it clears, begin to see in your mind yourself as a mother, holding this newly arrived baby. Notice how you hold the baby. Notice how you touch the baby and how you look at and watch your baby. Look at your baby and notice how that baby looks back at you. Explore the smells, the textures, the colors, and the emotions you get when you look at your baby. Allow your mind to wander, continuing to explore your fantasies about yourself and your baby. If any difficult or uncomfortable thoughts come up, do not fight them; instead just let them float right through your mind, allowing the gentle warm breeze to wash them away. Refocus then on the loving relationship you are focusing on.

Now journal your fantasies in your own journal or the worksheet provided.

DATE_____

My fantasy was about...

INTERVENTION 6

Gifts to Your Body

TASK
To help the mother-to-be learn to nurture herself through giving gifts to her body.

REFERENCE
Chapter 1, 2

ABOUT THIS INTERVENTION
It is not always easy to separate mind and body. Thoughts, at any particular time, are often connected to the state and comfort of the body. Pregnancy forces the body adjust to differences in many ways. The body learns to work in different ways. For instance, the pregnant woman's body has to continually reconfigure how to maintain balance as the unborn baby grows. Leg muscles need to work a little harder to move around the added weight that normally comes with being pregnant. There are many things the pregnant woman's body does for mother and her unborn child, so it is important to think about what can be done to take care of and nurture her body.

INTRODUCING THIS INTERVENTION
When you are pregnant, your body has to cope with many changes. As the baby grows, your balance is thrown off and your body has to adjust to new ways of walking, sitting down, and standing up. You're carrying more weight, so your legs have to work a little harder.

Because your body is adjusting to so many changes, it is important to think of things you can do to take care of your body.

INTERVENTION
1. Review the Gifts to Your Body handout.

2. Explore the items listed as possible ways to give a gift to your body.

3. Think of your own ideas.

4. Add to the list.

5. Elaborate or modify the items to suit you, your budget, and your lifestyle.

Gifts To Your Body

The following are some ideas for gifts you can give your body.

GIFT IDEA	DESCRIPTION	ALTERNATIVES/MODIFICATION
MASSAGE	A total body massage is, of course, a wonderful gift for your body. Some massage therapists offer special massage designed for pregnant women.	1. Foot or hand massages can be equally as helpful to the body. 2. Some massage schools give discount rates on massages.
MANICURE/ PEDICURE	A manicure is a simple and short but very pampering activity you can give to your body. Pedicures are equally as pampering, especially as it becomes difficult to polish your toes.	1. Some mothers-to-be help prepare for delivery by getting a manicure and pedicure near the time of delivery. 2. These activities can also be done with a group of girl friends, or get your spouse's help.
FACIALS	Facials can be very pampering. There are many different types, and it will be most helpful to explore the type that sounds best for you.	1. If a professional facial seems unreasonable, again, a girl friend get-together can be fun. 2. There are many home facial products that may be fun and pampering to try.
PAJAMA DAY	Some days call for staying home and relaxing in your own surroundings. Staying in your favorite pajamas all day can help this be a certainty.	1. Plan the day off by stocking up your most pampering foods, music, books, magazines, and/or movies. 2. If you do not have the whole day, breakfast in bed can be a very pampering experience. This will depend on a friend or spouse who is willing to wait on you.

Think of your own gifts to your body and write them below.

INTERVENTION 7

Vitamin L: Laughing It Out

TASK
To learn to relax and feel better about yourself through humor and laughter.

REFERENCE
Chapters 1, 2

ABOUT THIS INTERVENTION
Laughing is one of the most natural releases available for stress and tension. Everyone has had moments when they began to laugh at something that could not possibly be funny. But they laughed anyway. Why? Because it is the body's natural way to move out of difficult places and to help get rid of difficult feelings. Everyone needs to make sure they have enough humor and laughter in their lives. Think of it as Vitamin L for well-being and peace of mind, similar to Vitamin C for physical health. Each of these helps to both heal and protect from future problems. In this intervention, the goal will be to add some Vitamin L back into everyday life.

INTRODUCING THIS INTERVENTION
Some folks say laughter is the best medicine. It releases chemicals in your body that make you relax and feel better, so it is a great medicine. Have you ever laughed at something that wasn't really funny? Why? Laughter helps us get rid of difficult feelings.

It also expresses joy and pleasure. And we all need those feelings in our lives. While you're pregnant, it is especially important to have joy and humor in your life. Think of laughter as Vitamin L. It's as important to your mental well-being as Vitamin C is to your physical well-being. Laughter, Vitamin L, can heal current hurts and help prevent future problems. Let's look at ways to keep laughter in your life.

INTERVENTION
1. Explore and discuss the Vitamin L worksheet.

Vitamin L

When was the last time you really laughed a great belly laugh? Think about how that felt.

What makes you laugh now?

What kinds of things do you think are funny?

Can you laugh at yourself? Can you laugh at some of your mistakes and let them go?

Add to the list below things you might do to help add some extra Vitamin L into your life and laugh!

- Watch a funny movie
- Play with a child
- Dance naked in your living room
- Read a joke book
- Listen to others laugh
- Talk to an old friend about some fun times you shared
- Ask your mom about what you used to do as a child that made her laugh
- Write a story remembering as many details as possible of the funniest day of your life
- Go out for a night of stand-up comedy at a comedy club
- Draw or paint a picture of the funniest thing you have ever seen
- Play charades with some friends
- Allow yourself to make mistakes
- Do something backwards
-
-
-
-
-
-
-
-

INTERVENTION 8

Playing

TASK
To help the mother-to-be reconnect with the part of her that loved to play.

REFERENCE
Chapters 1, 2

ABOUT THIS INTERVENTION
Play is a remedy for many of life's stresses and difficulties. Playing helps the body heal and relax. Playing helps the mind release many of the numerous thoughts and worries it carries around. Playing can just be fun. There are an endless number of ways to play and many wonderful advantages to playing:

- Play doesn't require money. Play that is free is just as easy as play that can cost a small fortune.
- Play can be done alone, with one other person, or with a group.
- Play is diverse in nature; one can play by making crafts, through using drama and imagination, by exploring a playground, through a board game, by silly body actions, or through participating in a sport.
- Play can be competitive or skill building.
- Play can be done by anyone.

INTRODUCING THIS INTERVENTION
What were some of your favorite activities when you played as a child? Did you play games, dance or sing to music, make mud pies, pretend you were a superhero, or what? How did playing make you feel?

Play can relax you, release tensions and worries, and make you feel better. Some forms of play cost money; others are free. Some have to be done with teams; others can be done alone.

Let's look at the play you've enjoyed during earlier stages of your life and list things you can do now for play and relaxation. If the play you want to do is physically strenuous, check with your health care provider to find out whether it's safe for you and your baby at this stage of your pregnancy.

INTERVENTION
1. Complete the When I Played—Then and Now worksheet on play.
2. Discuss and process what you discover.
3. Explore the Ways to Play handout.
4. Discuss some of these ideas.

Remember: Never begin a new level of activity without consulting with your health care provider and making sure it is safe during your pregnancy.

When I Played—Then and Now

List some of the ways you used to play as a child:

What was fun about these things you used to do? Could you do them now?

Which of these things can you imagine yourself doing with your child as he or she grows?

What do you do now that you would consider play? How do you feel while you are doing these things? How do you feel afterwards?

The Play I Do	Feelings When I Play	Feelings After I Have Played

What kinds of play would be fun and relaxing for you during this time in your life when you are pregnant?

Take one of your ideas and do it! Just go out and play!
Relax and have fun!

Ways To Play

Sculpt something out of clay or play dough

Make a sand castle

Paint a picture with watercolors

Color in a coloring book

Play Jacks

Bounce a ball

Swim

Have a tea party

Make a mask

Dress up

Play the game Candyland

Play in a sand box

Play peek-a-boo with a friend's baby

Play hide and seek in your house with a 4-year-old

Make cookies with a 6-year-old

Paint your feet with watercolors

Sing out loud

Take a walk

Go to a park and sit on a swing (bet you can't resist actually swinging!)

Have a picnic in your living room

Build a fort out of blankets and pillows

Play Go Fish

Make a sculpture with shaving cream

Finger paint

Build a Lego castle

Stack blocks

Play with baby dolls

Sail boats in the bathtub

Blow bubbles

Use markers to create a picture of a tree with flowers

Make an ice cream sundae

REMEMBER...

THE BEST WAY TO LEARN TO PLAY AGAIN

IS FROM A CHILD

Unit 4

Points To Remember

Knowing how to relax and maintaining a positive sense of well-being are helpful to everyone throughout life. During pregnancy, the ability to relax is especially helpful in minimizing the impacts of the many changes and accommodations required. A positive sense of well-being may enhance the experience of pregnancy and protect the woman's energies from unnecessary stress. Let us review the interventions:

- *The Art of Pondering Poetry* allows for a time of reflection through the medium of poetry. Poetry often provides a gentle rhythm carrying us back to our own childhoods, allowing us to let go of the stresses of the day. Relaxing in this manner allows the imagination to take over.

- *Exercise: The Body's Release* is an activity based on exercise. We know that exercise is powerful in combating the stresses of daily life and things like depression. Remember, however, no pregnant woman should begin an exercise program without the approval and supervision of her medical provider.

- *Breathe...1...2...3...*is an activity that makes use of deep breathing as a way of centering on and releasing stored up stress and frustration.

- *Reach for the Stars!* uses stretching as a way of relaxing the body and the spirit. Stretching can be helpful in releasing stored up stress and frustration. It is also a gentle way to get the body moving (again, every woman should check with her medical provider before beginning any exercise program, even stretching).

- *Fantasizing for Calmness and Child* provides a simple step-by-step approach to becoming calm, centered, and focused on the unborn child.

- *Gifts to Your Body* gives the pregnant woman permission to pamper herself—always a source of nurturance and relaxation.

- *Vitamin L: Laughing It Out* emphasizes humor as a way of letting go of the daily stresses we all encounter through our own sense of fun and laughter.

- *Playing* is designed to reconnect the pregnant woman with the fun side of life. Playing is a natural release enjoyed daily by children—it should be a daily requirement for all women, pregnant or not, as well.

"You cannot know what you do not feel."

MARYA MANNES

Unit 5

Honoring the Woman in Me

KEY CONCEPT

Healthy relationships of any type begin with a healthy sense of self-esteem and positive self-image. Feeling good about one's self decreases the impact of outside stressors and instills a sense of control over one's life. Self-confidence is supportive of a healthy, normal course of pregnancy. When a woman can feel satisfied with who she is and what her skills and talents are, she will most likely be able to approach mothering in the same fashion.

OUTCOME GOALS

The mother-to-be will:

Verbalize statements of increased self-esteem.

Report feelings of having some control over her life (as opposed to feeling powerless).

Describe two activities she engages in to support her feelings of self worth and self-confidence.

INTERVENTIONS

1. Nurturing the Woman in Me

2. Conserving Energy: Saying NO

3. The Sexual Me

4. Affirmations

5. Inner Healing: Ghosts of the Past

6. Inner Child

7. Celebrations of Me: Marking the Occasion

8. What Kind of Baby Was I?

INTERVENTION 1

Nurturing the Woman in Me

TASK
To recognize and nurture the woman inside the pregnant body.

REFERENCE
Chapter 2

ABOUT THIS INTERVENTION
When a woman becomes pregnant, she begins to go through many changes and transformations. One of these transformations occurs with her body. Her breasts begin to swell and enlarge in preparation for feeding her child. Her belly swells with the growth of her unborn child. She may become uncomfortable at times, unable to find a good position for sitting or falling asleep. She may feel the baby is taking over her body, and she may begin to lose her sense of who she is now as well as who she used to be. Her clothes no longer fit, her routines need adjustment, her energy may vary, and even her skin and hair may change. Some women ride out these changes without any difficulty; some eagerly accept them as signs of their child and become excited with each new change; others become uncomfortable and distressed with the changes, often to the point of depression and lethargy; and still others resist or ignore the changes and make no adjustments in their lives.

The woman having no or little difficulty may want to use this intervention just to get ideas of how to continue to care for herself and nurture herself during her pregnancy. The woman having moderate to severe difficulty with accepting the changes to her body may need more directive interventions.

INTRODUCING THIS INTERVENTION
Your pregnancy is causing a lot of changes in your body. Your breasts may be enlarging in preparation for feeding your baby. Your belly is getting bigger. You may have trouble finding a comfortable position for sitting or sleeping. Your energy levels may vary. You're having to change some of your routines.

In the midst of all these changes, you need to find ways to take care of yourself. What makes you feel happy, pampered, loved? Find ways to nurture yourself that also help your baby.

INTERVENTION
1. Have the woman complete the What Makes Me Feel Good worksheet. Review and discuss the ideas generated.

2. Have the woman choose one of the things off her list to do each day just to pamper herself.

3. Explore the lists of Nurturing Activities that the woman might not have thought of but might like to try.

What Makes Me Feel Good

Make a list below of the things that make you feel good or warm or safe or nurtured or taken care of. You might include things that others did for you that you found comforting or made you feel better. You might include things that make you feel good in your mind, in your heart, or with your body.

1.

2.

3.

4.

5.

6.

7.

8.

9.

10.

11.

12.

13.

14.

15.

16.

17.

18.

19.

20.

Nuturing Activities

Bubble baths

Lighted candles

Incense

Fresh flowers

Wearing pajamas all day

A warm mug of tea

A warm mug of tomato soup

Lavender scented lotion

Rubbing lotion on your body

Reading a short book

Getting deep into a novel

Calling an old friend

Writing letters

Watching an old movie

Watching a new movie

Macaroni & cheese

Resting with your childhood blanket

Music

Having a manicure

Having a pedicure

Having a professional massage

Hot spiced cider

Watching your favorite Disney movie

Finding memories in an antique store

Feeding ducks

Hot chocolate (with or without marshmallows)

Apple pie (with or without ice cream)

Drinking tea from a real teacup

Popcorn with real butter

Lying in the sun

Having a fire in the fireplace

Buying a pair of fuzzy slippers

Rocking in a rocking chair

Mashed potatoes with gravy

Looking at old photographs

Reading your old diaries

Letting someone just hold you

Silence

Daydreaming

Keeping a journal

Preparing a party just for you

Having a girlfriend sleep over

Grilled cheese sandwiches

Sitting on a park bench

Watching children play

Getting a library book on "comfort"

Painting a picture

Strolling in a park

Shopping

Pretending the baby has been born and you are sharing a quiet moment in his or her room

INTERVENTION 2

Conserving Energy: Saying NO

TASK
To reinforce the conservation of personal energy through saying NO.

REFERENCE
Chapter 2

ABOUT THIS INTERVENTION
Many people have difficulty saying NO. They have trouble saying NO to purchases, NO to extra activities, NO to additional work. An idea exists that the more you do, the better and stronger you are. Not true! A strong person is able to balance the amount of resources they have with the demands on those resources. It is much healthier to decline a party invitation, stay home, and relax with a quiet activity than to go to a party tired, stay late creating more of a burden on your body, then go home only to be exhausted and cranky the next day. It is better to say NO to watching a friend's children for the evening than to take on this responsibility depleting your energy and finding it hard to find the time to pay your bills or do your grocery shopping. Pregnancy puts a large demand on personal resources. The body needs energy to create the changes necessary for a healthy mother and child. Energy is needed to supply the unborn child. Food intake that used to sustain only you, now sustains a growing child, which creates added demands on the body.

INTRODUCING THIS INTERVENTION
Do you ever have trouble saying NO to people or activities? Lots of us have trouble saying NO and end up overcommitted, tired, and stressed. During your pregnancy, your energy levels may not be as high as at other times in your life. As a result, you need to be able to say NO and mean it if you are going to get the rest you and your baby need.

You are important, and so is your baby. You have the right to put yourselves first— before demands of friends, family members, and coworkers. Save your energy for the essentials of you and your baby.

NO is stronger and more believable if you avoid excuses. Excuses are ways to avoid things; reasons are explanations of needs, priorities, and prior commitments. You can also say NO without giving an explanation. The important thing is to know what is best for you and your baby and not be swayed by pleas of others who aren't thinking about what is best for you.

INTERVENTION:
Who will want to be involved in your baby's life? Think of people in your life. What about people from the father's family? Which people will be helpful and supportive to your baby? Are there some people who should not be around your baby?

1. Discuss Types of NO handout.
2. Complete the Meaning of NO worksheet.
3. Review and discuss this worksheet.

4. Review the Beliefs and Behaviors of NO worksheet. With the woman, discuss each point and indicate which ones she believes in and does now and which she has difficultly accepting or trouble doing now. For the ones she has trouble with now, assist her in making a plan that will move her closer to achieving the self confidence to say NO when she needs to.

5. Use the Role-Plays handout to practice saying "NO."

6. Explore feelings for each person in saying NO and hearing NO. Variations on this might include:

    - sharing the most difficult time of saying NO
    - sharing the easiest time of saying NO
    - sharing the scariest time of saying NO

Types of NO's

NO	REASON	TYPE
NO	*I have something else planned for that night.*	Prior commitments take precedence over doing favors for others.
NO	*I have plans to finish my laundry and pay my bills tonight so I can have my weekend free.*	Personal priorities take precedence over doing favors for others.
NO	*I have had to stay up late the last three nights and need to go to bed early tonight.*	Caring for self and attending to personal needs take priority over doing favors for others.
NO	(Saying or doing nothing.)	Avoidance—not saying anything, not answering the phone, avoiding answering the door, etc.
NO	*Sure I can do that (but then not following through or cancelling at the last minute when you knew you did not want to in the first place).*	Passive-aggressive—this type of NO sets others up. It creates problems and creates an impression that you cannot keep your word and that you are not strong enough to stand up for youself.
NO	*I won't be able to do that tonight.*	Setting limits without the need to share reasons for your decisions.
NO	*I can't do that tonight but maybe I could help you out next Thursday. Then I can get more prepared and have more energy to be there for you.* *I'll think about it and get back to you.*	This is a negotiation, setting limits on the present but remaining open to a later arrangement. This is great to do if you really want to do both—just do it on your terms. Gives you time to think about it and decide what you can and cannot do, as well as what you do and do not want to do.
NO	*Being pregnant is great, but I find I am getting tired more easily than I used to. So I need to stay home tonight and take care of me and my baby.*	Taking care of yourself anytime, especially when pregnant, is a way of respecting yourself and your baby. It also lets others know you are worthy of being treated like number one.
NO	*Well, I would like to but I really have a lot of stuff to do...my brother might come over tonight...I am not sure if I have to help Cindy tonight...I can see...but I think that Tim might need me to do something for him....*	Excuses—these are not reasons but numerous excuses. They indicate ambivalence and make you less believable. They also suggest false promises that you might work something out, when that is not what you are planning.

Meaning of NO

1. Make a list of the ways in which you say no to others. For each of these indicate if you think what you say is a reason or an excuse. Think about ways you can make your NO more powerful and also help yourself to feel more in charge of your time, your body, and your life.

WAYS I SAY NO	REASON	EXCUSE	WAYS I MIGHT IMPROVE MY "NO"

2. What does NO mean to you when you hear it from others?

   Think about your relationships with others. How do they change when you hear NO from the different people in your life?

3. Say the following three times each day when you wake up:

   I have the right to say NO and I will not feel guilty about it.

Beliefs and Behaviors of NO

Indicate whether you agree or disagree with each belief statement. Indicate whether you do or do not do each of the behavior statements.

BELIEFS	AGREE	DISAGREE
1. I have the right to say NO.		
2. I do not have to apologize for saying NO.		
3. It is fine to provide a reason for saying NO.		
4. I do not need to make a list of excuses when I say NO.		
5. My needs are just as important as those of others.		
6. I need to put the needs of my baby and myself above those of others.		
7. Other people cannot bully or manipulate me into saying Yes when I need to say NO.		
8. When I say NO, it does not mean I am rejecting the other person; it merely means I cannot meet their needs right now.		
9. I am important and my needs and wants can come first.		
10. Caring for my unborn child takes precedence over other people's needs.		
BEHAVIORS	**DO**	**DON'T DO**
1. When I say NO, I look people in the eye and speak clearly.		
2. When I say NO, I am direct and honest.		
3. I do not change my mind when someone begs, pleads, or tries to manipulate me into saying Yes.		
4. I avoid making excuses for not saying yes.		
5. I avoid making promises I do not mean and cannot keep.		
6. I do not say yes when I mean NO.		
7. I hang up the phone when someone calls asking me to buy things.		
8. I avoid the people I have said NO to before or I avoid people I have said yes to and then have never followed through with.		
9. I speak in a firm voice and do not begin to waiver in my decision.		
10. I do not feel guilty for saying NO when I have other things in my life that take priority—for instance, my unborn child and me.		

"NO" Role-Plays

Use these situations to discuss saying No, how to do it, and how to feel good about it.

It is Wednesday night and your best friend asks you to watch her three kids tonight so she can go out dancing. You are three months pregnant and have been experiencing a lot of morning sickness and you need to work at 8 a.m.	Your mother-in-law calls to say Aunt Goldie has just dropped by. They invite themselves for dinner at your home tonight. You have just worked 8 hours, have nothing prepared, and your feet are tired and a little swollen.	Your sister asks if she can have your car tonight. She promises she will bring it back early enough for you to do the shopping you had planned.
You are in your seventh month of pregnancy and your mother asks you to clean her house for Thanksgiving dinner and make three pies.	Your husband asks you to wash his favorite jeans for tomorrow even though you have just finished all the laundry.	The PTA from your older child's school asks you to head the Crafts Bazaar this fall. You will be 8 months pregnant when the Bazaar takes place.
The doctor has ordered you on bedrest for the next week because she says you have been doing too much. Your friends insist you come over and join them for a night of movies.	You receive a phone call from someone telling you that you need this new crib that has just come out. It rocks the baby to sleep on its own. It is only $1600. They tell you it will cut the time you need to spend with your baby in half.	It is your anniversary and your boyfriend has brought over a bottle of champagne. He wants you to celebrate with him and tells you a little champagne will not hurt your unborn child. He is sure because his cousin Patty drank all the time during her pregnancy and her baby seems just fine.
Your friends, Sally and Dan, have invited you and your husband over to play cards with them. Your husband wants to go. Last time you went, however, Sally and Dan drank quite a bit and got into a big fight. This fight was very scary and your husband was almost drawn into it because Dan was beginning to get violent with Sally.	This week you have been invited to a Tupperware party on Monday, a wedding shower on Wednesday, a birthday dinner on Friday, and your company party on Saturday. In addition, you have your usual pregnancy support group on Tuesday night and plans with a friend to see a movie Thursday—which you made three weeks ago. Who do you say no to? How do you do it?	Your brother has asked to come by with his friend Max tonight because he wants to pick up some of his sports equipment he left there. Whenever your brother comes, he generally visits for a couple of hours and eats whatever he can find in your kitchen. You have a lot of fun with your brother, but Max scares you. He has a long history of drug use and you heard he often carries a gun.

Address these questions:

How do I say NO? What kind of reason can I give? How do I feel when I say NO? How does the other person feel when they hear me say NO? How can I resist giving in and saying yes when I really want to say NO?

INTERVENTION 3

The Sexual Me

TASK
To recognize and validate sexual feelings and needs during pregnancy.

REFERENCE
Chapter 2

ABOUT THIS INTERVENTION
The purpose of this intervention is not to encourage or promote sexual behaviors during pregnancy but instead it is designed to support and validate the sexual feelings and intimacy issues that may arise. Sex during pregnancy should always be discussed with the primary health care provider. During a normal pregnancy progressing well, sex during pregnancy is not a problem even into the last trimester. If, however, there are any complications or concerns, certain restrictions or prohibitions may be necessary to support the mother and her unborn child through the pregnancy.

Discussion with the primary health care provider can often lead to a decrease in anxiety and the development of increased comfort over sex during pregnancy for both the woman and her partner. Completing the worksheets included for this intervention may also be helpful. The goals of this intervention are to increase comfort levels with sex during pregnancy, increase communication between partners, and support a woman's natural sexuality.

INTRODUCING THIS INTERVENTION
Pregnancy may or may not impact a woman's sexual feelings, her sexual preferences, or her sexual behaviors. For some women, the changes in their bodies make various parts of their bodies more or less sensitive than before the pregnancy. Other women lose their sexual desire altogether during pregnancy. Some woman experience pain during intercourse that is not only uncomfortable but may also create anxiety over the safety of the baby. And some women find that their partner's sexual behaviors change because they become fearful that they may in some way harm or hurt the woman or her unborn child. In actuality, the fetus is well protected by the muscles of the uterus, the bag of waters or amniotic sac, and the mucous plug, which prevents outside organisms and substances from entering the womb.

INTERVENTION
1. Fill out the three worksheets.
2. Discuss the first one with your health care provider.
3. Role-play ways to bring up ideas related to sexuality with your partner.

Sexuality During Pregnancy
TALKING WITH MY HEALTH CARE PROVIDER

This worksheet is designed to help you organize your questions for your health care provider. Several common questions are listed. Add any of your own questions or other issues you may be concerned about as well. You can discuss these with your health care provider or you can share this worksheet with him or her.

- Would it be okay for me to have sexual intercourse during my pregnancy?

- Is there a limit on how often I can have sex?

- Can intercourse hurt my baby? If my husband goes in very deep when we have intercourse, can that hurt the baby?

- What if I feel pain during intercourse?

- Are other types of sexual activity okay? Such as masturbation, oral sex, etc.

- Will having an orgasm hurt my baby or cause me to go into labor?

- Sometimes when my partner and I are being close to each other without having intercourse (kissing, hugging, making out, and so forth), I begin to feel strong sexual feelings that seem to cause sensations in my uterus; can these harm my baby or cause me to go into labor?

- What if my partner or I have a history of (or currently have) sexually transmitted diseases?

- Sometimes when we have been trying to make love, we have some difficulty because I seem so dry in my vagina; is this normal and what can I do to help?

- Will sexual activity with my breasts cause my breasts to start making milk or cause leaking?

- Things I used to like or things that used to make me feel excited are not the same since I became pregnant. Is this normal? Is there anything I can do about it?

Other questions or concerns:

Sexuality During Pregnancy

LISTENING TO MY BODY AND MY FEELINGS

- I have checked with my health care provider that sexual activity during pregnancy is safe for me: YES   NO

- Since I became pregnant, I have noticed the following changes in how my body feels before, during, or after sexual activity (things that excite me, body sensations, pain, etc.)

- Since I became pregnant, I have noticed the following changes in my emotions before, during, or after sexual activity (emotional ups and downs, feeling like crying, feeling more sexually satisfied than ever before, no sexual desire at all)

- Sexual activities I feel like trying since I have become pregnant. Examples: Different sexual positions, shared masturbation, etc.

- What I wish my partner and I might do when we are being sexual or making love. Examples: More foreplay, manual stimulation of clitoris, use of a lubricant, etc.

- How I might discuss this with my partner or ask for what I need. Examples: I can make a list and talk to him/her, I can share a picture of the position, hide a new book on sexual intimacy under his/her pillow, etc.

- What no longer feels good when we are being sexual or making love. Examples: Fondling of my breasts, the sexual position of him on top, etc.

- How I might discuss this with my partner or ask for what I need. Examples: Suggest other ideas for positions or touch, share openly what has changed for me, etc.

Sexuality During Pregnancy
TALKING WITH MY PARTNER

- I have checked with my health care provider that sexual activity during pregnancy is safe for me: YES   NO

- What I want my partner to know about how my body feels right now. Examples: My body is easily excited and seems more sensitive; I have no sexual desire, etc.

- What I want my partner to know about my feelings and desires right now. Examples: I feel closer to my partner now than ever before, I feel like crying all the time, etc.

- These are some sexual positions I would like to try that might increase my comfort and satisfaction during sex:

Man on top	Side by side, face to face
Woman on top	Side by side, from behind
Standing	Rear entry
Sitting	Others:

- These are some other things I would like to try:

Shared masturbation	Using sexual toys, vibrators, etc.
Showering together	Bathing together
Creating a romantic atmosphere	Reading romantic stories to each other
Watching films together	Total body massage
Play acting scenes	Sex in different rooms of the house
Being pursued	Being the pursuer
Oral sex	Others:

Remember:

- Sexual feelings are normal and natural, even during pregnancy.
- There are more ways of being sexual than intercourse.
- Be creative and respectful of each other. It is okay to say NO, even to your partner.
- It is your body and you are experiencing many changes right now.
- Open communication about sexual issues is always important, anytime.

INTERVENTION 4

Affirmations

TASK
To recognize and affirm the rights each person has as a human being.

REFERENCE
Chapter 2

ABOUT THIS INTERVENTION
Affirmations are positive statements that affirm or support the positive aspects of ourselves as well as our rights as a human being. Many women and men often forget they do have certain rights that pertain to their humanness, their bodies, and their feelings. Women often feel powerless when interacting with various agencies and institutions. To counteract those feelings of powerlessness, it is important to remind ourselves of the rights that we do have and the power that we each control. Affirmations read and said out loud on a regular basis can become part of who we are and help change our thinking about ourselves, what we do, and who we involved in our lives. They can also help us to feel better about ourselves and the world.

INTRODUCING THIS INTERVENTION
People who succeed in life often say they focus on positive things and picture themselves as winners. They believe they are worthwhile and important. Well, everyone is worthwhile and important. We all have rights as human beings—the right to control our bodies and express our feelings. Affirmations are positive statements that remind us of our strengths and our rights.

It is important that we remind ourselves of the rights we have and the powers we control. When others compliment us on our strengths, we should believe them—not discount them. If others don't tell us our strengths and rights, we can remind ourselves with affirmations. If we repeatedly make affirmations to ourselves, we begin to believe them and to act in stronger and more positive ways. We feel better about ourselves and our world.

INTERVENTION
1. Read and discuss each affirmation.

2. Encourage home interventions using the worksheets provided.

Affirmations

I am lovable.

I have a right to my feelings.

I have a right to dream and to pursue those dreams.

My body is my own.

My body is beautiful.

I have a right to say NO.

I do not have to pay a price for receiving love or affection.

I have a right and a responsibility to protect myself.

I have a right to set boundaries on my time and relationships.

I am worthy of good things in my life.

I am responsible to get my own needs met.

I have a right to dream and to pursue those dreams.

I can choose my own path in life.

I am responsible for my own decisions.

I do not need another person in my life in order to feel good about myself.

I have a right to express my talents.

I have a right to receive good things in my life without feeling I owe someone something.

I have a right to ask for help.

I have a right to be powerful and take charge of my life.

I have a right to relationships free of shame or fear.

Making Changes Affirming Myself

Choose one or two of the affirmations from the Affirmations worksheet that you have had difficulty believing in for yourself. Write these out below. For each one think of an example or situation that demonstrates the difficulty you have had. Describe an alternative way of handling that situation that would have made the situation more affirming for you.

AFFIRMATION	SITUATION AFFIRMING	CHANGES
I have a right to receive good things in my life without feeling I owe someone something.	My boyfriend and I were shopping. He offered to buy me this new CD I wanted because he loved me. Later, at home, he wanted to take my car to go out with his friends. I told him I had my evening class. He said that he bought me the CD so I had to let him take my car. I reminded him he said he bought it because he loved me. He said, "I guess you don't love me then."	• I could refuse to let him take my car, he might get mad, he might break up with me—but I do not have to let him take my car when I have plans. My school plans take precedence. • I could give him back the CD. • I could tell him I do love him but loving someone shouldn't involve giving up all your plans. • I can just say no and practice not feeling guilty.

Affirming Myself Today

Write out your favorite affirmation and hang it on a mirror or the refrigerator. Each time you pass by it, read it out loud to yourself. Start with a new one each week (or day).

INTERVENTION 5

Inner Healing: Ghosts of the Past

TASK
To recognize unfinished old business and begin to move past it through inner healing.

REFERENCE
Chapters 1, 2

ABOUT THIS INTERVENTION
A woman by the name of Selma Fraiberg once referred to *ghosts in the nursery*. By this, she meant that a woman's past experiences and relationships can act as ghosts and can affect the way a woman mothers her child, as well as the relationship she develops with her child. Ghosts are often not seen but their presence is felt; they quietly bring the past with them, haunting the present with old business.

For example, a woman might have grown up in a family where her parents fought a lot. She might have thought that the fights, as well as her mother's crying and yelling at her to "get away, you can't help" after the fights, were because of something she had done.

Children often feel responsible for problems their parents have. They think that if they were only nicer or behaved better or if they never got angry, then everything would be all right. While we know this is not true, it is very hard to erase those childhood ideas and feelings.

As that woman grows up, the same feelings and thoughts can often become connected to any fighting between people she cares about or any crying she witnesses. When she herself has a child, the baby's crying may be interpreted as anger towards her. She may feel responsible and not be able to properly interpret what the baby needs. The woman would not understand why she feels that way and might begin to feel bad about her ability to mother her child.

The first thing that needs to happen to begin to get rid of the ghost that haunts this woman would be for her to identify some of her past childhood experiences that she remembers as troubling or hurtful.

Any other work on past issues is best done with a qualified therapist, especially where trauma is involved.

INTRODUCING THIS INTERVENTION
Selma Fraiberg, a noted psychoanalyst, referred to ghosts in the nursery as the past experiences and relationships that affect our current behaviors. Some of the ghosts may be friendly ones that help us behave in positive ways. Others may have been harmful and can have negative effects on relationships with family, friends, and children.

For example, if a woman grew up watching her parents fight, she may have felt guilt—"if I were a better girl, maybe they wouldn't fight as much." If the girl tried to comfort a crying mother after the fights and was told, "Go away, you can't help," the girl may have associated crying with personal rejection. If she carries those ghosts of feelings into her future, she may feel a crying baby is rejecting her. She may not be able to correctly interpret her baby's cries as "I'm hungry. Feed me" or "I'm wet. Change me." She would need to recognize and shed those ghosts of past experiences to relate positively to her baby.

Many new parents can benefit from dealing with the ghosts from their past.

INTERVENTION
1. Complete and discuss Ghosts From My Past worksheet.(A case example is included in Appendix I.)
2. Discuss feelings associated with these ghosts.
3. Discuss ways to get rid of those ghosts and any bad feelings, such as tearing them up and throwing them away, throwing them into a fireplace, crumpling them up and tossing them in the garbage, or shredding them.

Ghosts From My Past

The ghost from my past is called:

_____

The ghost is here because:

_____

This ghost makes me feel:

_____

I do not need this ghost in my life. I do not
need to carry around bad feelings any more.
I will get rid of this ghost by:

_____

_____

_____

The ghost from my past is called:

_____

The ghost is here because:

_____

This ghost makes me feel:

_____

I do not need this ghost in my life. I do not
need to carry around bad feelings any more.
I will get rid of this ghost by:

_____

_____

_____

INTERVENTION 6

Inner Child

TASK
To reconnect with the "inner child" inside us, strengthening our beliefs and
experiences of playfulness, fun, and relaxation.

REFERENCE
Chapter 2

ABOUT THIS INTERVENTION:
Everyone has within them what is referred to as their inner child. The inner
child is the part of each person that is playful. Some people easily tap into the
playful part of themselves, creating fun in much of what they do and how they
live. Others struggle with so many things in their everyday lives that feeling or
behaving in a playful manner seems almost impossible. But playfulness is
important! Laughing, relaxing, playing, and having a sense of humor can
decrease stress and increase enjoyment of life overall. During pregnancy, these
behaviors can do two things:

- they can decrease the stress of pregnancy;
- they can begin to prepare women to be playful with their children.

Playfulness within parent-child interactions can not only support a close and
loving relationship, but can also assist the child in developing cognitive, gross
motor, fine motor, and social skills.

INTRODUCING THIS INTERVENTION
*There is a playful inner child in each of us. Some folks find playful activities easy;
others are so bound up in the struggle to survive that play seems impossible. Yet,
playing is important. During your pregnancy, it can help you relax. After your
baby is born, playing together helps you develop a loving relationship. It also helps
your baby learn to talk, think, and develop motor skills. Play helps us learn and
increases our enjoyment of life.*

INTERVENTION
1. Complete and discuss the Things Just for Fun worksheet.

2. Use the Some Fun Things list to demonstrate the wide range of fun and
   enjoyable activities available.

3. Complete and discuss the Playful With My Child worksheet.

4. Provide client with the list of recipes for childhood fun. In a group or
   individually, make one or two of the recipes and PLAY with the final product.
   (This is very important for women who have not had the experience of a lot
   of play in their lives. They need to experience it to feel comfortable playing
   with their child.)

Things Just For Fun

Make a list of things you like to do just for fun or how you like to play.

1. _____

2. _____

3. _____

4. _____

5. _____

6. _____

7. _____

8. _____

9. _____

10. _____

Some Fun Things

This is a list of some fun and playful ideas compiled from clients and others. Add your own ideas as you think of them.

1. Dancing
2. Taking a walk under a full moon
3. Sewing
4. Making a new recipe
5. Going to garage sales
6. Watching a favorite movie fromchildhood
7. Feeding ducks, seagulls, geese, or pigeons
8. Swimming
9. Bowling
10. Building something with legos
11. Playing with play dough
12. Making a collage of babies
13. Making a collage of anything
14. Painting
15. Coloring in a coloring book
16. Swinging in the park
17. Playing Candyland
18. Playing Chutes & Ladders
19. Playing jacks
20. Jump-roping
21. Finger painting with pudding
22. Making a mountain out of your mashed potatoes
23. Giving your peanut buttersandwich raisin eyes and a raisin mouth before eating IT
24. Making a jack-o-lantern at Halloween
25. Making snowmen out of rice krispies and marshmallows
26. Decorating cookies
27. Playing a game of cards
28. Playing hide and seek
29. Decorating Easter eggs
30. Making an Easter basket
31. Decorating your house for St. Patrick's day or any other holiday
32. Making red oatmeal for Valentine's Day
33. Making orange oatmeal for Halloween
34. Making green oatmeal for St. Patrick's Day
35. Making a cornhusk doll
36. Cutting out paper dolls
37. Face painting
38.
39.
40.
41.
42.
43.
44.
45.
46.
47.
48.

Playing With My Child

Make a list of things you might want to do with your child as he or she grows up.

AGE	ACTIVITY
1-3 months	*Playing "hold my finger," singing lullabies, playing "watch me"*
4-6 months	
7-9 months	
10-12 months	
1 year	
2 years	
3 years	
4 years	
5 years	
6 years	
7 years	
8 years	
9 years	
10 years	
11 years	
12 years	

Recipes to Grow With

FINGER-TRAY PAINT
For Baby

1 package instant vanilla (or any flavor) pudding

Milk (or the specific formula for your baby)

High chair tray (once baby can sit in the high chair, this is a great activity)

Directions: Mix pudding with milk or formula, adding liquid little by little until the consistency of finger paint. Smear a thin layer over the clean high chair tray. Encourage and allow baby to smear and explore pudding.

PLAY DOUGH
For Toddler and Older

1 cup flour

1/2 cup salt

1 tablespoon cooking oil

1 cup water

2 teaspoons cream of tartar (find in spice section)

Food coloring

Directions: Mix together and cook over low heat. Stir constantly until firm.

FINGER PAINT
For Toddler and Older

1 can sweetened condensed milk

Food coloring

Finger paint paper

Directions: Divide milk into small cups and add a different color to each. Mix well. Use as finger paint on finger paint paper. Pictures can be dried and kept for about a week.

CORNSTARCH CLAY
For Toddler and Older

1 cup cornstarch

2 cups salt

1 and 1/3 cups cold water

Directions:

1. Put salt and 2/3 cup of water in a pot and bring to a boil.

2. Mix cornstarch with remaining water and stir well.

3. Blend these two mixtures together and knead into clay.

4. Objects made can be dried and painted. Unused clay should be kept in a covered container.

Hand or Foot Print Plaque

For Any Age Child

Dough for plaque:

1 box baking soda (16 ounces)

1 cup corn starch

1 and 1/4 cups cold water

1 tablespoon vegetable oil

Optional: Food coloring

Directions:

Mix baking soda and corn starch together. Put into a pot and mix with water, oil, and food coloring. Cook over medium heat, stirring constantly. Mixture should become the consistency of mashed potatoes. This will take about 10-15 minutes. Do not cook too long or the plaque may crack later.

Remove mixture to a bowl or plate, cover with a damp cloth so it will not dry out, and wait for it to cool. When it is cool enough to handle, knead on a breadboard or table that has been dusted with cornstarch. Knead until smooth. Shape it into the shape you want for the plaque.

Gently press your baby or child's hand or foot into the shaped dough while it is still damp and soft. You can either carve the name and date into the soft dough or wait until it dries and write on it with permanent markers. When dry you may also paint it. You can leave it natural or apply a coat of clear acrylic. You can also glue a picture hanger to the back so it can be hung on the wall. Repeat this project every now and then as your child gets older.

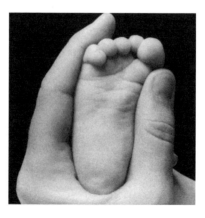

INTERVENTION 7

Celebrations of Me: Marking the Occasion

TASK
To recognize and celebrate our accomplishments during pregnancy.

REFERENCE
Chapter 2

ABOUT THIS INTERVENTION
When asked what is the most special thing about being a mother, women often reply that it is not the big things like birthdays or holidays. Rather, it is the little everyday things like laughing with their child at something funny in the grocery store, or snuggling on the couch, or holding their sleeping baby. This seems to be true in many areas of life. And realizing and embracing this idea can improve the quality of life and help encourage enjoyment of the normal, everyday days.

Celebrations do not need to be big, elaborate parties with a lot of people, food, and activity. Celebrations can acknowledge accomplishments, taking another step toward completing a project, or moving past a normal point of development. Completing a school assignment or getting through a class presentation are reasons to celebrate. Painting a room being remodeled or completing the initial application materials for a multi-step process are reasons to celebrate. Feeling the first flutter of an unborn child within the womb, moving from the first to the second trimester, and buying a first baby outfit are equally important and special reasons to celebrate.

Many of the occasions experienced during pregnancy are quiet moments— things that are personal or things shared with very few other people. These are subtle but powerful experiences and should be honored. Women today take very little time to honor themselves during pregnancy, motherhood, or even woman-hood. But women today, maybe more than any other time in history, deserve to be honored and acknowledged for the things they accomplish. No one sends a card or brings gifts or even speaks words of acknowledgment when passage through these special moments occurs. Women can do these things for them-selves, though. Women feel better when their experiences and actions are acknowledged. They also learn to understand and identify the smaller special things in life and may develop new ways of celebrating the everyday accomplish-ments and achievements of children.

INTRODUCING THIS INTERVENTION
We often have parties or ceremonies to celebrate big events in our lives, but we also need everyday ways to celebrate everyday joys and triumphs—painting the nursery, feeling your baby move for the first time, moving from the first to the second trimester, buying your first maternity outfit, or making something for your baby. Some of these events may involve other people and be shared with them; some may be private and shared with few people or none.

If others are unaware of your accomplishments or forget to congratulate you about them, you can congratulate yourself and give yourself a treat to celebrate the occasion. When your accomplishments are recognized and valued, you feel better about yourself. You're also more apt to recognize and praise the accomplishments of your child. This will help your child grow up feeling valued and self-confident.

INTERVENTION
1. Complete and discuss the Celebrating Me Every Day worksheet provided.

Celebrating Me Every Day!

Complete the following table. Begin to think about the little things you do, accomplish, or experience every day; how you feel about them; and ways in which you can celebrate.

DAY	WHAT HAPPENED?	HOW DID I FEEL? WHAT DID I THINK?	HOW TO CELEBRATE?
Example: Thursday 7/15	Today I felt my baby kick for the first time!	Excited, nervous scared, happy— I wasn't sure about it at first but then I figured out what it was and wanted it to happen some more. It was like he was communicating with me now.	I made a journal entry describing what it was like. I told my husband and we ate our favorite dinner and then we sat together and he tried to feel it, too.
Example: Friday 7/16	I had to put on my first pair of maternity pants!	Excited, surprised my old pants did not fit, fat—but it was okay because I knew it was really my baby.	I went shopping and bought a new maternity top. I told the clerk about my celebration and she was excited, too.

INTERVENTION 8

What Kind of Baby Was I?

TASK

Exploring personal history of early infancy and childhood.

REFERENCE

Chapters 1, 2

ABOUT THIS INTERVENTION

Women who are able to get in touch with their own beginnings develop ways of thinking about the babies they will have, the reality of having a baby in their arms, and their own personal connections to babyhood. It can be important for some women to know what the world, or at least their family, was like while waiting for their arrival into this world. Knowing what they were like as babies, how others anticipated them, and reactions to arrival into this world can provide them with windows into past family relations.

Some women who have been adopted, who have no one available who knows their history, or who come from other similar situations where they may not have access to information about their birth may not feel comfortable with this intervention. Instead, they may want to begin at the age that they do have access to information and memories. For example, with my own adopted daughter we tell the story of how many planes it took to get to her and how she cried when I first held her but how she was smiling at me by the end of the day. She cherishes each of these stories. Neither of us will ever know about her actual birth; we do know about our births into each other's lives.

INTRODUCING THIS INTERVENTION

As you prepare for your baby's birth, it might help to know more about your own birth. Have people talked to you about your mother's pregnancy and labor or about how family members reacted to your arrival? Did your family keep a baby book to document your age when you first spoke, walked, or had your first haircut? If you can learn more about yourself as a baby, you may get clues that will help you understand your baby and how your family will welcome him or her.

INTERVENTION

1. Complete the What Was I Like as a Baby and the What Others Say About Me as a Baby worksheets.

2. Discuss and process them.

What Was I Like as a Baby?

Interview or question parents and other family members about
your early childhood. Getting different perspectives from
multiple people can help fill in any potential holes in the story.

BEFORE BIRTH
What did people do to prepare for my arrival? Did they think I was going to be a
boy or a girl? Were they financially set for my arrival?

TIME OF BIRTH
When did labor begin? Who was in the hospital awaiting my arrival? How long
was labor? Who cut my cord? What did I look like upon arrival? Were there any
worries about MY health or safety? What time did I arrive? What were the
hospital rules at the time?

GOING HOME
How long did I have to stay in the hospital? When I went home, who was
waiting for me? Who took care of me initially? Were there people helping my
primary caretaker? How did my sisters or brothers react to my arrival home (if
applicable)?

YOUR ADJUSTMENT
When did I sleep through the night? What kind of feedings did I receive? When
did I first recognize the important people in my family? When did I first smile?
Did I have any problems initially? How did my mother and/or father adjust to
having a baby? Did they think I was an easy or hard baby? What favorite
memories do people have about me?

What Others Say About Me as a Baby

Unit 5

Points To Remember

Pregnancy is often a time when a woman's sense of being a woman becomes lost in the anticipation of the child on the way. It is important for women to maintain that sense of who they are as women. They need to think about how to take care of themselves, how to get their needs met, and how to give attention and resolution to what parts of them might have been awakened by the pregnancy. Let us review the interventions:

- *Nurturing the Woman in Me* helps the pregnant woman focus on the smaller, everyday things she might do to be kind to herself.

- *Conserving Energy: Saying NO* reminds the pregnant woman that she can say no to others who might be making demands on her time and energy. Her priorities will shift to the care and nurturing of her child, often requiring a letting go of some of her caretaking role of others in her life.

- *The Sexual Me* encourages the pregnant woman to embrace and enjoy her sexuality throughout her pregnancy.

- *Affirmations* are simply positive self-statements. Sometimes we need to be very conscious in the things we think and say about ourselves in order for us to truly believe those good things and feel good about ourselves.

- *Inner Healing: Ghosts of the Past* encourages a re-examination of past relationships that may still be difficult to deal with and may interfere with the kind of relationship she wants to develop with her child. This activity allows the pregnant woman to work through some of those past issues.

- *Inner Child* is an activity based in play. It encourages a re-connection with one's own inner child, facilitates having fun, and prepares the pregnant woman to play with her child.

- *Celebrations of Me: Marking the Occasion* helps the pregnant woman to develop ways to celebrate and enjoy the smaller, everyday events that make one's life special.

- *What Kind of Baby Was I?* provides a path to the pregnant woman's personal past—her own history as a baby. Getting in touch with who she was as a baby can be supportive of her ability to connect with her own child, based on their similarities and differences.

"Call it a clan, call it a network, call it a tribe, call it a family. Whatever you call it, whoever you are, you need one."

JANE HOWARD

Unit 6

Making Space

KEY CONCEPT

One of the most important tasks a woman needs to deal with as she is preparing to welcome her child into the world is to establish a place in her personal world for her baby. She needs to prepare for her child personally and she needs to prepare her family and friends not only to welcome her baby but also to make space in their lives and to accept her baby into the circle.

OUTCOME GOALS

The mother-to-be will:

Prepare a place in the world physically, emotionally, and socially for her baby.

Build a network of "healthy and safe" persons for both her and the baby to be involved with.

INTERVENTIONS

1. Personal Circle of Support

2. Baby's Circle of Support

3. Circle of Safety

4. Family Tree

5. Exploring the World

6. Play and Toy Making

7. Baby Book

8. Welcome Video

INTERVENTION 1

Personal Circle of Support

TASK
To help the mother develop an awareness of the support network around her, to establish or improve on a support network as needed, and to explore how these support networks may or may not impact the baby.

REFERENCE
Chapters 3, 4

ABOUT THIS INTERVENTION
A circle of support is essentially a diagram of all of the people significant in the mother's life. These are the people who may or may not become significant in the baby's life. It is now that the mother needs to begin to think about how her baby will fit into her existing circle of support and which members of her circle will be available and appropriate for the baby to interact with.

For some mothers, the significant people around her may be the same ones she wants to have her baby involved with. They are generally people who are supportive and positive in her life. For other mothers, it may be difficult just to identify anyone she can place on this list. This suggests she is quite isolated and may need help finding supportive others and building a support network that will be advantageous to her and her baby.

INTRODUCING THIS INTERVENTION
Who are the people in your life? Think of family members, friends, people at work and church, medical people, neighbors, and others. Can any of them give you support in the form of help, friendship, transportation, or other needs during your pregnancy or after your baby is born? Which ones already know about your baby? Which ones do you want to be around your baby?

INTERVENTION:
1. Begin by deciding, based on your goals for the mother and/or a joint decision between you and the mother, what type of circle of support would be most a appropriate to create.

    Some variations include:

    -   Differentiating groups of people, i.e. family, friends, neighbors, agency workers by using different shapes or colors (for anyone)

    -   Listing phone numbers by names for everyone, (helpful for the mother who needs help in organizing her network and access to it)

    -   Creating a list for those moms who do not have support by learning names and numbers of significant persons in her community (for the mother with very little social support or no existing network)

    -   Making a three-dimensional network (for the artistic or creative mother or for mothers who have difficulty learning or reading)

    -   Making a network using a collage technique (for the mother who needs an alternative to a straight handout)

- Placing the persons identified in various proximities to the "ME" heart based on her assessment of their significance in her life (for the mother who is assessing those important in her life). See Circle of Support handout.
- Creating a network using not only names and phone numbers but also pictures of the significant people (for the mother needing visual cues or who has difficulty with reading or processing written information)

2. Have mother discuss the significant people in her life. Discuss in terms of those:
   - offering support
   - offering safety
   - necessary for life's necessities
   - who know about the baby
   - who are not safe
   - who may be okay for them to be around but who the baby should be protected from
   - who can be contacted for everyday things
   - who can be contacted for emergencies (babysitting, transportation)
   - who contribute to her life and what they contribute (money, food, attention, intimacy, advice, etc)

3. Discussion questions you ask:
   - How long have you known this person?
   - How has this person been helpful or supportive to you?
   - Which of these people know about your pregnancy?
   - How do these people feel about the pregnancy?
   - How often do you see them?
   - When is the last time you saw them? (This is actually a very important question since people can feel they see someone often when it is really very infrequent. Asking the last time can give you a good estimation of contact.)

4. Two case examples are provided in Appendices J and K. Each example illustrates how two different mothers used shapes and symbols to code the significant people in their lives. These examples may be helpful to share with the women you are working as they are working on their own Circle of Support.

MY Circle of Support

Baby's Circle of Support

TASK
To help the mother develop an awareness of the support network around her baby and to establish or improve on this support network as needed.

REFERENCE
Chapters 3, 4

ABOUT THIS INTERVENTION
Just as a circle of support is essential in the mother's life, it is equally important to develop a circle of support for the baby. The baby's circle may or may not mirror the mother's. One difference might be that people on the father's side of the family could be more active in the baby's life than they are in the mother's life. Additionally, the mother may have folks in her life who are not safe or appropriate to be around or near the baby.

INTRODUCING THIS INTERVENTION
Who will want to be involved in your baby's life? Think of people in your life. What about people from the father's family? Which people will be helpful and supportive to your baby? Are there some people who should not be around your baby?

INTERVENTION
1. Develop network baby in the same manner as done with the mother in intervention one (refer to intervention one, page 421, for details of the intervention.)

My BABY'S Circle of Support

INTERVENTION 3

Circle of Safety

TASK

To help the mother develop an awareness of the protective nature and risk factors of the support network around her, to increase the protective nature of her network, and to decrease the risk related to her network.

REFERENCE

Chapters 3, 4

ABOUT THIS INTERVENTION

Support networks and the Circle of Support were both discussed in interventions 1 and 2 of this unit. In this intervention the "safety" of the support networks of the mother and the baby will be more closely examined. It is important to examine all the members of each support network and decide on the "safety" of that individual. Sometimes, a person may be safe for the mother because she is an adult and has resources and skills to lessen the danger or risk. That same person, on the other hand, may be a significant risk to the safety and well being of the baby who is vulnerable and unable to defend and protect him or herself.

INTRODUCING THIS INTERVENTION:

Now that you have listed people who are involved in your life and might be involved in your baby's life, let's put them in categories according to how safe and supportive they are for both you and your baby.

INTERVENTION

1. Create a support network using circles of red, yellow, and green to note which people are safe and unsafe. Red for unsafe, yellow for safe for mom but not baby, and green as safe for all. The support network can also be done using boxes of red, yellow and green and listing individuals as in the Safety Zones worksheet.

    RED or STOP: People who are not safe. Those who have hit or hurt before. Those who become abusive in any way. Those that become out of control and dangerous at various times.

    YELLOW or Questionable (?): People who can be unsafe to be around but with whom some contact may need to occur at times; for instance, an abusive parent whose abusiveness is limited to periods of alcohol usage. These people might be tolerated by the mother or she might have developed ways of dealing with them; however, she knows they would not be safe for her baby to be around.

    GREEN or GO: People who are safe, supportive, and willing to be there for both mother and baby.

Safety Zones

RED

YELLOW

GREEN

INTERVENTION 4

Family Tree

TASK
To develop a visual picture of the parents' families and where the unborn child will fit into this family system.

REFERENCE
Chapters 3, 4

ABOUT THIS INTERVENTION
Having an understanding of family history can be helpful in understanding the way a family has come to be. Family trees inform us of the persons responsible for bringing us to into the world. They can also be helpful in identifying family patterns and relationships we could never really think about until we saw it mapped out. Finally, it is also a very good way to begin to get others to share their knowledge and experiences, some that may never have been talked about before.

INTRODUCING THIS INTERVENTION
Children often ask questions about their relatives and how everyone fits into the family. One way to answer these questions is to have a family tree. This can show your parents and grandparents, aunts and uncles, cousins, brothers and sisters, and other children if you have them. Can you supply similar information about the father's family? Making a family tree can clarify information for you and start some interesting conversations that may help you understand more about your family.

INTERVENTION
1. Use the model provided to make the family tree or encourage the mother to create one of her own. (A second model of a family tree is included in Appendix L.) Families come in all different shapes, styles, and configurations so using a pre-made model and filling in the blanks can be difficult and cause a focus on what is missing and what cannot be filled in rather that what is known and present.

2. Fill in as much of the information that can be collected based on personal knowledge and asking others to share their remembrances and stories.

3. Think about different symbols to indicate different aspects of the family tree. The following list provides some examples:

    a. Squares for males/circles for females

    b. Different colors for different sides of the family

    c. Use a specific color for those who have died

    d. Use dashed lines between persons together and partnered without marriage

    e. Make a slash through lines where divorces have occurred

    f. Develop a code for certain characteristics you want included; for instance, A for alcoholic, C for college graduate, NY for a relative living in New York, B for a blonde person, etc.

4. Determine a good place to keep the family tree. It might be posted on a wall or placed in the baby's book.

Family Tree

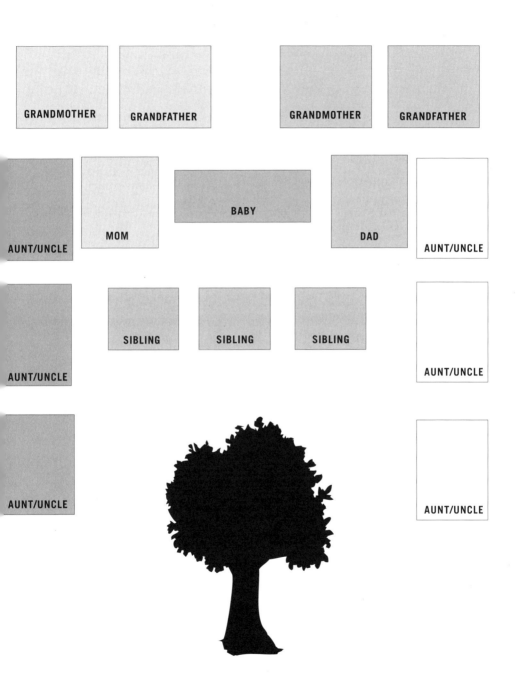

INTERVENTION 5

Exploring the World

TASK
To develop a visual picture of the world where the baby will be born.

REFERENCE
Chapters 3, 4

ABOUT THIS INTERVENTION
It is important to know what a community or neighborhood has to offer for individuals, families, and children. With first babies, women have not often explored their neighborhoods or communities from a "mother and child" perspective. Neighborhoods and communities will often offer mother and baby groups and activities. In addition, many areas have public parks, community pools, and playgrounds. It is important to know what each area has to offer to both mother and baby. In this intervention, the goal will be to explore what the neighborhood and community has to offer.

INTRODUCING THIS INTERVENTION
Every neighborhood has a predominant feature—malls, businesses, apartments, houses, factories, farms, or whatever. What's the predominant feature of the area where you live? When you walk around your immediate neighborhood, what does it offer to mothers and children? Are there parks, playgrounds, community centers, daycares, classes, swimming pools, or other facilities that might be helpful or interesting for you and your baby?

INTERVENTION
1. Use the Community Resources worksheet to list ways to explore and learn about what your community has to offer.

2. Create a Mother and Baby Friendly Community Map of your community or neighborhood with the best mother and baby spots highlighted. An example is provided in Appendix M.

Community Resources

Become a detective! Develop a list of ways you can learn about your community or neighborhood. Below are a few of the ways that are commonly found to be helpful. Think of other ways and list them below. Check off each idea as you try it and list what mother and child friendly activity or place you learn about.

WAYS TO FIND OUT ABOUT MY COMMUNITY

1. Local newspaper
2. Local hospital mailings or flyers
3. Store bulletin boards
4. Baby magazines
5. Community center mailings
6. My health care provider

7. _____
8. _____
9. _____
10. _____
11. _____
12. _____

OTHER PLACES AND EVENTS TO LOOK FOR RESOURCES
(Place a checkmark next to those you know of or use)

___PEPS groups

___Mother and baby massage classes

___Parks

___Places to take walks

___Mother and baby yoga classes

___Early childhood programs

___New mother support groups

___Places for children to play safely

___Mother and baby groups

___Baby gym or play times

___Early Head Start Programs

___Healthy Start

___Birth to Three (0-3) programs

___Parenting classes

___Preschools and daycares

___Elementary schools

MOTHER & CHILD FRIENDLY EVENTS OR PLACES IN MY COMMUNITY

_____   _____

_____   _____

_____   _____

_____   _____

_____   _____

_____   _____

INTERVENTION 6

Play and Toy Making

TASK
To prepare for baby's needs by learning games and songs and by making toys.

REFERENCE
Chapters 3, 4

ADDITIONAL MATERIALS
Karo syrup, plastic bottle, sparkles, tape; laminated family pictures, string, sticks or dowels.

ABOUT THIS INTERVENTION
Play is a child's first language. This is how babies learn about their world, work out their fears and worries, and communicate with others. For the very young child, play is best when it is one on one, or child and parent. Toys and objects are not always necessary for play. *Peek-A-Boo, I'm Gonna Get You,* and *This Little Piggy* are wonderful games for babies and parents. Through *Peek-A-Boo,* children learn about surprise, they learn about getting excited and getting calmed down, and they learn you can disappear from view and that you come back again. Through *I'm Gonna Get You*, children learn about getting excited and surprised and how to calm down again, they learn to anticipate what might come next, and they learn how to laugh with their parent. Through *This Little Piggy*, children learn about their toes from having each one touched, they learn to differentiate each toe and what each toe comes to represent, they learn to anticipate, and they again learn to get excited and to calm down again.

Toys can be fun and interactive. Children can learn to focus attention, track objects, and learn that what they do with their bodies can impact other things. In this intervention, both non-toy games and toys will be explored.

INTRODUCING THIS INTERVENTION
Your baby will learn about the world by playing. You can help your baby learn by playing games. A simple game like Peek-A-Boo can teach your baby about surprises. Your baby will also learn that you can disappear from view and come back again. This can help if you have to leave your baby with a sitter or in daycare. Your baby learns about getting excited and calming down again. All of these are helpful lessons.

Toys can also be fun and interactive. A baby who tries to follow a moving object learns to focus attention, track objects, and move eyes and body toward a goal. Today, we'll talk about games and toys for your baby.

INTERVENTION
1. Explore and discuss the Baby Games handout.
2. The Toys worksheet provides two baby toy ideas. Choose one or both and make a new toy for your baby.

Baby Games

PEEK-A-BOO

Position the baby so you are face to face and each of you have your hands free. Your baby might be in a reclining baby chair or propped safely on a bed or sofa. Move to within 18-24 inches from baby and cover your face with your hands. Say some of the following things to try and engage baby in the game:

Where's baby?

Where's Momma?

Baby, baby

Where'd I go?

Then open your hands so the baby can see your face. (Be careful with your timing. If you wait too long, the baby may become frightened you are not coming back; if you move too soon, the baby might not have had time to build up any excitement for the game. Watch your baby for signs of these feelings.) Then say:

Peek-a-boo, Peek-a-boo

Or

Peek-a-boo, I see you

Or

Here I am (or there you are)

You can also reward baby with a kiss or a little tickle on the tummy.

THIS LITTLE PIGGY

With your child lying on his or her back, remove any socks so the little toes are free (this activity is great during a diaper change or after a bath before dressing). Using the following rhyme, wiggle each toe with each line of the rhyme and on the littlest toe, walk your fingers up to the tummy and give a little tickle.

This little piggy went to market

This little piggy stayed home

This little piggy ate roast beef

This little piggy ate none

And

This little piggy ran "wee, wee, wee" all the way home!

Toys

MAGIC BOTTLE

Materials

1 plastic soda pop bottle with screw on top

1 bottle of karo syrup

3-4 tablespoons of glitter, sparkles, shiny metallic shapes (like fish, animals, hearts, etc.)

Super glue

Duct tape or other similar tape in other colors

Directions

Wash out bottle with soapy water and clean off any outside paper or plastic wrappers. Rinse well. Pour karo syrup into pop bottle until it is about 1/2 to 2/3 full. Pour in sprinkles, glitter, and sparkles. Roll the bottle around until sparkles are spread throughout the syrup. When it is well blended, clean off the top part of pop bottle so no glitter or syrup is on the outside screw top area. Dry thoroughly and spread super glue around the threaded area where the top screws on. Put on top of bottle, secure it tightly. Let dry about an hour. When dry, use tape and wrap several layers around the screw top. Make sure ends and edges of tape are trimmed so no little threads are hanging down.

Use as a toy for baby. Turning it over and over causes the sparkles to move and make different patterns.

PICTURE MOBILE

Materials

Photos of family members, which have been laminated (can be done at copy centers and poster shops)

String

Duct tape

Hole punch

Two straight sticks or dowels, about 12-14 inches long

Directions

Punch four holes in each picture, near each corner. With picture face down, tie two pieces of string to picture, one piece from one corner to the opposite corner (diagonally) and the same with the other piece so you make an "X" on the back of the picture. Tie a piece of string to the middle of the "X" where the other strings have crossed. Repeat with all pictures. Cross sticks or dowels into an "X", secure the "X" at the middle with string or duct tape. Tie a picture on each of the ends of the four sticks and one down the middle. You can make the lengths equal or you can alternate them with some long and some shorter. When finished a string can be attached to the center and mobile can be hung from the ceiling. The pictures of family members should be hanging face down so baby will be able to see the pictures. Be sure to tie the mobile so baby will be able to view it but not touch it. One of the best spots is over the changing area, so the parent can point to the pictures and discuss who is who. Strings should be kept as short as possible and the mobile should be out of baby's reach range to ensure safety from choking or strangulation.

INTERVENTION 7

Baby Book

TASK
To begin to see the world the baby will be born into through the environment, interactions, and experiences of the mother.

REFERENCE
Chapters 3, 4

ABOUT THIS INTERVENTION
Baby books are wonderful ways to create a history of what happens in a baby's life. Stories, pictures, tokens, and mementos are all cherished as time goes on. Organizing them as events occur is often best since ideas and events are fresh and more easily remembered. Books can be purchased or created.

INTRODUCING THIS INTERVENTION
A baby book is a great way to record special events in your pregnancy and in your baby's life. It can include pictures, stories, a bit of hair from your baby's first hair cut, and other special mementos. You can buy a baby book or make your own. If you fill it out when an event occurs, you will include more detail. As your child grows up, the two of you can enjoy going through the book and talking about special happenings. This book can become your baby's first picture book and become something very special to the two of you.

INTERVENTION
1. Explore different baby books in bookshops or card & gift shops. Get an idea of the things you like and the style you like (journal style vs. storybook style).

2. Either purchase a baby book that you feel fits your style or begin to create one with the computer or using your own art skills.

3. Another option is to explore some of the memory book classes and groups that might be offered in your community.

4. See the Baby Book Ideas handout for some ideas of what to include in your book.

Baby Book Ideas

- Pictures of family members
- Ultrasound pictures
- Any paper or note that confirms your pregnancy
- Any hospital bracelets you have to wear
- Pictures of your home, inside and out
- Picture of your car
- Important news headlines
- Current articles on baby care
- A diary of when you first felt baby, when baby first kicked, when you felt baby with the hiccups
- A diary of when you told others about your pregnancy and how they responded
- A summary of any baby showers—who was there, what you did, what you received, the type of cake
- Any cards you receive
- A list of any gifts you receive
- What kinds of foods you craved
- The measurements of your belly as it grew
- Other ideas:

INTERVENTION 8

Welcome Video

TASK
To develop a recorded memory of the home the baby will be welcomed into.

REFERENCE
Chapters 3, 4

ADDITIONAL MATERIALS
Video camera, blank tape

ABOUT THIS INTERVENTION
Today with the wonders of technology almost any event can be recorded. One recording that can be helpful in preparing for baby is to make a welcome video which can be used later to show the baby the home he or she was born into, the place where he or she lived, and what had been prepared for him or her.

INTRODUCING THIS INTERVENTION
Do you have access to a video camera? If so, then you can plan a "welcome home" video for your baby. When your child is older and asking, "Where did you live when I was born?" you can bring out the video and share it. Let's discuss the kinds of things you could include in the video.

INTERVENTION
1. Prepare the home the way you would like. Think about what you would want your baby to see.

2. Have one person be the cameraperson and film while you conduct the tour of the home.

3. Using the planning worksheet, think about including the things listed as well as the many ideas you want to be sure to add.

4. Be sure to label the tape with the date, the address of the home you are in, and who was living in the home at the time of the video.

Welcome Home Video

THINK ABOUT INCLUDING:

- Where baby will sleep
- Where baby will have diapers changed
- Where baby will be bathed
- Where the baby's clothes are kept
- What toys you have bought
- What books you have collected
- Special family items
- Parents' room
- Where in the home you do special activities
- Each room in the home or apartment
- Any current family members living in or outside the home
- The outside of the house
- The doorway you first walk through with the baby

YOUR IDEAS:

_____

_____

_____

_____

_____

_____

_____

_____

_____

Unit 6

Points To Remember

This unit provides a series of interventions designed to help the pregnant woman make space in her life and her world for the unborn child. Let us review the interventions:

- *Personal Circle of Support* provides a way for the pregnant woman to explore her own circle of support, as well as a framework in which to add to that circle of support or create a new or different one.

- *Baby's Circle of Support* stresses that the circle of support for the baby may or may not be the same as the circle of support for the mother. Mother and child have different needs and may require different people in their lives.

- *Circle of Safety* provides a way to look at present support through the lens of safety. Pregnancy can increase one's vulnerability and a child requires certain considerations for safety that may not have been necessary for the woman in her pre-pregnant state.

- *Family Tree* allows the pregnant woman to explore who is in her family and who will be in the baby's family.

- *Exploring the World* encourages the pregnant woman to explore her local environment, but from the perspective of what is and is not child-friendly.

- *Play and Toy Making* provides several pathways to preparing the environment and home for the baby. Making toys for the baby and learning games and songs are ways that make the world baby-friendly.

- *Baby Book* is an activity that helps prepare the pregnant woman for the place her baby will occupy in her world and to begin anticipating her child's development and progress.

- *Welcome Video* is an activity that makes use of video technology to make a visual memory of how the pregnant woman prepared for her child and the first home the child was welcomed into.

"If men had to have babies they would only ever have one each."

Unit 7

Enhancing My Baby's Brain and Development

KEY CONCEPT

Brain development during the fetal period is rapid. Through the prenatal period, the fetus is learning various things from the world outside the mother's womb. Interacting with the unborn child in specific ways can be fun, exciting, and can both support and encourage enhancement of the child's brain development.

OUTCOME GOAL

The mother-to-be will:

Demonstrate an increased knowledge of fetal brain development.

Demonstrate an increased knowledge of how her behaviors and choices may impact her developing child during the prenatal period.

INTERVENTIONS

1. Feeding My Unborn Baby's Brain

2. Brain Building Dinner

3. I Know You Are Out There!

4. Brain Activity

5. Baby's First Classroom

6. My Baby-To-Be Can Hear!

7. Seeing the Light at the End of the Tunnel

8. Making Connections That Rock!

INTERVENTION 1

Feeding My Unborn Baby's Brain

TASK
To develop an awareness of the nutritional needs of the unborn baby's developing brain and how the mother's choices and behaviors need to facilitate this development.

REFERENCE
Chapters 3, 4, 5

ABOUT THIS INTERVENTION
During pregnancy the unborn child takes all needed nutrients from the mother. The unborn baby will receive the variety of nutrients needed to develop if the pregnant woman makes a variety of healthy food choices. Making healthy food choices during pregnancy is important to a healthy mom and a healthy baby.

INTRODUCING THIS INTERVENTION
The foods you eat nourish you and your baby. Your baby needs certain nutrients to grow strong bones and to avoid some problems. As you learn about the helpful and harmful ingredients in food, you can plan a diet that will be healthy for you and will help your baby's bones and brain grow stronger and healthier.

INTERVENTION
1. Review the food pyramid and food choices in each of the categories of recommended foods.

2. Review the foods that provide specific nutrients needed for the baby's development.

3. Using Brain Building Foods for My Baby and Me worksheet, have the mother-to-be list the foods she likes in each category.

4. Encourage the mother-to-be to post this list on her refrigerator or in the kitchen in an alternate place to serve as a supportive reminder of making healthy choices.

Options: Enlarge the pyramid and develop a collage using photos out of magazines and newspapers.

Food Pyramid

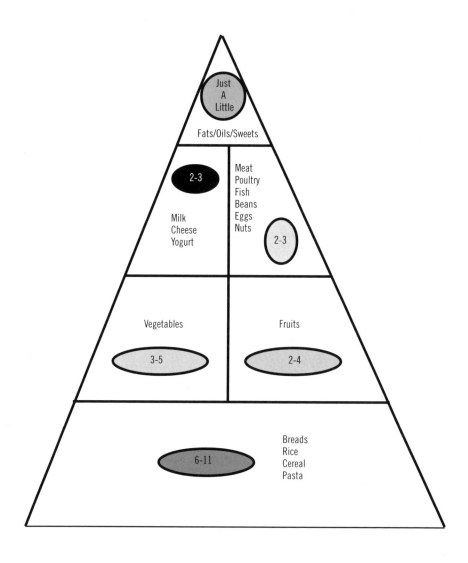

Nutrients for the Unborn Baby's Development

FOODS	NUTRIENTS FOR BABY	HOW THEY HELP
Oranges, black beans and other dried peas/beans, asparagus, oatmeal, spinach and other dark green leafy vegetables	**Folic Acid (Folate)**	• Helps to prevent neural tube defects such as spinal bifida • Aids in building red blood cells
Milk, hard cheeses, ice cream, yogurt and other dairy products, dark green leafy vegetables, calcium fortified orange juice, breads, & cereals	**Calcium**	• Supports the fetal development of strong bones
Lean red meats, certain cooked fishes (for instance farm raised salmon), poultry, green leafy vegetables, dried peas/beans, iron fortified foods	**Iron**	• Aids in building red blood cells • Helps to decrease the risk of premature delivery
Oranges, grapefruits and other citrus fruits, strawberries, some green vegetables like broccoli	**Vitamin C**	• Supports the fetal development of strong bones • Aids in building red blood cells
Cooked seafoods, whole grain breads and cereals, dried peas/beans	**Copper**	• Aids in building and establishing nerve tissue • Aids in building red blood cells • Supports fetal development of strong bones
Dried peas/beans, bananas, nuts, cooked eggs, whole grain breads and cereals, lean red meats,	**Vitamin B6**	• Aids in the body's ability to use protein for developing and maintaining body systems
Cooked seafoods (beware of fish that may contain heavy metals or chemicals), dried peas/beans, lean red meats	**Zinc**	• Helps to decrease the risk of premature delivery
Milk, hard cheeses, ice cream, yogurt and other dairy products, cooked eggs, lean red meats	**Vitamin B12**	• Aids in building red blood cells
Milk, hard cheeses, ice cream, yogurt and other dairy products, cooked eggs, whole grain breads and cereals, some green vegetables like asparagus and broccoli, foods fortified with riboflavin such as certain breads and cereals	**Riboflavin**	• Aids in building red blood cells • Aids in building fetal tissue

Brain Building Foods for My Baby and Me

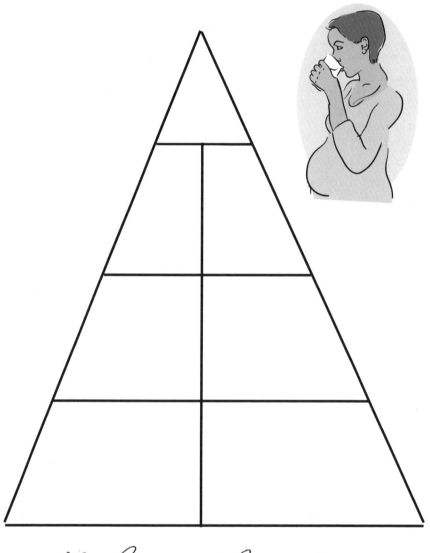

My Pyramid. gov

INTERVENTION 2

Brain Building Dinner

TASK
To develop an awareness of how the nutritional choices of the mother can benefit her unborn baby's developing brain.

REFERENCE
Chapters 3, 4, 5

ABOUT THIS INTERVENTION
Foods, of course, hold many of the nutrients needed to develop and survive throughout our life. Thinking about what nutrients the foods we choose contain can often seem confusing and too scientific. But, choosing foods that are good for both the mother and baby can be fun and interesting. This intervention is designed to explore food options and then to use these food options to design a menu of things we like to eat.

INTRODUCING THIS INTERVENTION
We know babies need certain nutrients to grow strong. But sometimes we wonder if nutritious foods will also be delicious to our tastes. Let's look at some foods that are good for the baby and see what kinds of delicious meals you can design for yourself. It's nice to know that foods you enjoy can be good for the baby, too.

INTERVENTION
1. Review the Foods With Important Nutrients handout. It lists foods with nutrients that assist in the development of the unborn child and are good for supporting the health of the mother-to-be.
2. Circle or underline the things that sound appetizing or interesting.
3. Think about ways to put these foods together in various menu plans for a any meal or snack.
4. Using Menu to Enhance My Baby's Brain worksheet, design a menu that both fits in many of these foods and is something the mother-to-be might actually eat.
5. Use Menu Example handout as an example of a menu.

Options: As a group project, develop a meal menu that the group can prepare and eat together. For the enthusiastic person, develop a daily or weekly menu.

Caution: As with any major changes in diet or activity, women should consult with their health care providers.

Foods With Important Nutrients

FOLIC ACID	CALCIUM	IRON	VITAMIN C	COPPER	VITAMIN B6	ZINC	VITAMIN B12	RIBOFLAVIN
Lettuce	Nonfat yogurt	Spinach	Orange juice	Blackstrap molasses	Liver	Lean meat	Liver	Cottage cheese
Beans	Waffles	Walnuts	Lemons	Kelp	Spinach	Tuna	Meat	Sweet potatoes
Legumes	Tofu	Pistachios	Oranges	Almonds	Bananas	Nuts	Fish	Cornbread
Liver	Almonds	Liver	Grapefruits	Brazil nuts	Lean red meat	Cheese	Eggs	Dark chicken meat
Some fruits	White beans	Lean red meat	Tomatoes	Fish	Yeast	Rice	Dairy products	Almonds
Enriched cereals	Broccoli	Chicken	Strawberries	Cashews	Carrots	Milk	Oysters	Avocados
Enriched breads	Sesame seeds	Salmon	Green peppers	Hazelnuts	Chicken	Almonds	Pork	Brussels sprouts
Orange juice	Spinach	Egg yolks	Potatoes	Pecans	Eggs	Plain yogurt	Blue cheese	Corn
Raspberries	Turnip greens	Potatoes	Citrus juices	Pine nuts	Whole grain cereals	Whole grain cereals	Eggs	Buttermilk
Lentils	Figs	Iron fortified products**	Broccoli	Pistachios	Spinach	Yeast	Kelp	Ice cream
Black beans	Cranberries	Broccoli	Watermelon	Walnuts	Potatoes	Potatoes	Seafood	Kelp
Spinach	Corn tortillas	Kidney beans	Cantaloupe	Cooked sea foods	Peas	Spinach	Margarine	Hard cheeses
Sunflower seeds	Hard cheeses	Lentils	Papaya	Dried peas	Walnuts	Sunflower seeds	Soy products	Yogurt
Beets	Ice cream	Bran	Vitamin C fortified juices & foods**	Dried beans	Eggs	Cooked sea foods	Yogurt	Frozen yogurt
Artichokes	Frozen yogurt	Raisins	Cabbage	Whole grain breads and cereals	Chicken		Hard cheeses	
Asparagus	Fortified orange juice and breads**	Enriched rice** fortified juices & foods**	Collard greens		Cooked sea foods		Ice cream	
Broccoli	Buttermilk	Peanut butter	Spinach		Potatoes			
Cauliflower	Chocolate milk	Apricots	Cranberries					
Endive		Cranberries						
Mustard greens		Onion						
Whole grains		Radishes						
Most berries		Chili peppers						
Okra		Green beans						
Oatmeal		Corn						
Oranges		Cucumbers						
		Carrots						
		Brussels sprouts						
		Cabbage						
		Celery						
		Cauliflower						

**Enriched and fortified foods are those with the specific nutrients added to the product

Note: This is only a partial list of foods put together for this intervention; consult package labeling, nutritional information sources, and/or a registered dietitian or nutritionist for more specific information.

A Menu to Enhance My Baby's Brain

Design a breakfast, lunch, or dinner menu that combines as many of the nutrients as possible listed on the Foods With Important Nutrients handout. Be creative and think about how you could incorporate some of these foods into what you are already eating. An example of a dinner and snack menu is provided on the Menu Example handout.

My Mom knows
what to do to help
me grow and to be
the smartest I can
be!

Menu Example

Spinach salad with dried cranberries & walnuts Raspberry vinaigrette dressing	Calcium, folic acid, iron, zinc, vitamin B6, copper, vitamin C
Steamed asparagus	Folic acid, vitamin C
Whole dinner roll w/ 1 tsp. Butter or margarine	Folic acid, vitamin B6, zinc, vitamin B12
Calcium enriched pasta	Calcium
Chicken breasts baked with olive oil, Sliced green and red peppers, and toasted pine nuts	Vitamin B6, vitamin C, copper, iron
Orange milkshake made with Skim milk, frozen vanilla yogurt, And calcium fortified orange juice concentrate	Vitamin C, calcium, vitamin B12
Snack: Skim milk and two ginger snap cookies made with Blackstrap molasses	Calcium, copper

INTERVENTION 3

I Know You Are Out There!

TASK
To increase the mother-to-be's awareness of the abilities of her unborn child to be aware of and interact with the outside world.

REFERENCE
Chapters 4, 5

ABOUT THIS INTERVENTION
Babies begin in utero to discover the outside world through their mothers' bodies and experiences. Babies become used to the way their mothers interact and behave. They seem to be able to sense when their mother is going to rest, become active, eat, or sleep. This is often not easy to see, as the mother is usually too preoccupied with daily living to take a great deal of notice of her daily patterns. Her unborn child, however, can notice those changes! This can be seen in changes in the unborn child's activity level when the mother experiences a disruption in her normal routines.

INTRODUCING THIS INTERVENTION
Your baby is old enough to react to your experiences. For instance, what does your baby do when you lie down to rest? When you exercise? When you eat? Have you noticed any patterns of behavior from your baby when you stick to a predictable schedule? When you change your routine? If you keep records of what you and your baby do, you can start recognizing how your baby reacts to your actions.

INTERVENTION
1. Record your sleep, exercise, and eating patterns for a few days or a week on the My Activities and Baby's Responses worksheet.

2. At the same time, record your baby's activity patterns.

3. When the second week begins, make some small changes in your schedule; for example, if you usually go to bed at 10 p.m.., try going to bed earlier at 9 or later at 11. If you usually eat breakfast at 9, try eating at 7, or postpone dinner for an hour. If you had been exercising in the morning when you wake up, try moving your exercise to the afternoon or evening.

4. You can experiment with other things as well; for instance, if you usually watch TV in the evening, try taking a bath and reading a book instead.

5. Record your activities and your baby's for the second week.

6. Compare the recordings between the weeks and explore how or if your baby reacted to those changes.

Options: This can also be done when unusual events come up; for example, a vacation trip or a holiday—make recordings before and during those periods and observe for changes.

My Activities and Baby's Responses

Day:_____   Routine Day: Yes   No

MOTHER CODES:	BABY CODES:
S = sleep	S = sleep or quiet time
R = rest or quiet time (reading, TV, visiting with friends)	0 = some activity
0 = exercise or activity (cleaning, walking, and so forth)	+ = very active
E = eating meals or snacks	U = unusual or new behavior or activity
X = any other activity or pattern	X = any other activity or pattern

Example   **One square equals 15 minutes

Time	9			10			11			12			1			2		
Mom	E	E	R	R	R	0	0	0	E	0	0	R	R	R	E	E	S	S	S	S	S	R	E	R
Baby	X	0	+	0	S	S	S	S	0	S	S	0	0	0	S	+	S	S	S	S	S	S	0	+

9A.M.- 3 P.M.

Time	9			10			11			12			1			2		
Mom																		
Baby																		

3P.M.- 9 P.M.

Time	3			4			5			6			7			8		
Mom																		
Baby																		

9P.M.- 3 A.M.

Time	9			10			11			12			1			2		
Mom																		
Baby																		

3A.M.- 9 A.M.

Time	3			4			5			6			7			8		
Mom																		
Baby																		

New things I tried today:

Changes I noticed in my baby's behavior:

My feelings and thoughts about these changes:

INTERVENTION 4

Brain Activity

TASK
To develop an awareness of the activity of the different parts of the brain.

REFERENCE
Chapters 4, 5

ABOUT THIS INTERVENTION
The brain is involved in much of our bodies' functions. It functions to help us understand our environment and to figure out what to do in that environment. It controls our emotional responses, our language, our habits, and our physical reactions. It is heavily involved in movement. The brain is responsible for our vision, our hearing, our sense of taste, our ability to feel things against our skin, and our ability to smell things. The brain is involved in our personalities and the ways in which we interact with others. The brain helps us to differentiate colors and to know the differences between different objects. The brain is also involved in our breathing, heart rhythm, swallowing, digestion, temperature regulation, balance, reflexes, and ability to be alert or to sleep. The brain is a very important organ in our bodies and needs to be nurtured, fed, stimulated, and cared for.

The brain begins to develop abilities to work for the body during the prenatal period. In fact, brain activity in the unborn child or fetus has been recorded as early as 8 weeks in utero, using Electro Enchephalogram (EEG). As it is beginning to build the necessary pathways and structures to support the body, it is already beginning to assume responsibility for the body's functions and actions. In this intervention, the focus will be on what the different parts of the brain are responsible for.

INTRODUCING THIS INTERVENTION
The brain controls most of the things we do. It gathers and interprets information so we can think, understand, decide, and react. It gives our body orders so we can move, see, touch, hear, smell, and taste. It controls body functions like breathing, digesting, pumping blood, and sleeping so we don't have to consciously order those things. Because the brain is involved in everything we do, we need to care for it.

Your baby's brain is already active 8 weeks after conception. As the baby grows, it forms the brain and nerves that will control body functions. Just as different body parts like your hands, feet, ears, and nose perform different functions, so do different parts of the brain control different functions. Today we'll find out which parts of the brain control different things—vision, hearing, breathing, balance, and so on.

INTERVENTION
1. Review the Parts of the Brain handout.
2. Complete The Colorful Brain worksheet.
3. Explore the worksheet and handout together.

Parts of the Brain

THE FRONTAL LOBE OR CEREBRUM
Emotions, habits, being alert and conscious, knowing what is in our environment and how to interact with that environment, planning, worrying, thinking

PARIETAL LOBE
Ability to pay attention to what we see, ability to figure out what we are touching or feeling, body awareness

OCCIPITAL LOBES
Involved in vision, understanding colors

TEMPORAL LOBES
Hearing, assists with memory, speech center

BRAIN STEM
Heart rate and rhythm, breathing, ability to be alert and/or asleep, swallowing, digestion, balance

CEREBELLUM
Helps with balance and motor coordination

HYPOTHALAMUS
Assists with drives and actions

THALAMUS
Helps to pass information from the rest of the body to other parts of the brain

The Colorful Brain

Using the Parts of the Brain handout, fill in each part of the brain with a different color (see below).

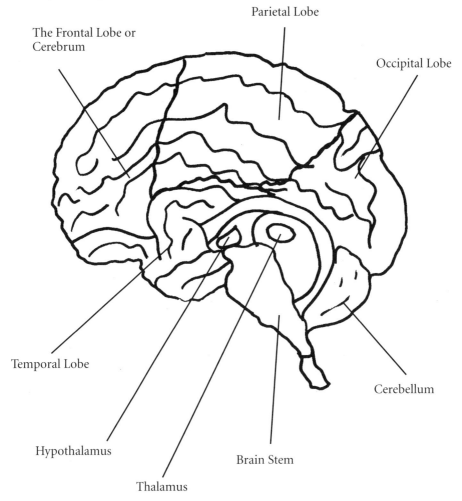

The Frontal Lobe or Cerebrum: Orange
Parietal Lobe: Green
Occipital Lobes: Purple
Temporal Lobes: Blue
Brain Stem: Pink
Cerebellum: Lavender
Hypothalamus: Navy Blue
Thalamus: Brown

INTFRVENTION 5

Baby's First Classroom

TASK
To develop an awareness of how the unborn baby's developing brain is receptive to teaching and how the mother can begin to teach and connect with her child.

REFERENCE
Chapters 4, 5

ABOUT THIS INTERVENTION
More and more research is supporting the notion that babies begin learning while still in utero; the mother's womb is the baby's first classroom. News sources and television have often reported on stories where reading or singing to your baby before birth can increase intelligence and may even produce a "super baby." While creating a super baby is probably not possible or desired, we do have evidence that some of the experiences and actions of the mother can impact the developing fetus and may have lasting effects after birth. To fully understand this, it is important to think about both positive and negative experiences. Babies who have heard their mothers repeat a rhyme, story, or song during the prenatal period have shown a preference for those same rhymes, stories, or songs after birth. These babies would turn their heads to the familiar words when given a choice between two stories, rhymes, or songs. Other studies have found that when babies are given a choice between two nipples that cause the recording of a rhyme, story, or song, the baby will choose to suck on the one that causes the familiar words to be played.

While these findings are very exciting, some of the findings have raised concerns and cautions. Babies of mothers who were exposed to high degrees of stress during their pregnancy often demonstrated higher levels of stress hormones present in their bodies at the time of birth. Stresses could include domestic violence, a chaotic home, or even a trauma such as a car accident. In addition, babies would often show a "remembering" of an event they experienced while in utero when they were again exposed to it after birth. Other research has demonstrated a connection between mother's depression during pregnancy and depressive symptoms in the baby at birth.

While we are still examining what and how babies begin to learn during the pregnancy period, we do know that learning does begin during this period. We know that the mother's womb is indeed the baby's first classroom.

INTRODUCING THIS INTERVENTION
Did you know that your womb is your baby's first classroom? As your baby's brain develops, the baby starts to hear things you hear or say. Your voice becomes familiar. You can share happy times and comfort your baby with stories or songs you enjoy. Do you have a favorite nursery rhyme, lullaby, song, or poem? If you start now telling the same story or singing the same song to your baby, you'll find the baby recognizes that story or song after birth.

INTERVENTION
1. Choose a rhyme, a short story, or a song and read or sing it to your baby on a daily basis during pregnancy.

2. Keep track of each time the rhyme, story, or song is shared with your unborn baby.

3. After your baby's birth, have the baby lie in a safe and comfortable position (in the crib, on a blanket on the floor) and sit to one side of the baby. Recite the rhyme, story, or song in the same manner as it was done during pregnancy. Notice your baby's reaction.

4. Now sit on the opposite side of your baby and recite a similar rhyme, story, or song and notice your baby's reactions.

Optional: Have someone else recite the words on each side of the baby or record during the pregnancy a reading or singing time and use that to play after birth as part of this intervention.

Rhymes, Songs, and Stories

RHYMES

HUMPTY DUMPTY

Humpty Dumpty sat on a wall.
Humpty Dumpty had a great fall.
All the king's horses and all the king's men
Couldn't put Humpty together again!

TWINKLE, TWINKLE, LITTLE STAR

by Jane Taylor

Twinkle, twinkle, little star,
How I wonder what you are.
Up above the world so high,
Like a diamond in the sky.

HUSH LITTLE BABY

Hush, little baby, don't say a word,
Papa's going to buy you a mockingbird.
If that mockingbird won't sing,
Papa's going to buy you a diamond ring.
If that diamond ring turns brass,
Papa's going to buy you a looking glass.
If that looking glass gets broke,
Papa's going to buy you a billy-goat.
And if that billy-goat runs away,
Papa's going to buy you another today.
And all of these things your Papa will do
Because of the way that he loves you.

THIS LITTLE PIGGY WENT TO MARKET

This little piggy went to market,
This little piggy stayed at home,
This little piggy had roast beef,
This little piggy had none,
And this little piggy cried,
Wee-wee-wee-wee-wee,
All the way home.

PEASE PORRIDGE HOT

Pease porridge hot
Pease porridge cold
Pease porridge in the pot
Nine days old.

JACK AND JILL

Jack and Jill
Went up the hill
To fetch a pail of water.
Jack fell down
And broke his crown
And Jill came tumbling after.
Up Jack got
And home did trot
As fast as he could caper
Went to bed
And plastered his head
With vinegar and brown paper

MARY HAD A LITTLE LAMB

Mary had a little lamb
Its fleece as white as snow.
And everywhere that Mary went
That lamb was sure to go.
It followed her to school one day,
Which was against the rules,
It made the children laugh and play,
To see a lamb at school.

RUB-A-DUB-DUB

Rub-a-dub-dub
Three men in a tub,
And how do you think they got there?
The butcher, the baker, the candlestick-maker —
They all jumped out of a rotten potato!
'Twas enough to make a fish stare.

THE TEENSY WEENSY SPIDER

The Teensy Weensy Spider went up the water spout.
Down came the rain and washed the spider out.
Out came the sun and dried up all the rain,
And the Teensy Weensy Spider went up the spout again.

SONGS

YOU ARE MY SUNSHINE
You are my sunshine
My only sunshine
You make me happy
When skies are gray
You'll never know dear
How much I love you
Please don't take my
Sunshine away.

TAKE ME OUT TO THE BALL GAME
Take me out to the ball game
Take me out to the crowd
Buy me some peanuts and Cracker Jack
I don't care if I ever come back.
So it's root, root, root for the home team
If they don't win it's a shame
Oh, it's one, two, three
Strikes you're out!
At the ol' ball game.

ROW, ROW, ROW YOUR BOAT
Row, row, row your boat
Gently down the stream.
Merrily, merrily, merrily, merrily,
Life is but a dream.

DO YOU KNOW THE MUFFIN MAN
Do you know the Muffin Man,
The Muffin Man,
The Muffin Man?
Do you know the Muffin Man
Who lives in Drury Lane?
Yes, I know the Muffin Man,
The Muffin Man,
The Muffin Man.
Yes, I know the Muffin Man
Who lives in Drury Lane.

NOTE:
• Any theme song you are familiar with can also be used
• A recorded song can be used as well; however, using the mother's voice would be the best choice.

STORIES

- A short children's book
- Snow White
- Cinderella
- The Three Pigs
- Goldilocks and the Three Bears
- One or two pages of your favorite book

My Teaching Schedule

DATE	TIME	RESPONSE OF UNBORN BABY/MY THOUGHTS & FEELINGS

After the Baby Is Born

Write a little about how your baby reacted when he or she heard the rhyme, story, or song you had been sharing with him/her before birth.

INTERVENTION 6

My Baby-To-Be Can Hear!

TASK
To develop an awareness of the hearing abilities of the unborn baby.

REFERENCE
Chapters 4, 5

OPTIONAL MATERIALS
Bells, radio/stereo, alarm clock, musical instruments, spoons, etc.

INTRODUCING THIS INTERVENTION
The unborn child begins to develop the ability to hear in the second trimester. This hearing is thought to be well developed by 24 weeks. The unborn child can not only hear sounds coming from both inside and outside the mother but can react to them with movement.

INTRODUCING THIS INTERVENTION
By the time your baby is 24 weeks old, it can hear sounds from inside and outside your body. How have you noticed your baby reacts to sounds? Does your baby react in the same way to your voice and to a stranger's voice?

INTERVENTION
1. Throughout a day or a week, make a list of all of the noises and sounds you believe your unborn baby can hear.

2. Experiment with these sounds. When your baby is moving around, change the sounds in the environment, such as putting on music, turning off the TV, beginning or stopping a conversation with others, etc. Try both adding sounds and removing sounds and see how the movement changes. These sounds may include ringing a bell, listening to the alarm clock, electronic toys, a child's xylophone, etc.

3. Continue the experiment when your unborn baby is quiet or still, clap your hands over your belly and see if there is a response. While taking a bath, tap the side of the tub with a stick or metal spoon and notice any responses.

4. Try to keep a record of all the sounds you feel your baby responds to.

5. Remember, unborn babies often respond to familiar sounds but will often respond to an unfamiliar sound. Likewise, they may begin to get so used to certain sounds, like their mother's voice, that they may not respond as much to her voice as to the father's or a grandparent's voice.

My Baby Can Hear!

Sounds I noticed my baby responding to:

How my baby reacted to other sounds I found:

How my baby reacted to voices of the family:

Other things I observed:

INTERVENTION 7

Seeing the Light at the End of the Tunnel

TASK
To develop an awareness of the developing sight skills of the unborn baby.

REFERENCE
Chapters 4, 5

NEEDED MATERIALS
Flashlight

ABOUT THIS INTERVENTION
The unborn child's ability to sense light begins at the start of the second trimester. By 29 weeks, the unborn child's eyes can open and shut. Responding to a light source while in utero can become apparent at this time as well.

INTRODUCING THIS INTERVENTION
At 29 weeks old, your baby's eyes can open and close. This means your baby can react to light or darkness around you. Let's experiment with a flashlight to find out how your baby reacts to light.

INTERVENTION
1. Have the mother-to-be get into a relaxed position.
2. After dimming the lights in the room and turning off any televisions or other noise sources, have the mother-to-be expose her belly.
3. Using the flashlight, have the mother-to-be place the light on her skin and shine the light into her belly. Notice the unborn baby's response.
4. Try moving the light around to different areas of her belly to test for other responses. As the fetus matures, he or she might even begin to turn toward the light source.
5. Experiment with different times of the day, to see if there is a difference in response patterns.
6. Explore with the mother-to-be how it feels to have her baby begin to respond to her actions more directly.

My Baby Can See!

How my baby acted when I shined a light into my belly:

How my baby acted when I moved the light to different places on my belly:

Other observations I made:

INTERVENTION 8

Making Connections That Rock!

TASK
To help the mother-to-be begin to develop an understanding of what the baby needs to develop a healthy and active brain.

REFERENCE
Chapters 4, 5

ABOUT THIS INTERVENTION
The science of the human brain can be very complicated and often includes many complex words and terms. Without getting too scientific, we know the unborn child's brain becomes active while the child is in utero. The brain rapidly develops throughout the before-birth period and the first several years of childhood. In fact, the brain actually continues to develop throughout our lifetimes.

As far as the before-birth period is concerned, the structures of the brain are being laid down. Within these structures, there are neurons or nerve cells, which could be thought of as islands. In between these islands are streams connecting them, called synapses. The streams carry the messages between the islands. For example, in the brain there are a group of islands that help in the understanding and knowing about a ringing telephone. When the phone rings, the phone ringing island is activated. Before there is a chance to answer the phone, the phone ringing island has sent a message down to the next island, which is the behavior island of answer it, which sends a message onto the next island called say "hello," which sends a message to converse with friend island (now, of course, there are many, many more islands involved and many more scientifically significant transactions between the neurons). The reason this series of messages gets activated and each of these islands exists is because past experience has reinforced what occurs when the phone rings. Understanding is established of what a ringing phone means, what to do about it, how to behave, and over time an understanding that a ringing phone can mean different things was developed. For instance, if it rings during dinner, it is probably a solicitor wanting a commitment to do business with them. The only way knowledge of these events is developed is through how they happen over and over again to the point where a deep stream of communication was established between the islands. Each repetition of experience deepens the stream and makes it more and more permanent. This same phenomena occurs for all of our everyday activities and experiences.

Babies have not had many experiences before birth that have laid down such a complicated network of communication. But the beginnings for many experiences have been established. It is helping to establish these beginnings that is the subject of the intervention presented here. In this intervention the focus will be on helping the unborn child to connect being rocked by mom as a soothing experience.

INTRODUCING THIS INTERVENTION

Our brains grow and develop throughout our lives. Before birth, your baby's brain grows into sections that control different body functions. To help the parts coordinate their actions, the brain lays pathways between the sections to speed communication. You can think of the brain as a collection of islands with paths or bridges between them. Every time your baby's brain uses a path, the path gets smoother and faster.

Travel over some well-used paths becomes so easy it becomes automatic and requires little thought. For instance, if the phone rings, you don't have to think much to know the expected action is to answer the phone and to speak to the caller. You've used that brain path so often, you can do the expected thing automatically.

You can start now before birth to teach your baby some useful, calming reactions. You can help your baby develop calming pathways in the brain.

INTERVENTION

1. Review Islands of Communication handout.

2. Review New Experiences handout.

3. Practice for a week or more, recording results on the Connections That Rock worksheet.

4. Discuss thoughts and experiences about the intervention.

Islands of Communication

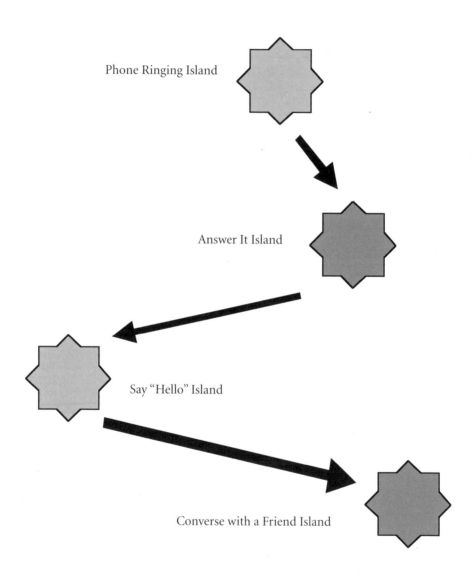

New Experiences

Mom does or experiences something new or different from her usual activities. She may refrain from something that she usually does at this time, she may decide to eat, or she may be engaging in something totally new. Baby's excitement can come from a variety of sources— anticipation of something mom routinely does at this time, such as eating, or she may have done something new that has caused the baby to be surprised.

In the womb, the baby senses this new event or experience. Baby's brain and body get the message Something New!

Baby's systems get excited. He or she begins to move around a lot, kicking, twisting, or turning somersaults. The excitement continues to increase, as baby does not know what the new experience is or what it means. He or she does not know what will happen next.

When mom feels baby's movement and activity, she begins to sway her hips back and forth, rocking the baby and soothing the increasing excitement.

Baby feels soothed and calmed. First, the baby's body begins to feel comforted, then the brain. Baby has now developed the beginning of a group of islands with streams of communication or a neuronal pathway. When he or she is born, the beginnings will be there and when mom soothes her crying baby, he or she will have one option of reaction—to be soothed by mom's holding and rocking. Each time mom responds to baby's excitement, the streams get deeper and deeper, becoming better established each time.

Connections that Rock!

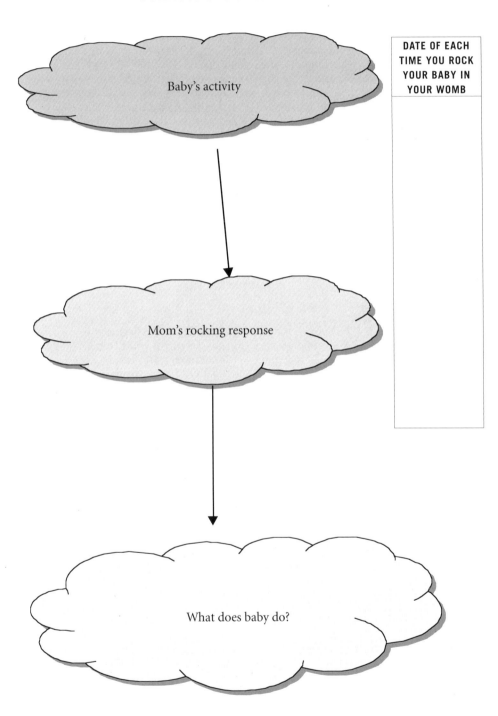

Baby's activity

DATE OF EACH
TIME YOU ROCK
YOUR BABY IN
YOUR WOMB

Mom's rocking response

What does baby do?

Unit 7

Points To Remember

The interventions in Unit 7 are based on many of the most current ideas on what can be done to enhance the brain development of the unborn child. At the very least, these activities help the pregnant woman to take care of herself, make decisions based on the welfare of her unborn child, and interact with her unborn child. Let us review these interventions:

- *Feeding my Unborn Baby's Brain* encourages healthy eating by the pregnant woman and helps her to connect her choices and decisions to the welfare of her baby. Remember, changes in a pregnant woman's diet should always be explored with her medical provider or a nutritionist specializing in pregnancy.

- *Brain Building Dinner* is a simple one meal activity that encourages exploration of the foods that are thought to be most helpful during fetal development.

- *I Know You Are Out There*! is an activity that helps the pregnant woman to connect and interact with her baby. The purposeful interaction is thought to enhance the baby's development while in utero.

- *Brain Activity* is an introduction into the complexity of the human brain and to the potential it holds.

- *Baby's First Classroom* supports the pregnant woman's role as a teacher for her child. This activity helps to link what the unborn child absorbs in utero and shows a connection with after birth.

- *My Baby-to-be Can Hear!* stresses the hearing abilities of the unborn child.

- *Seeing the Light at the End of the Tunnel* stresses the unborn child's ability to perceive and react to light while still in utero.

- *Making Connections That Rock!* helps the pregnant woman to understand how activity and stimulation help to create pathways in the developing child's brain.

Appendices

APPENDIX A

Pregnancy Assessment Format

IDENTIFYING INFORMATION
(date of birth, age, marital status, month of pregnancy, etc.)

PRESENT ISSUES
Current Pregnancy

Pregnancy Background

Medical Background

Mental Health

Self Care

Work and Education

Relationships

Stressors

PAST HISTORY
Loss and Trauma

Childhood Experiences

Relationship with Mother

FUTURE VISIONS
Image of Baby

Images of Becoming a Mother

Images of How This Baby Will Change Daily Life

APPENDIX B

Transcript of Interview Excerpts

TOPIC: PREGNANCY HISTORY OF A 23 YEAR OLD EUROPEAN AMERICAN WOMAN

INTERVIEWER (I): I would like to ask you about your past. Is this is your first pregnancy?

PREGNANT WOMAN (PW): Mm-hmm.

I: Okay, so you have never been pregnant before, is that correct?

PW: Well, I was pregnant before, but this is my first baby.

I: Oh, okay. When were you pregnant before?

PW: I was pregnant when I was 21.

I: Okay.

PW: And I was pregnant a couple months.

I: And what happened with that pregnancy.

PW: I had an abortion.

I: Uh-huh.

PW: And then I had a miscarriage and I had another abortion.

I: Okay. So this is your fourth pregnancy?

PW: Uh-huh.

I: How old were you when you were first pregnant?

PW: Nineteen.

I: So, 21 was the first time you were pregnant?

PW: Mm-hmm.

I: Was that with the boyfriend you were with for quite a while.

PW: Mm-hmm.

I: Okay. When were you pregnant the second time?

PW: Awhile after that. We really wanted that one.

I: Just so I can understand better...When you miscarried with your second pregnancy that was also in a relationship with him?

PW: Mm-hmm.

I: And your third pregnancy, when you decided on an abortion?

PW: Mm-hmm. That was with him, too.

I: Okay. So that was all really within the last three years then.

PW: Mm-hmm.

I: So what made you decide to parent this child you are now pregnant with?

PW: *Because...well the second time I got pregnant I was going to keep it. And then when I miscarried I was going to keep that pregnancy. And the third time it was...he...it was like bad thing; we were like fighting and stuff and he hit me and he went to jail and all kinds of stuff was happening so...he was in jail and I moved out for two weeks and like I just stopped talking to him for a while. And so I just I didn't want to have that...in my life. I didn't want that in front of my kid, I didn't want...I just didn't want any part of it, you know. And I decided to keep this baby because I wanted it, I felt like it was supposed to be here and I felt really bad about having the other abortions. But I felt like it was the right thing to do. And I just felt like this baby was supposed to be here and enough was enough, basically. You know like I had gotten myself into the situation again so I needed to take responsibility. And also I do not want my other boyfriend in my life for the rest of my life. I can...we had like the worst relationship. I mean I...I wouldn't go have a kid by him today it was so bad.*

I: But it sounds like when you miscarried that was kind of a different point in your relationship?

PW: *Yeah we were doing good then, he wanted it and we were like...we were doing good. He was like going to Alcoholics Anonymous. He was like trying to get his life together and you know he was really excited about the whole thing so. It was...at that time I had a really good job and everything was going good, so...*

I: So it must have been real difficult for the two of you then when you miscarried.

PW: *Like it was. I was like really upset.*

I: Did that change your relationship with him?

PW: *Mmm no I think...yeah things got kind of bad you know again but it was probably just 'cause they were going bad again anyway so you know so.*

I: So it was just kind of the nature of the relationship not necessarily losing the baby.

PW: *Mm-hmm.*

I: Do you think about your first three pregnancies much?

PW: *Mmm not really, not any more, I used to. I just feel bad about it you know and I feel like if this baby...you know like supposed to be here you know like why shouldn't the other ones you know like had a chance too. I think about things like that but then I think like...like him and just the whole thing and my life would have just been horrible. I would have been a wreck you know like as a mom and stuff. Being...*

I: Do you think your experiences with your first three pregnancies will influence at all the way you're going to mother this child? Or your relationship with this child?

PW: *No because I just try to put that stuff in the past, I try not to hold on to it.*

I: So how do you do that? How do you kind of resolve it and let it go?

PW: *Time is helpful.*

I: So for you that's a real important thing.

PW: Mm-hmm.

I: Just kind of letting things...

PW: Yeah because it used to be...I used to like be more like...I was like really depressed you know and I felt really bad about it so I think time is just mainly you know kind of the way.

DISCUSSION

In this excerpt it is apparent that the pregnant woman is having a difficult time talking about her pregnancy history. In fact, on three other occasions (one with an intake staff) this woman failed to even acknowledge any previous pregnancies. This reluctance or avoidance of the topic suggests some unresolved feelings around these previous pregnancies. Unresolved loss issues and unresolved issues over her choices to abort would be areas to explore further as her unresolved feelings-possibly guilt, grief, sadness, sorrow, anger, and so forth—have the possibility of interfering with her ability to transition into the role of mother. Other comments she made outside this interview support this concern, such as "I just know something is going to go wrong, I've done too many bad things in my life."

A second major issue to come up in this excerpt is the relationship she had with her boyfriend, which was extremely volatile and abusive. In this section the goal was to learn more about her pregnancy history. Her comments about the relationship with her boyfriend provide a good opening to exploring that area as well. However, she is having some difficulty sharing her pregnancy history and this did not seem like a good time to switch focus to the boyfriend. These issues will be discussed further when the section on relationships comes up. At that time, it would be helpful to go back to the statements she has made here about him.

Finally, some comments on the interviewer. It is important to note how some questions were gently repeated in different ways in an attempt to gather the information. As you can see the pregnant woman provided more clarity as the questions were repeated in different ways. The interviewer also made an effort to continue gathering information so she could be clear on the history. No judgments or criticisms of either the pregnant woman's ability to provide the information, her past choices, or her experiences were introduced into the interview. The goal was simply to gather information in a manner that was respectful and supportive of a developing relationship. Finally, note how at the end of this section, the information and topics are tied back into the potential effects on the baby. It is important to see all of the content of a pregnancy assessment in terms of how it will impact mothering and the relationship to the baby.

TOPIC: PAST RELATIONSHIP HISTORY WITH HER FATHER

I: Now, I'm going to focus on your past history which we've talked about just a little bit. I know you said you lost your father when you were very young and so you really don't have a lot of memory of him. Is that correct?

PW: Mm-hmm. I don't really remember anything about him.

I: Except for what people have told you, is that correct?

PW: Mm-hmm.

I: Do you have pictures and things of him?

PW: Mm-hmm.

I: What was he like?

PW: He was tall and handsome. I have one picture where he is holding me and smiling. I was just lying there.

I: It sounds like this is still difficult for you sometimes?

PW: Mm-hmm.

I: Do you think about him a lot? Or do you think about the impact of...the loss of your father?

PW: Just the fact that I never had him...you know...there. And I feel like I wouldn't have gotten into these relationships...you know, if I had that father figure in my life.

I: Mm-hmm.

PW: And I kind of think about that also with my baby and I don't want her to, you know, get into relationships like that 'cause she doesn't have her daddy around...

I: You mean abusive relationships?

PW: Mm-hmm. Controlling relationships. And I feel like my dad would have protected me, you know, a lot, also—you know, those type of things.

I: How do you plan to make things different for your baby?

PW: I don't know, I just know I want to. For me, I never thought I was going to be in a bad relationship...he was like a drug to me this guy [referring to the boyfriend that fathered her first three pregnancies.] I...I was like so in love with him I loved him so much and I never...when he was...when we weren't around each other I felt like you know like I needed him back you know. And it was just a sick relationship. It was really unhealthy. But yeah it was. I never thought I was going to actually be without him so. I can't do that no more.

I: Mm-hmm.

PW: Also, I just have to...I can't be like how I was before. Like I used to, you know. Like be like out there, you know, with guys and stuff like I always had a different boyfriend and I can't do that, I can't bring different guys home and stuff you know and have them around her. I got to be more independent and selective you know of who I actually decide you know can be in my life.

I: Well it sounds like you've thought a lot about what changes you want to make.

PW: Mm-hmm. Mm-hmm.

DISCUSSION

The young woman in this interview seems to already to searching for connections between her early loss of her father and her current relationships with men. She has the fantasy that her the presence of her father in her life would have had such a powerful influence that she would have experienced different life circumstance, made different choices, and been protected. This fantasy is also pushing her to fantasize on how her daughter's life will be different from her own. She is already realizing she will have to make changes and set some new rules for herself with regard to the men in her life. This passage not only provides information on her memories, fantasies, and wishes, it also provides a door to intervening in some of these areas. Notice, at the end of this section of questioning, it again tied back to the relationship between the mother's experiences and how this will impact her baby.

APPENDIX C

Special Items List

UNIT 2, INTERVENTION 3: STETHOSCOPE

There are many varieties of stethoscopes available. Some of the brand names include 3M, Sprague, Prestige, and Littman. They range from very inexpensive on up. Some stethoscopes will be better than others at hearing fetal heart tones. You will need to test out brands and types and see what works for you.

First Sounds Prenatal Listener: This is the only device that we could locate that is actually made to hear prenatal sounds. It allows the mother to not only listen to the sounds of her baby in utero, but the mother can also record the sounds she hears. This device can also be used for the father and others to listen to the baby. First Sounds is made by Unisar and can be purchased on line from many of the baby retailers such as Right Start (rightstart.com). We purchased ours locally for about $35.00.

UNIT 2, INTERVENTION 4: TAPE RECORDER

Any tape recorder should work well. Some have built in microphones others have microphones that can be attached and allow the speaker to be closer to the microphone. It is best to use a standard recorder that takes standard tapes (rather than the micro-cassettes). Tape recorders and tapes can be purchased at a variety of outlets such as office equipment stores, department stores, and on-line. There are several brand names of both recorders and tapes, but basically it is personal preference that makes the final decision.

UNIT 3, INTERVENTION 4: SOFT BABY CARRIER(S)

There are many, many varieties of baby carriers including the front pack, the sling, and the back carriers. Many companies offer several varieties. The decision as to which carrier is best for the mothers you work with should be based on their comfort level with the specific carriers, the cost, and the style. If she does not like it or feel comfortable in it she will never wear it. Some of the different companies include: Baby Bjorn, New Native, Prince Lionheart, Evenflo, Fisher Price, Theador Bean Adventure Company, Bill Amberg, Maws, Kelty, Gerry-Snugli, Heart to Heart, and No Jo. Most of these are available on-line or at baby/pregnancy retailers. Many can also be found at garage sales and thrift shops in very good condition.

UNIT 7, INTERVENTION 6: BELLS

Any bell or bell-sounding instrument can be used. Embryonics makes a line of toys and tapes that offer a complete range of musical sounds. If you need to purchase a bell, a child's bell instrument might be a good selection. They are made to be safe for children and the baby can use the bell as he or she gets older. They can be found in children's toy stores, retail stores, and on some on-line sites.

UNIT 7, INTERVENTION 8: FLASHLIGHTS

Most household type flashlights or penlights will work well for these exercises. The larger lantern types are often too large. Flashlights can be purchased in any hardware store, department store, or even some grocery stores.

FOR ALL UNITS

Crayons, other art supplies such as markers, colored pencils, art paper, and so forth: Any art supplies can be used. They can be found in department stores, on-line, and in office supply shops.

APPENDIX D

Suggested Interventions for the Individual Client

For the individual pregnant woman in a normal, typical pregnancy:

ACTIVITY	RATIONALE
The Many Hats of Motherhood	Helps to begin thinking about the many new roles that will need to be taken on.
Baby Kicks & Wiggles	Helps to connect the mother with her baby, helps to make the baby "real".
My Own Relationships	Facilitates a personal examination of the mother's own relationships.
Preparing to be an Attachment Focused Parent: Feeding Time	Helps push thinking in the direction of the mother-child relationship and what the character of that relationship will be about.
Breath…1…2…3…	Encourages the development of simple relaxation skills that are also supportive of many birthing techniques.
Conserving Energy: Saying NO	Encourages the mother to begin thinking about the most important places to focus her energy and supports the fact she will have limited energy and cannot do all.
Personal Circle of Support	Helps the mother explore who is in her life and who is important. Begins thinking in the direction of how her baby will fit into this circle.
Seeing Light at the End of the Tunnel	Helps the mother to connect to another aspect of her baby, that he or she is real and active and has the capacity to interact with her even in utero.

For a high-risk individual pregnant woman, I would make the following adjustments to the above:

1. Circle of Safety rather than Personal Circle of Support, in order to facilitate thinking about who is and is not safe and encourage a rethinking of who they want involved in their lives.

2. Affirmations rather than Conserving Energy, in order to facilitate positive self thinking as a beginning to making changes beneficial to the self.

3. Making Connections that Rock rather than Seeing the Light, in order to assist the mother in developing skills that will not only comfort her baby but will also be self-soothing for her.

APPENDIX E

Suggested Interventions for the Group

ACTIVITY	RATIONALE
Other Mothers	To facilitate the group to look at the variations on mothering and to explore with each other what kind of mothers they want to be.
Baby Predictions	A fun way of beginning discussion of having a baby in their future. The issue of predicting can also be helpful in bringing the group back together postpartum to "discuss their predictions" but also to reconnect and gain support from each other.
Family Traditions & Celebrations	A nice activity to share ideas. Each person of the group could share their ideas and experiences. Supports group interaction.
Gifts to your Body	Sharing with each other can make this a fun, interactive activity where women can learn from each other how to be kind and gentle to themselves.
Playing	Helps to force a shift from some of the harder and more difficult issues of real life to the lighter side. Also supports ways of connecting the woman with fun things in her own childhood and what she wants to provide for her child.
Conserving Energy: Saying NO	The role-plays in this activity are a great opportunity to share, be creative and laugh with each other. The group should also be able to share examples from their own experiences. Supports self-care.
Personal Circle of Support	Individually this encourages the mother to take a look at who is there for her. Group-wise this activity can facilitate a sharing group within and may forge some supports between the group members.
Brain Building Dinner	A nice and fun way to share with each other, nourish the group members and their unborn babies, and to celebrate and honor each other.

Groups of high-risk women really need to be nurtured, to learn how to nurture each other, and to feel good about the idea of nurturing their children-to-be. All of these group activities can be nurturing so they would be appropriate for the higher risk group. Substituting Circle of Safety for Circle of Support (or combining the two) may be helpful when safety issues need to be examined. Also, Family Traditions and Celebrations might be difficult or threatening for the mothers who have not had supportive families who do these types of things, instead the focus might be on only creating new traditions rather than exploring past traditions.

APPENDIX F

Guidelines for Developing a Group

The following are some guidelines for developing a group for the pregnant women you see in your practices. Consider each of these areas for the most successful group experience:

Who will be in this group?
Ages of women, stage of pregnancy, level of risk, current relationship status (i.e. single, married, partnered, recently broke up), etc.

What is the purpose of the group?
Education, development of relationships, support, processing emotions, working on personal issues related to pregnancy, etc.

Who will run this group?
One leader, multiple leaders, qualifications of leader, amount of group-running experience, position or job role, etc.

How would this group look?
Number of participants, number of group sessions, length of time for group (1 or 1 1/2 hours), rules for participation, behavioral rules (cannot come to group under the influence of drugs or alcohol, no smoking, etc.), where group will be held, time of group, transportation, inclusion of food or snacks, will childcare be provided, etc.

What would be the attendance rules?
Come to all groups, call if sick, must leave group if more than one group missed, etc.

How will sessions be structured?
Time for warm-up, information piece, activity, sharing, eating, etc.

What information or topics would you want to cover?

Why would those be most important for your group of women?

How will you incorporate the women's goals with your group goals?

How will you define confidentiality for your group?

How will you support confidentiality between group members as well as between group sessions?

How will you handle issues that might come up around someone's bad memories or past trauma?

How would you handle a situation where someone shares with the group that they are suicidal?

How would you handle a situation where someone shares that they (or someone else in their family) has been abusing a child, either sexually, physically, or emotionally? Or neglecting to provide proper care for a child?

How would you handle a situation where someone shares that they themselves have been sexually abused? How would your strategy change if that group member is under 18 years of age?

How might you handle arguments or conflict between group members?

How available will you or the other group leaders be between group sessions?

What are the limits to that availability?

What types of activities do you want to include?

What types of activities can your budget allow?

What other limitations might you have?

Will you want to involve any outside agencies or speakers?

How will you reward successful group participation?
A graduation, certificate, acknowledgment, party, etc.

How will you evaluate the effectiveness and meaningfulness of your group experience?

APPENDIX G

Your Response to Poetry Example

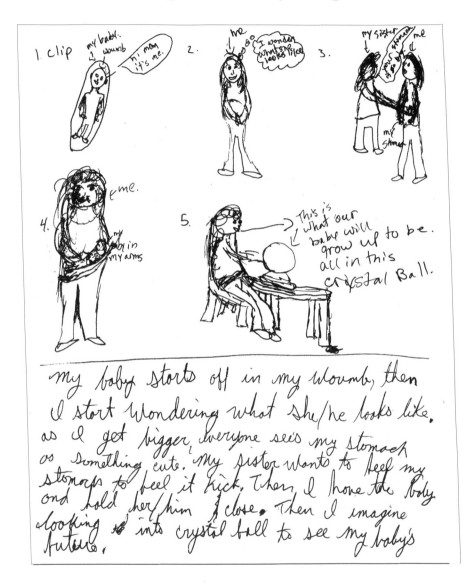

This Response to Poetry worksheet was done by a 19 year old in her 21st week of gestation. She grew up with an abusive and neglectful alcoholic mother. She is focused on bonding and putting her baby first to break the cycle of abuse.

APPENDIX H

How Your Baby Might Respond to Poetry Example

mommy,
it's scary here,
please don't let anyone harm
me. I'm fragile, please protect me!
I wanna smile, Just like you are
smile at me. I want to walk and
explore the world, Will you teach me.
When I cry, will you make me happy.

Please give me a nice, warm, place to
sleep and nourish me so I grow
healthy. I'm Your baby.
   I love You.

What might your child say to you?

This Response to Poetry worksheet was
done by the same young woman during
her 21st week of gestation. She grew up
with an abusive and neglectful alcoholic
mother. She is focused on bonding and
putting her baby first to break the cycle
of abuse.

APPENDIX I

Ghosts of the Past Example

The ghost from my past is called:

My mom

The ghost is here because:

she wants to hurt me

This ghost makes me feel:

hurt & betrayed

I do not need this ghost in my life. I do not need to carry around bad feelings any more I will get rid of this ghost by:

showing her how to love without the need to hurt.

The ghost from my past is called:

The Fallen

The ghost is here because:

it wants me to die.

This ghost makes me feel:

Scared I won't wake up.

I do not need this ghost in my life. I do not need to carry around bad feelings any more. I will get rid of this ghost by:

getting over the Fear off heights.

This Ghosts From My Past worksheet was done by the same young woman at 22 weeks. She had planned a ceremonial burning of her written ghosts. She chose to cut them up in very small pieces and reports feeling freer from the hurt imposed by her mother after this intervention.

APPENDIX J

Circle of Support Example 1

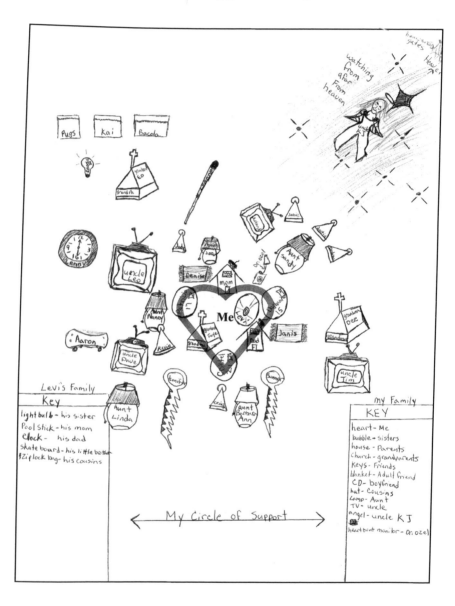

This worksheet was done at 27 weeks. On first glance, it appears that this young woman has a large support system. After following the discussion questions posed by the intervention guidelines, we discovered she has almost no reliable, accessible supports.

Circle of Support Example 2

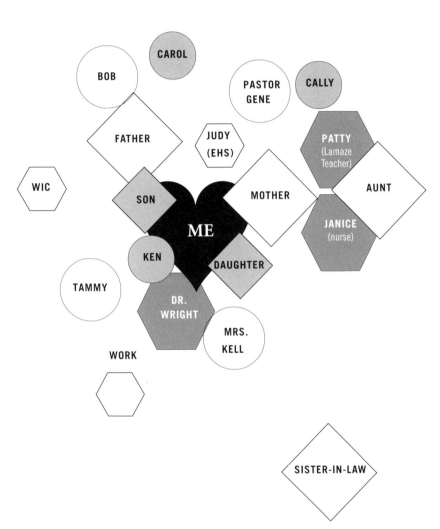

MY CIRCLE OF SUPPORT

Heart—Me
Small Squares—Children
Big Squares—Family
Big Circles—Church
Small Circles—Friends
BiG hexagons—Pregnancy Supports
Small Hexagons—Work/Agencies

Back side of My Circle of Support Handout

This example illustrates how one mother used both color and shape to code the significant people in her life. She included herself, her children, her family, friends, pregnancy supports, work, agencies, and church members. On the front side of her network she has listed everyone fairly close to her, with the exception of her sister-in-law, who she states is "all right but not really a good person." Whereas on the back side of the handout she places her brother, who she initially describes as "real mean and not good to be around." Several weeks following this session, the mother elaborated on the abuse she had suffered from her brother. This allowed the home visitor to do some work on the issues of keeping the baby safe from him as well as helping her to set safe boundaries.

APPENDIX L

Family Tree Alternative

APPENDIX M

Community Map Example

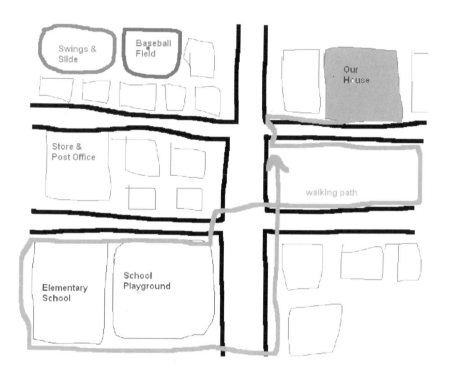

References

CHAPTER 1 *Child Welfare, gov*

1. Center for Disease Control, National Vital Statistics Reports. (2000). *Deaths: Final data for 1998.* Series 48, Number 11, July 24, 2000.

2. Center for Disease Control, Vital & Health Statistics. (2000). *Trends in pregnancy and pregnancy rates by outcome: Estimates for the U.S.76-96. Series 21,* Number 56, January.

3. Center for Disease Control and Prevention, National Center for Chronic Disease prevention and Health Promotion. (2000). *Chronic disease notes & reports; Special focus: Safe motherhood, Vol. 13* (2), Spring/Summer.

4. Ahmad, K. (1999). United Nations agencies join forces to cut worldwide maternal death rates. *Lancet,* November 6, 1999.

5. Center for Disease Control and Prevention, National Center for Chronic Disease prevention and Health Promotion. (2000). *Chronic disease notes & reports; Special Focus: Safe Motherhood, Vol. 13* (2), Spring/Summer.

6. Child Abuse and Neglect National Statistics. (2001). Child maltreatment, 1998. *http://www.calib.com/nccanch/pubs/factsheets/canstats.htm*

7. U.S. Department of Health and Human Services, The Third National Incidence Study of Child Abuse and Neglect, Washington, D.C.: U.S.Government Printing Office, 1996.

8. America's Children Key National Indicators of Well Being 1997. Federal interagency forum on child and family statistics, *http://www.cdc.gov/nchs/data/amchild.pdf*

9. National Center for Health Statistics, Healthy People 2000 Review. (1997). Hyattsville, MD: Public Health Service, 1997.

10. Child Abuse and Neglect National Statistics (2001) Child maltreatment, 1998.*http://www.calib.com/nccanch/pubs/factsheets/canstats.htm*

11. Child Abuse and Neglect National Statistics (2001) Child Maltreatment, 1998.*http://www.calib.com/nccanch/pubs/factsheets/canstats.htm*

12. Olds, D.L., Henderson, C.R., Kitzman, H.J., Eckenrode, J.J., Cole, R.E., Tatelbaum, R.C. (1999). Prenatal and infancy home visitation by nurses: Recent findings. *The Future of Children, Home Visiting: Recent Program Evaluations, 9*(1), Spring/Summer, 44-65.

13. Fraiberg, S. (1980). *Clinical studies in infant mental health: The first year of life.* New York: Basic Books.

14. Johnson, L.M. (2001). Effects of prenatal exposure to marijuana, parenting babies and toddlers. *http://babyparenting.about.com/parenting/babyparenting/library/weekly/bIDBmarij.htm*

15. Olds, D.L., Henderson, C.R., Kitzman, H.J., Eckenrode, J.J., Cole, R.E., Tatelbaum, R.C. (1999). Prenatal and infancy home visitation by nurses: Recent findings. *The Future of Children, Home Visiting: Recent Program Evaluations, 9*(1), Spring/Summer, 44-65.

16. Newsweek Special Issue. (2000). *Your child.* New York: Newsweek.

17. Dietz, P.M., Spitz, A.M., Anda, R.F., Williamson, D.F., McMahon, P.M., Santelli, J. S., Nordenberg, D.F., Felitti, V.J., & Kendrick, J. S. (1999). Unintended pregnancy among adult women exposed to abuse or household dysfunction during their childhood. *JAMA, 282*(14), 1359-1364.

18. Dietz, P.M., Spitz, A.M., Anda, R.F., Williamson, D.F., McMahon, P.M., Santelli, J. S., Nordenberg, D.F., Felitti, V.J., & Kendrick, J. S. (1999). Unintended pregnancy among adult women exposed to abuse or household dysfunction during their childhood. *JAMA, 282*(14), 1359-1364.

19. Bibring, G., Dwyer, T.F., Huntington, D.S., & Valenstein, A.F. (1961). A study of the psychological processes in pregnancy and of the earliest mother-child relationship. *Psychoanalytic Study of the Child,16*, p. 25.

20. Bibring, G., Dwyer, T.F., Huntington, D.S., & Valenstein, A.F. (1961). A study of the psychological processes in pregnancy and of the earliest mother-child relationship. *Psychoanalytic Study of the Child, 16*, 9-72.

21. Benedek, T. (1959). Parenthood as a developmental phase: A contribution to the libido theory. *Journal of the American Psychoanalytic Association, 7*, 389-417.

22. Rubin, Reva. (1975). Maternal tasks in pregnancy. *Maternal-Child Nursing Journal, 4*(3), 143-153. Citation from page 144.

23. Miller, L.J. (1993). Psychiatric disorders during pregnancy. Chapter 4 in D.E. Stewart and N.L. Stotland's (Eds). *Psychological aspects of women's health care: The interface between psychiatry and obstetrics and gynecology.* Washington, DC: American Psychiatric Press, Inc.

24. Fraiberg, S. (1980). *Clinical studies in infant mental health: The first year of life.* New York: Basic Books.

25. David, H. P., Dytrych, Z., Matejcek, Z., & Schuler, V. (Eds.). (1988). *Born Unwanted: Developmental Effects of Denied Abortion.* New York: Springer Publishing.

26. Rubin, R. (1984). *Maternal identity and the maternal experience.* New York: Springer Publishing Company.

27. Benoit, D., Parker, K. C. H., & Zeanah, C. H. (1997). Mothers representations of their infants assessed prenatally: Stability and association with infants' attachment classifications. *Journal of Child Psychology and Psychiatry, 38*(3): 307-313.

CHAPTER 2

1. Bailey, L.A. & Hailey, B.J. (1986). The psychological experiences of pregnancy. *International Journal of Psychiatry in Medicine, 16*(3), 263-274.

2. Caplan, G. (1960). Emotional implications of pregnancy and influences in family relationships. In H.C. Stuart and D.G.Prugh (Eds.) *The healthy child*, Cambridge: Harvard Universities Press.

3. Loesch, J. & Greenberg, M. (1962) Some specific areas of conflict observed during pregnancy: A comparative study of married and unmarried pregnant women. *American Journal of Orthopsychiatry, 32*, 624-636.

CHAPTER 3

1. Rubin, R. (1984). *Maternal identity and the maternal experience*. New York: Springer Publishing Company.

2. Mercer, R.T. (1985). The process of maternal role attainment over the first year. *Nursing Research, 34*(4), 198-204.

3. Cranley, M. S. (1993). The origins of the mother-child relationship—a review. *Concepts in Fetal Movement Research,* The Hawthorne Press, pp. 39-51.

4. Cote-Arsenault, D. & Mahlangu, N. (1999). Impact of perinatal loss on the subsequent pregnancy and self: Women's experiences. *Journal of Obstetric, Gynecology, & Neonatal Nursing (JOGNN) 28*(3), pp. 274-82.

5. Wilson, M.E., White, M.A., Cobb, B., Curry, RL, Greene, D., & Popovich, D. (2000). Family dynamics, parental-fetal attachment and infant temperament. *Journal of Advanced Nursing, 31*(1), 204-210.

6. Barnhill, L. (1979). Healthy family systems. *Family Coordinator, 28*, 94-108.

7. Wilson, M.E., White, M.A., Cobb, B., Curry, RL, Greene, D., & Popovich, D. (2000). Family dynamics, parental-fetal attachment and infant temperament. *Journal of Advanced Nursing, 31*(1), p. 208.

8. Caplan, G. (1959). *Concepts of mental health and consultation*. Washington, DC: U.S. Department of Health, Education, and Welfare.

9. Colman, A. & Colman, L. (1971). *Pregnancy: The psychological experience*. New York: Herder and Herder.

10. Bibring, G.L. (1959). Some considerations of the psychological processes in pregnancy. *Psychoanalytic Study of the Child, 14*, 9-24.

CHAPTER 4

1. Carter-Jessop, L. (1981). Promoting maternal attachment through prenatal intervention. *Maternal-Child Nursing, 6*, 107-112.

2. Stainton, M. C. (1990). Parents' awareness of their unborn infant in the third trimester. *Birth, 17*(2), 92-96.

3. Davidoff, R. & O'Grady, J. P. (1985). Disorders of mother-infant attachment. Chapter 12 in J. P. O'Grady and M. Rosenthal's (Eds.) *Obstetrics: Psychological and Psychiatric Syndromes.* New York: Elsevier, pp.181-195.

4. Benoit, D., Parker, K. C. H., & Zeanah, C. H. (1997). Mothers representations of their infants assessed prenatally: Stability and association with infants' attachment classifications." *Journal of Child Psychology and Psychiatry, 38*(3): 307-313.

5. Bowlby, J. (1958). The child's lie to his mother. *International Journal of Psychoanalysis, 39*, 350-373.

6. Bowlby, J. (1969/1982). *Attachment and loss: Volume 1. Attachment.* New York: Basic Books.

7. Bowlby, J. (1973). *Attachment and loss: Volume 2. Separation.* New York: Basic Books.

8. Bowlby, J. (1979). *The making and breaking of affectional bonds.* London: Tavistock.

9. Bowlby, J. (1980). *Attachment and loss: Volume 3. Loss: Sadness and depression.* New York: Basic Books.

10. Bowlby, J. (1988). *A secure base.* New York: Basic Books.

11. Ainsworth, M.D. S., Blehar, M.C., Waters, E., & Wall, S. (1978). *Patterns of attachment: A psychological study of the strange situation.* Hillsdale, NJ: Erlbaum.

12. Spitz, R.A. (1946a). Anaclitic depression. *Psychoanalytic Study of the Child, 2*, 313-342.

13. Spitz, R.A. (1946b). Hospitalism: A follow-up report on investigation described in Volume I, 1945. *Psychoanalytic Study of the Child, 2*, 113-117.

14. Klaus, M.H. & Kennel, J.H. (1976). *Maternal-infant bonding.* St. Louis: CV Mosby.

CHAPTER 5

1. Janus, L. (1995). The prenatal dimension: Its relevance to psychosomatic obstetrics. In J. Bitzer and M. Stauber (Eds.) *Psychosomatic Obstetrics and Gynecology: 11th International Congress of Psychosomatic Obstetrics and Gynaecology,* Basil, Switzerland, Monduzzi Editore International Proceedings Division, pp. 59-64.

2. Janus, L. (1995) The prenatal dimension: its relevance to psychosomatic obstetrics. In J. Bitzer and M. Stauber (Eds.) *Psychosomatic Obstetrics and Gynecology: 11th International Congress of Psychosomatic Obstetrics and Gynaecology,* Basil, Switzerland, Monduzzi Editore International Proceedings Division, pp. 59-64.

3. Laughlin, C.D. (2001). Pre- and perinatal brain development and enculturation: A biogenetic structural approach. Part I. *http://www.carleton.ca/~claughli/dn-art1a.htm.*

4. Gable, S. & Hunting, M. (2000). Nature, nurture and early brain development. Human Environmental Sciences, publication GH6115, January 31, 2000; *http://www.muextension.missouri.edu/xplor/hesguide/humanrel/gh6115.htm.*

5. Wadhwa, P.D, Sandman, C.A, Proto, M, Dunkel-Schetter, C., & Garite, TJ (1993). The association between prenatal stress and infant birth weight and gestational age at birth: A prospective investigation. *American Journal of Obstetrics and Gynecology, 169*(4), pp. 858-65.

6. Lederman, R. (1995). Anxiety in pregnancy: Recent results. In J. Bitzer and M. Stauber (Eds.) *Psychosomatic Obstetrics and Gynecology: 11th International Congress of Psychosomatic Obstetrics and Gynaecology,* Basil, Switzerland, Monduzzi Editore International Proceedings Division, pp. 77-83.

7. Monk, C., Fifer, W.P, Myers, M.M, Sloan, R.P, Trien, L, & Hurtado, A. (2000). Maternal stress responses and anxiety during pregnancy: Effects on fetal heart rate. *Developmental Psychobiology, 36*(1), pp. 7-77.

8. Teixeira, M.A, Fisk, N.M, & Glover, V. (1999). Association between maternal anxiety in pregnancy and increased uterine artery resistance index: Cohort based study. *British Medical Journal, 318,* pp.153-157.

9. Copper, R.L., Goldenberg, R.L., Das, A., Elder, N., Swain, M., Norman, G., Ramsey, P., Collins, B.A.,Johnson, F., Jones, P., & Meier, A.M. (1996). The preterm prediction study: Maternal stress is associated with preterm birth at less than thirty-five weeks' gestation. *American Journal of Obstetrics and Gynecology, 175*(5), pp. 1286-92.

10. Lou, H.C., Hansen, D., Nordentoft, M., Pryds, O., Jensen, F., Nim, J., & Hemmingsen, R. (1994). Prenatal stressors of human life affect fetal brain development. *Developmental Medicine and Child Neurology, 36*(9), pp. 826-32.

11. Hansen, D., Lou, H.C., & Olsen, J. (2000). Serious life events and congenital malformations: Anational study with complete follow-up. *The Lancet, 356,* pp. 875-80.

12. Orr, S.T., Miller, C.A., James, S.A., & Babones, S. (2000). Unintended pregnancy and preterm birth. *Paediatric and Perinatal Epidemiology, 14*(4), pp. 309-313.

13. Neiderhofer, H., & Reiter, A. (2000). Maternal stress during pregnancy, its objectivation by ultrasound observation of fetal intrauterine movements and child's temperament at 6 months and 6 years of age: A pilot study. *Psychological Reports, 86*(2), pp. 526-8.

14. Sandman, C.A., Wadhwa, P.D., Chicz-DeMet, A., Dunkel-Schetter, C., & Porto, M. (1997). Maternal stress, HPA activity, and fetal/infant outcome. *Annuls of the New York Academy of Sciences, 814,* pp. 266-75.

15. Wadhwa, P.D., Sandman, C.A., Proto, M, Dunkel-Schetter, C., & Garite, T.J. (1993). The association between prenatal stress and infant birth weight and gestational age at birth: A prospective investigation. *American Journal of Obstetrics and Gynecology, 169*(4), pp. 858-65.

16. Sandman, C.A., Wadhwa, P.D., Chicz-DeMet, A,. Dunkel-Schetter, C., & Porto, M. (1997). Maternal stress, HPA activity, and fetal/infant outcome. *Annuls of the New York Academy of Sciences, 814*, pp. 266-75.

17. Ponirakis, A., Susman, E.J., & Stifter, C.A. (1998). Negative emotionality and cortisol during adolescent pregnancy and its effects on infant health and autonomic nervous system reactivity. *Developmental Psychobiology, 33*(2), pp. 163-74.

18. Edwards, C.H., Cole, O.J., Oyemade, U.J., Knight, E.M., Johnson, A.A., Westney, O.E., Laryea, H., West, W., Jones, S., & Westney, L.S. (1994). Maternal stress and pregnancy outcomes in a prenatal clinic population. *Journal of Nutrition, 124*(6), pp. 1006-1021.

19. Lundy, B.L., Jones, N.S., Field, T., Nearing, G., Davalos, M., Pietro, P.A., Schanberg, S., & Kuhn, C. (1999). Prenatal depression effects on neonates. *Infant Behavior and Development, 22*(1), pp.119-129.

20. Abrams, S.M., Field, T., Scafidi, F., & Prodromidis, M. (1995). Maternal "depression" effects on infants' Brazelton Scale performance. *Infant Mental Health Journal, 16*, pp. 231-235.

21. Lundy, B.L., Field, T., & Pickens., J. (1996). Infants of mothers with depressive symptoms are less expressive. *Infant Behavior and Development, 19*, pp. 419-424.

22. Sommer, K.S., Whitman, T.L., Borkowski, J.G., Burke, J., Maxwell, S.E., & Weed, K. (2000). Prenatal maternal predictors of cognitive and emotional delays in children of adolescent mothers. *Adolescence, 35*(137), pp. 87-112.

23. Brown, A.S. & Susser, E.S. (1996). Prenatal risk factors in schizophrenia. *Psychiatric Times, 13*(1).

24. Tsuang, M. (2000) Schizophrenia: Genes and environment. *Biological Psychiatry, 1*(47), 210-220.

CHAPTER 7
PREGNANCY LOSS

1. Nikcevic, A.V., Tunkel, S.A., Kuczmierczyk, A. R., and Nicolaides, K. H. (1999). Investigation of the cause of miscarriage and its influence on women's psychological distress. *British Journal of Obstetrics & Gynaecology, 106*(8), pp. 808-813.

2. Swanson, K. M. (1999a). Research-based practice with women who have had miscarriages. *Image: Journal of Nursing Scholarship, 31*(4), pp. 339-345.

3. Stirtzinger, R.M., Robinson, G.E., Stewart, D.E., & Ralevski, E. (1999) Parameters of grieving in spontaneous abortion. *International Journal of Psychiatry and Medicine, 29*(2), pp. 235-249.

4. Swanson, K. M. (1999b). Effects of caring, measurement, and time on miscarriage impact and women's well-being. *Nursing Research, 48*(6), pp. 288-298.

5. Swanson, K. M. (1991). Empirical development of a middle range theory of caring. *Nursing Research,* 40, pp. 161-166.

6. Cote-Arsenault, D. & Mahlangu, N. (1999). Impact of perinatal loss on the subsequent pregnancy and self: Women's experiences. *JOGNN, 28*(3), pp. 274-282.

FAMILY PLANNING

1. Dietz, P.M., Spitz, A.M., Anda, R.F., Williamson, D.F., McMahon, P.M., Santelli, J. S., Nordenberg, D.F., Felitti, V.J., & Kendrick, J. S. (1999). Unintended pregnancy among adult women exposed to abuse or household dysfunction during their childhood. *JAMA, 282*(14), pp. 1359-1364.

2. Orr, S.T., Miller, C.A., James, S.A., & Babones, S. (2000). Unintended pregnancy and preterm birth. *Paediatric and Perinatal Epidemiology, 14*(4), pp. 309-313.

3. David, H. P., Dytrych, Z., Matejcek, Z., & Schuler, V. (Eds.) (1988). *Born unwanted: Developmental effects of denied abortion.* New York: Springer Publishing.

CONTROVERSY OF ULTRASOUND

1. Brazelton, T.B. (1992). *Touchpoints: The essential reference.* Reading, MA: Perseus Books, p. 5.

2. Scheele, M. (1995) What does the ultrasonographic examination contribute to the perception of the pregnancy? In J. Bitzer and M. Stauber's (Eds.) *Psychosomatic Obstetrics and Gynaecology,* Switzerland: Monduzzi Editore, International Proceedings Division.

3. Scheele, M. (1995). What does the ultrasonographic examination contribute to the perception of the pregnancy? In J. Bitzer and M. Stauber's (Eds.) *Psychosomatic Obstetrics and Gynaecology,* Switzerland: Monduzzi Editore, International Proceedings Division.

4. Scheele, M. (1995) What does the ultrasonographic examination contribute to the perception of the pregnancy? In J. Bitzer and M. Stauber's (Eds.) *Psychosomatic Obstetrics and Gynaecology,* Switzerland: Monduzzi Editore, International Proceedings Division.

DOMESTIC VIOLENCE

1. Center for Disease Control, Vital & Health Statistics. (2000). Trends in pregnancy and pregnancy rates by outcome: *Estimates for the U.S.76-96. Series 21,* Number 56, January.

2. Canterino, J.C., VanHorn, L.G., Harrigan, J.T., Ananth, C.V., & Vintzileos, A.M. (1999). Domestic abuse in pregnancy: A comparison of a self-completed domestic abuse questionnaire with a directed interview. *American Journal of Obstetrics and Gynecology, Nov; 181*(5), pp.1049-51.

3. Gazmararian, J.A., Lazorick, S., Spitz, A.M., Ballard, T. J., Saltzman, L.E., & Marks, J. S. (1996). Prevalence of violence against pregnant women. *JAMA June 26; 275*(24), pp. 1915-20.

4. Hedin, L. W., Grimstad, H., Moller, A., Schei, B., & Janson, P.O. (1999). Prevalence of physical and sexual abuse before and during pregnancy among Swedish couples. *Acta Obstetrics Gynecology Scandinavia, 78*(4), pp. 310-315.

5. Stewart, D.E. & Cecutti, A. (1993). Physical abuse in pregnancy. *CMAJ, 149*(9), pp. 1257-1263.

6. Mattson, S. & Rodriguez, E. (1999). Battering in pregnant Latinas. *Issues in Mental Health Nursing, 20*(4), pp. 405-22.

7. Stewart, D.E. & Cecutti, A. (1993). Physical abuse in pregnancy. *CMAJ, 149*(9), pp. 1257-1263.

8. Leung, W.C., Leung, T.W., Lam, Y.Y., & Ho, P.C. (1999). The prevalence of domestic violence against pregnant women in a Chinese community. *International Journal of Gynecology and Obstetrics, 66*(1), pp. 23-30.

9. Center for Disease Control and Prevention, National Center for Chronic Disease prevention and Health Promotion, (2000c). *Chronic disease notes & reports; special focus: Safe motherhood, Vol. 13* (2), Spring/Summer.

10. Center for Disease Control and Prevention, National Center for Chronic Disease prevention and Health Promotion, (2000c). *Chronic disease notes & reports; special focus: Safe motherhood, Vol. 13* (2), Spring/Summer.

11. Canterino, J.C., VanHorn, L.G., Harrigan, J.T., Ananth, C.V., & Vintzileos, A.M. (1999). Domestic abuse in pregnancy: A comparison of a self-completed domestic abuse questionnaire with a directed interview. *American Journal of Obstetrics and Gynecology, Nov; 181*(5), pp. 1049-51.

DEPRESSION AND PREGNANCY

1. Matthey, S., Barnett, B., Ungerer, J., & Waters, B. (2000). Paternal and maternal depressed mood during the transition to parenthood. *Journal of Affective Disorders, 60*(2), pp. 75-85.

2. Matthey, S., Barnett, B., Ungerer, J., & Waters, B. (2000). Paternal and maternal depressed mood during the transition to parenthood. *Journal of Affective Disorders, 60*(2), pp. 75-85.

3. Battegay, R. (1995). Masked depression in obstetrics and gynecology. In J. Bitzer and M Stauber (Eds.) P*sychosomatic Obstetrics and Gynecology: 11th International Congress of Psychosomatic Obstetrics and Gynaecology,* Basil, Switzerland, Monduzzi Editore International Proceedings Division, pp. 35-40.

4. Sugawara, M., Sakamoto, S., Kitamura, T., Toda, M.A., and Shima, S. (1999). Structure of depressive symptoms in pregnancy and the postpartum period. *Journal of Affective Disorders, 54*(1-2), pp. 161-9.

5. Steinberg, S.I., & Bellavance, F. (1999). Characteristics and treatment of women with antenatal and postpartum depression. *International Journal of Psychiatry in Medicine, 29*(2), pp. 209-233.

THE PREGNANT WOMAN ABOVE AGE 35

1. Reece, S.M., & Harkless, G. (1996). Divergent themes in maternal experience in women older than 35 years of age. *Applied Nursing Research 9*(3) pp. 148-153.

2. Solchany, J.E. (2000). *The nature of mothers developing relationships with their internationally adopted Chinese daughters.* Unpublished dissertation, University of Washington, Seattle.

3. Reece, S. M. (1995). Stress and maternal adaptation in first-time mothers more than 35 years old. *Applied Nursing Research* 8(2), pp. 61-66.

THE PREGNANT ADOLESCENT

1. Quinlivan, J.A., Petersen, R.W., & Gurrin, L.C. (1999). Adolescent pregnancy: Psychopathology missed. *The Australian and New Zealand Journal of Psychiatry, 33*(6), pp. 864-868.

2. Quinlivan, J.A., Petersen, R.W., & Gurrin, L.C. (1999). Adolescent pregnancy: Psychopathology missed. *The Australian and New Zealand Journal of Psychiatry, 33*(6), p. 866.

3. Sciarra, D.T., & Ponterotto, J.G. (1998). Adolescent motherhood among low-income urban Hispanics: Familial considerations of mother-daughter dyads. *Qualitative Health Research, 8*(6), pp. 751-763.

4. Hockaday, C., Crase, S.J., Shelley, M.C., & Stockdale, D.F. (2000). A prospective study of adolescent pregnancy. *Journal of Adolescence, 23*(4), pp. 423-438.

5. Center for Disease Control. (2000). Pregnancy in adolescents. *Adolescent Health, CDC's Public Health Surveillance for Women, Infants, and Children*, pp. 369-379.

PREGNANT WOMEN WITH DISABILITIES

1. Parents with disabilities online, *http://www.disabledparents.net/index.html*

2. Center for Research on Women with Disabilities. (2001). National study of women with physical disabilities: Pregnancy. *http://www.bcm.tmc.edu/crowd/national_study/PREGNANC.htm*

3. Blackford, K.A., Richardson, H., & Grieve, S. (2000). Prenatal education for mothers with disabilities. *Journal of Advanced Nursing, 32*(4), pp. 898-904.

4. Lipson, J.G. & Rogers, J.G. (2000). Pregnancy, birth, and disability: Women's health careexperiences. *Health Care for Women International, 21*, pp. 11-26.

5. Center for Research on Women with Disabilities. (2001). National study of women with physical disabilities: Pregnancy. *http://www.bcm.tmc.edu/crowd/national_study/PREGNANC.htm*

6. Kirshbaum, M. (1995). Serving families with disability issues: Through the looking glass. *Marriage & Family Review, 21*(1-2), pp. 9-28.

7. Lipson, J.G., & Rogers, J.G. (2000). Pregnancy, birth, and disability: Women's health careexperiences. *Health Care for Women International, 21*, pp. 11-26.

8. Parents with disabilities online, *http://www.disabledparents.net/medical.html*

9. Through the looking glass. *http://www.lookingglass.org/parent.org*

THE RISK OF AN IMPERFECT BABY: HANDICAPS, ILLNESS AND PREMATURITY

1. Curry, M.A. (1982). Maternal attachment behavior and the mother's self-concept: The effect of early skin-to-skin contact. *Nursing Research, 31*, pp. 73-78.

2. Stainton, M. C., Harvey, S., & McNeil, D. (1995). *Understanding uncertain motherhood: A phenom-enological study of women in high risk perinatal situations.* Calgary, University of Calgary Press.

3. Stainton, M. C., D. McNeil, et al. (1992). Maternal tasks of uncertain motherhood. *Maternal-Child Nursing Journal, 20*(3,4) pp. 113-123.

CHAPTER 9

1. Janus, L. (1995). The prenatal dimension: Its relevance to psychosomatic obstetrics. In J. Bitzer and M Stauber (Eds.) *Psychosomatic Obstetrics and Gynecology: 11th International Congress of Psychosomatic Obstetrics and Gynaecology,* Basil, Switzerland, Monduzzi Editore International Proceedings Division, pp. 59-64.

2. Maldonado-Duran, M., Lartigue, T., & Feintuch, M. (2000). Perinatal psychiatry: Infant mental health interventions during pregnancy. *Bulletin of the Menniger Clinic, 64*(3), Summer, pp. 317-343.

UNIT 2

1. Moore, M. & Hopper, U. (1995). Do birth plans empower women? Evaluation of a hospital birth plan. *Birth, 22*(1), pp. 29-36.

2. Peacock-Albers, M. (1996). Childbirth Education Plan, unpublished.

3. Simkin, P., Whalley, J., & Keppler, A. (1991). *Pregnancy, childbirth, and the newborn: The complete guide.* Deephaven, MN: New York: Meadowbrook.

Index